SEIVERD'S CHEMISTRY FOR MEDICAL TECHNOLOGISTS

Seiverd's
Chemistry for
medical technologists

WILMA L. WHITE, B.A.

Supervisor, Clinical Chemistry Laboratory, Barnes Hospital, St. Louis;
Member, American Association of Clinical Chemists, American
Chemical Society, and St. Louis Society of Analysts

SAM FRANKEL, Ph.D.

Director, Division of Biochemistry, Department of Laboratories,
The Jewish Hospital of St. Louis; Member, American Association of
Clinical Chemists and American Chemical Society

Second edition

THE C. V. MOSBY COMPANY

Saint Louis   1965

Dedicated to

Lora P. and Fredrick F. White

Mary E. Ude

and to

Sidney and Sylvia Shankerman

John and Etta Buchman

CONTRIBUTOR

Marilyn M. Erickson, B.S. (Appendix C. Reagents)

Supervisor, Clinical Chemistry Laboratory,
Barnes Hospital, St. Louis

CONSULTANTS

Mary L. Lear, A.B., B.S., M.A., Sc.D.

Professor Emeritus of Chemistry, Lindenwood College,
St. Charles, Mo.

Nancy Kay McAdam, A.B., MT(ASCP)

Assistant Supervisor, Clinical Chemistry Laboratory, and
Teaching Supervisor, Barnes School of Medical Technology.
Barnes Hospital, St. Louis

PANEL

Dorothy Harrison, MT(ASCP)

Supervisor, Clinical Microscopy

Norma Moss, RMT/ISCLT

Supervisor, Clinical Microscopy

Ronald Verdun

Clinical Chemistry Laboratory

All of Barnes Hospital, St. Louis

Preface

In the field of medicine the technologists are often lost in the chaos of human survival. In training, too little time is spent in preparing them for the demands of the profession; in working, too little time is available to guide each individual technologist. Although the progress of medical science has been recorded in many excellent reference and teaching books, there is yet a need for a helping hand on technique problems and a need for a basic review for the beginning and practicing technologist. This book is intended to fulfill these needs and to serve as an aid to technologists in their daily work. Many technologists from varied backgrounds have offered suggestions as to the material to be included in this text.

The following changes have been made from the first edition, published in 1958. The section including basic theory, techniques, solution preparation, and operation of colorimeters has been further developed with a new atomic weight table, an indicator table, and a more complete discussion of the analytical balance and flame photometry. Within the section on quantitative blood analysis, the methods taken from instrument manuals have been replaced with newer and more widely used procedures. New chapters on lipids and quality control have been added. The electrolyte section has been developed to include flame photometry, the Cotlove Chloridometer, manometric CO_2, and blood pH and pCO_2, with a full-page nomogram for calculating the pCO_2. New methods that have been added are ionized calcium with nomogram, transaminases, prostatic acid phosphatase, Barker's dry ash method for PBI's, serum iron, quantitative fibrinogin, and calculations for urea clearance.

Whenever possible, for the interest of the student, some history or discussion is given. With the methods a few disorders are listed in which abnormal results are found.

Although the authors, contributors, consultants, and reviewing panel are deeply involved with automation, it was felt that this is beyond the scope of a training book.

We hope that this book will prove valuable to students and technologists who use it and that they will not hesitate to make suggestions. Only in this way will we know whether the needs of the technologists have been fulfilled and in what ways future editions should be developed.

Wilma L. White
Sam Frankel

Contents

Chapter 15

Special chemistry tests, 254

Part 3

Spinal fluid analysis

Chapter 16

Spinal fluid examination, 277

Part 4

Gastric and duodenal analysis

Chapter 17

Gastric analysis, 285

Part 1

Essentials of elementary chemistry

This portion of the text presents the elementary chemistry that is significant to the medical technologist. The material is discussed in the following chapters:

In Appendix A there is a set of review questions. For the convenience of the student the answers are given.

Chapter 1

Basic theory

What causes chemical reactions? How are they expressed by the chemist? What are ions? What is the hydrogen ion concentration? These and other basic questions are considered under the following headings:

Elements and compounds
Chemical reactions
Chemical equations
Ionization
Acids, bases, and salts
Hydrogen ion concentration
Chemical indicators

ELEMENTS AND COMPOUNDS

All matter is composed of tiny particles called atoms. If a substance is made up of atoms that are all alike, it is known as an element. Atoms of gold, for example, make up the element gold, and in a single speck of gold dust there are millions of gold atoms. Consequently, atoms are the building blocks of elements.

When a substance, however, is composed of different atoms in definite proportions, it is called a compound. To illustrate, salt is made up of sodium atoms and chlorine atoms. When 1 sodium atom and 1 chlorine atom are chemically united they form a structure known as a molecule. In a single grain of salt there are millions of molecules. Molecules, therefore, may be called the building blocks of compounds.

In the early years of this century, scientists listed the number of naturally occurring elements as 92. Physicists then discovered methods for splitting the atoms (artificial disintegration), and in the years following 1934, some 11 new elements have been added to the list. Atoms of one kind react or combine with those of another, making possible the thousands of compounds necessary to our existence.

It is not difficult to list about 80 elements that are solids, 10 that are gases,

Table 1. Common elements

Solids			Gases	Liquids
Lithium	Manganese	Antimony	Hydrogen	Bromine
Carbon	Iron	Iodine	Helium	Mercury
Sodium	Cobalt	Barium	Nitrogen	
Magnesium	Nickel	Cerium	Oxygen	
Aluminum	Copper	Tungsten	Fluorine	
Silicon	Zinc	Gold	Chlorine	
Phosphorus	Arsenic	Mercury		
Sulfur	Molybdenum	Lead		
Potassium	Silver	Bismuth		
Calcium	Tin	Uranium		

and 2 that are liquids, among the elements occurring in *nature*. The more commonly known elements are listed in Table 1.

CHEMICAL REACTIONS

As you read these pages your body is undergoing millions of reactions per minute. These and other chemical reactions are all made possible by the simple transfer of material from one substance to another. The essential aspects of this transfer are discussed under the following headings:

> Composition of atoms
> Nature of reactions
> Reason for reactions
> Combining power or valence
> Oxidation and reduction

Composition of atoms

The idea of the atom has been pursued by the scientists for many centuries. In the last thirty years tremendous progress has been made in understanding the power of the atom. The atomic-powered submarines and ships and the atomic bomb are well-known examples of the Atomic Age. We should not look upon the new with awe and completely discredit the old. The new would not be possible if it had not been for the work done in earlier times.

At man's first exciting experience with fire, he was involved with chemistry. Throughout the ages there was little agreement among scientific philosophers. A lot of superstition prevailed. Hours of trial and error preceded modern atomic theory. Most citizens believed the alchemist and early scientists were moonstruck individuals who dealt with witchcraft.

However, in the fifth century B.C. two philosophers, Leucippus and Democritus, arrived at a theory of the atom not too far from the modern view: "All matter is composed of invisible, indestructible, and indivisible particles called Atoms, separated by voids."

By the nineteenth century approximately 60 elements had been found. The twentieth century is witnessing a revelation in atomic power.

The English chemist and physicist, John Dalton (1766-1844), developed the atomic theory. During the years 1803 to 1808, Dalton constructed the following principles:

1. Each element is composed of many invisible particles called atoms.

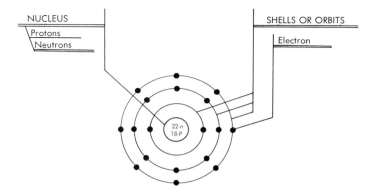

Fig. 1. Basic structure of the atom.

2. Atoms of each element are identical in mass and size.
3. Atoms of different elements have different mass and size.
4. In a chemical reaction atoms separate, change places, or combine in a simple integral ratio.

These four principles in Dalton's theory are still held useful today; however, it is now known that nearly all—but not all—the atoms of any one element are alike in mass, size, and structure. There may be a very small number of them differing slightly in the nucleus part of the atom. These slightly "off weight" atoms are the isotope atoms.

An atom is made up of protons (positively electrified particles) and electrons (negatively charged particles) (Fig. 1). The protons are always in the center or nucleus. Some electrons are in the nucleus, too, but it is the ones revolving around the nucleus in definite pathways that are responsible for the reactivity of the atom, particularly those electrons farthest from the nucleus.

About 1913 Niels Bohr described the electron movement around the atom nucleus as similar to the rotation of the planets around the sun. The electrons, although some distance from the nucleus, hold their course at various energy levels. These energy levels are also called shells. The electrons in their respective shells or energy levels form an electric field about the nucleus.

Although there are more components to the atom, we shall list only the three that concern us in this book: the proton, neutron, and electron.

The nucleus of the atom consists of protons and neutrons. The nucleus, we know, is positively charged because of the excess protons, each of which carries a positive charge. A neutron is a combination of an electron and a proton and has no electric charge. Therefore, it is neutral (Table 2).

The electrons, each carrying a negative charge, neutralize the atom in their various energy level arrangements. The outermost electrons are sometimes called valence electrons because they participate in chemical change. By gaining, losing, or sharing the electrons, atoms of one kind may combine with those of another element to form molecules. The number of the outer electrons will determine the valence of the atom (its combining power).

The number of protons in the atom's nucleus is known as the atomic number. This varies from 1 to 103 and identifies the atoms of different elements. For

Table 2. Particles of an atom

Name	Symbol	Atomic weight	Charge
Proton	p or $_1H^1$	1.00756	+1
Neutron	n or $_0n^1$	1.00893	0
Electron	e⁻	0.000548	−1

Table 3. Atomic numbers of the atoms

Atom	Atomic number	Atom	Atomic number
Hydrogen	1	Tin	50
Helium	2	Antimony	51
Lithium	3	Tellurium	52
Beryllium	4	Iodine	53
Boron	5	Xenon	54
Carbon	6	Cesium	55
Nitrogen	7	Barium	56
Oxygen	8	Lanthanum	57
Fluorine	9	Cerium	58
Neon	10	Praseodymium	59
Sodium	11	Neodymium	60
Magnesium	12	Promethium	61
Aluminum	13	Samarium	62
Silicon	14	Europium	63
Phosphorus	15	Gadolinium	64
Sulfur	16	Terbium	65
Chlorine	17	Dysprosium	66
Argon	18	Holmium	67
Potassium	19	Erbium	68
Calcium	20	Thulium	69
Scandium	21	Ytterbium	70
Titanium	22	Lutetium	71
Vanadium	23	Hafnium	72
Chromium	24	Tantalum	73
Manganese	25	Tungsten	74
Iron	26	Rhenium	75
Cobalt	27	Osmium	76
Nickel	28	Iridium	77
Copper	29	Platinum	78
Zinc	30	Gold	79
Gallium	31	Mercury	80
Germanium	32	Thallium	81
Arsenic	33	Lead	82
Selenium	34	Bismuth	83
Bromine	35	Polonium	84
Krypton	36	Astatine	85
Rubidium	37	Radon	86
Strontium	38	Francium	87
Yttrium	39	Radium	88
Zirconium	40	Actinium	89
Niobium	41	Thorium	90
Molybdenum	42	Protactinium	91
Technetium	43	Uranium	92
Ruthenium	44	Neptunium	93
Rhodium	45	Plutonium	94
Palladium	46	Americium	95
Silver	47	Curium	96
Cadmium	48	Berkelium	97
Indium	49	Californium	98

example, the sodium atom is the only one that has 11 protons. Because of this, it is known by its atomic number of 11. The chlorine atom, having 17 protons, consequently has the atomic number of 17. Now take time and check this with Table 3.

When an atom is in the neutral or uncombined state before it takes part in a reaction, the protons are balanced by an equal number of electrons. Thus, the sodium atom has 11 protons and 11 electrons, and the chlorine atom has 17 protons and 17 electrons. In each case, therefore, the atom as a whole may be called a neutral, balanced structure.

Nature of reactions

If two atoms are brought together, and the conditions are right, one atom may give electrons to the other. This converts the atoms to either ions or compounds, depending on solubility. *This tendency of atoms to transfer electrons becomes the basic principle involved in all chemical reactions.*

It is the nature or disposition of some atoms to give electrons and of others to take electrons. Some atoms are even content to share electrons. This giving, taking, and sharing of electrons makes for two general types of chemical reactions.

In the first type, there is a clear-cut transfer of electrons from one atom to another. One atom gives electrons; the other atom takes electrons. This reaction is known as a *transfer of electrons.*

In such a transfer, using the sodium and the chlorine atoms as an example, the sodium atom will give up its valence electron to the chlorine atom, forming a positive sodium ion and a negative chloride ion. These ions are held together by electrostatic forces or attraction that exists between unlike charged particles. This reaction involving a transfer of electrons is illustrated in Fig. 2, where it can

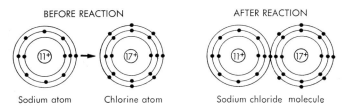

Fig. 2. Reaction between sodium and chlorine.

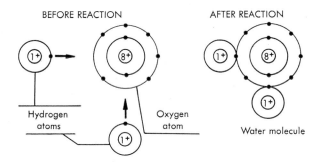

Fig. 3. Reaction between hydrogen and oxygen.

be seen that the sodium atom gives an electron to the chlorine atom. The result is sodium chloride:

$$
\begin{array}{ll}
\text{Na} & 11\ \text{p} \\
& \underline{10\ \text{e}} \\
& 1+
\end{array}
\qquad
\begin{array}{ll}
\text{Cl} & 17\ \text{p} \\
& \underline{18\ \text{e}} \\
& 1-
\end{array}
$$

In the second type of reaction, one atom furnishes electrons which are shared by both atoms. This reaction is known as a *sharing of electrons.*

A reaction that involves a sharing of electrons is illustrated in Fig. 3. Here the hydrogen atoms share their electrons with an oxygen atom. The result is a molecule of water. The oxygen atom's peculiar need for 2 electrons is pointed out.

Reason for reactions

Atoms, by forming chemical unions, apparently acquire a stable structure. This will be illustrated by considering the following reactions.

Return to the reaction between sodium and chlorine which is indicated in Fig. 2. Note that before the reaction sodium has 1 electron in its outer orbit and chlorine has 7 electrons in its outer orbit. After the reaction each atom has 8 electrons in its outer orbit! In most cases, when an atom has 8 electrons in its outer orbit, it neither gives nor takes electrons, for it has found a stable structure.

Consider the reaction between oxygen and hydrogen to form water (Fig. 3). The oxygen atom has 6 electrons in its outer orbit and, since it seeks a stable structure of 8 electrons, it needs 2 more. However, the hydrogen atom has only 1 electron to offer. Consequently, it takes 2 atoms of hydrogen to satisfy 1 atom of oxygen.

In order to attain a stable structure, a majority of the 103 atoms seek this arrangement of 8 electrons in their outer orbit. Several atoms already have 8 electrons in their outer orbit. These atoms, appropriately enough, are known as the inert group. They do not react. Then, there are a few atoms whose total number of electrons is less than 8. Helium, for example, has only 2 electrons in its one and only orbit, but this is all it needs for a stable structure.

Combining power or valence

The number of electrons an atom gives, takes, or shares during a reaction is called its combining power, or valence. For example, sodium gives 1 electron and therefore has a valence of 1. Chlorine, which takes 1 electron, also has a valence of 1. Since hydrogen gives 1 electron, it too has a valence of 1. Oxygen, however, in sharing 2 electrons, has a valence of 2.

The protons of an atom bear a positive charge of electricity, and the electrons a negative charge. You will recall that before an atom takes part in a reaction, its protons are balanced by an equal number of electrons. This means that the positive charges are balanced by an equal number of negative charges. The balance, however, is upset when an atom gives electrons. The atom then has excess positive charges and is said to have a *positive valence.* On the other hand, when an atom either takes or shares electrons, it takes negative charges. The negative charges then outnumber the positive charges, and the atom has a *negative valence.*

In the reaction between sodium and chlorine, sodium gives 1 electron. It therefore has a positive valence of 1. Chlorine, however, takes 1 electron and thus has a negative valence of 1.

Some atoms, by giving or taking, may have more than one valence. Carbon, by giving 4 electrons, may have a positive valence of 4; or by taking 4 electrons, it may have a negative valence of 4.

Oxidation and reduction

There are many reactions involving ions (electrically charged atoms), wherein no change in valence or electron number takes place. For example, in the action of an acid on a base, the positive hydrogen ion of the acid unites with the negative hydroxyl ion of the base to form a neutral molecule, water. There are no changes in valence of the ions—no change in the number of electrons for each.

But there is another large group of reactions, in which the numbers of electrons *are* changed. That is, the valence gains or loses. Such reactions are called reduction and oxidation or, more simply, "redox" actions.

When an atom *gives* electrons, the chemist says that it is *oxidized*. And when an atom *takes* electrons, it is said to be *reduced*. Quite often, when a substance is oxidized or is reduced, a color change takes place which becomes the basis for a test.

Consider, for example, a test for glucose in urine. When glucose reacts with copper, the copper takes electrons and is thus reduced. The reduced copper then forms a colored compound. The appearance of the colored compound tells the technician that glucose is present.

For a further illustration, consider the analysis of calcium. In this test, the following occurs: a purple compound, potassium permanganate, takes electrons; in so doing, it is immediately reduced to a colorless compound.

CHEMICAL EQUATIONS

A chemical equation is a statement, using symbols, of the exact relationships between atoms or ions undergoing change. The technician is seldom, if ever, called upon to write equations. However, he should be able to interpret those he meets in his work. This section deals with basic equations. The material is arranged as follows:

> Symbols
> Formulas
> Radicals and ions
> Atomic weights
> Molecular weights
> Expression of weights
> Writing basic equations

Symbols

The stenographer uses shorthand notes to simplify the taking of dictation, and the chemist uses symbols to simplify the discussion of atoms and their reactions. For example, the stenographer writes ∂๛ ∟ ⌒ for "chemistry is not difficult," and the chemist writes $Fe + S \longrightarrow FeS$ for "1 atom of iron reacts with 1 atom of sulfur to form 1 molecule of iron sulfide."

In most instances, the symbols have been derived by taking the first one or two letters of the element's English or Latin name. The symbols which the technician is most likely to meet are listed in Table 4.

Table 4. Symbols of some common elements

Aluminum	Al	Lithium	Li
Arsenic	As	Magnesium	Mg
Barium	Ba	Manganese	Mn
Bromine	Br	Mercury	Hg
Calcium	Ca	Nickel	Ni
Carbon	C	Nitrogen	N
Cerium	Ce	Oxygen	O
Chlorine	Cl	Phosphorus	P
Cobalt	Co	Potassium	K
Copper	Cu	Silver	Ag
Fluorine	F	Sodium	Na
Gold	Au	Sulfur	S
Hydrogen	H	Tin	Sn
Iodine	I	Uranium	U
Iron	Fe	Zinc	Zn
Lead	Pb		

Formulas

A recipe gives a cook the ingredients of a cake, and a formula gives a chemist the composition of a compound.

To illustrate, the formula for sodium chloride, which is NaCl, means that a molecule of sodium chloride contains 1 atom of sodium and 1 atom of chlorine. The formula for water is H_2O, meaning that a molecule of water is made up of 2 atoms of hydrogen and 1 atom of oxygen.

In the formula for water, H_2O, the figure 2 is known as a subscript. When a subscript is not written after a symbol, it is understood to be 1. For example, H_2O is understood to be H_2O_1.

By the same token, if there is no number before a molecule, it is understood to be 1. For example, H_2O is understood to be 1 H_2O.

Radicals and ions

It is possible for some atoms grouped together to act as single atoms. Such groups, if they are neutral, are called radicals. If a radical loses an electron or gains an electron, however, then it too is positively or negatively charged, as is the case with single atoms, and it is now called an ion. Ions are more commonly met among the acids, bases, and salts. Radicals are more common among the organic compounds—the carbon compounds related to life. (Tables 5 and 6.)

Atomic weights

In order to write equations and solve problems, the chemist must know something about the weight of atoms. Since he cannot actually weigh them, he does the next best thing: he finds and uses the relative weights of atoms. It is these relative values that are called atomic weights. They were derived as follows.

First, the early chemists picked out an atom which they could easily compare with other atoms. They chose oxygen. Second, they assigned oxygen an arbitrary weight of 16. The figure 16 was chosen because it gave them a means of

Table 5. Composition and symbols of some common radicals and ions

Name of radical or ion	Composition	Symbol
Hydroxyl radical or ion or Hydroxide ion	1 oxygen atom 1 hydrogen atom	OH^-
Ammonium ion	1 nitrogen atom 4 hydrogen atoms	NH_4^+
Sulfate ion	1 sulfur atom 4 oxygen atoms	SO_4^{--}
Ethyl radical	2 carbon atoms 5 hydrogen atoms	$C_2H_5^+$
Acetate ion	2 carbon atoms 3 hydrogen atoms 2 oxygen atoms	$C_2H_3O_2^-$

Table 6. Formulas of several compounds which contain radicals

Name of compound	Composition	Formula
Sodium hydroxide	1 sodium ion 1 hydroxyl ion	$NaOH$
Ammonium hydroxide	1 ammonium ion 1 hydroxyl ion	NH_4OH
Sulfuric acid	2 hydrogen ions 1 sulfate ion	H_2SO_4
Ethyl alcohol	1 ethyl radical 1 hydroxyl radical	C_2H_5OH
Acetic acid	1 hydrogen ion 1 acetate ion	$HC_2H_3O_2$

simple whole-number comparison with other atoms. Third, they compared the weights of all other atoms with oxgyen (Table 7).

For example, since oxygen was the standard (set at 16) and sulfur was found to be twice as heavy as oxygen, the relative or atomic weight of sulfur was 32. A hydrogen atom weighs only 1/16 as much as an oxygen atom; consequently, the atomic weight of hydrogen is 1. The carbon atom weighs 12/16 the weight of an oxygen atom; therefore, the atomic weight of carbon is 12.

In 1961 the International Union of Pure and Applied Chemistry prepared a revised atomic weight table, basing it on carbon-12. Atomic weights used in examples and problems are taken from the new source (Table 8). However, for the student's benefit in studying and adapting to the new table, the old form (Table 7) remains in the book also.

In Table 8, where the atomic weights of the atoms of the elements are given, note the following: the atomic weight of some atoms is carried out to the fifth decimal place, whereas the atomic weight of other atoms is carried out only to the first decimal place. The number of decimal places indicates the degree of accuracy with which the chemist has been able to make the measurement. For example, the atomic weight of sulfur is given as 32.064 and the atomic weight

Table 7. Atomic weights

Atom	Atomic weight	Atom	Atomic weight
Actinium	227	Molybdenum	95.95
Aluminum	26.97	Neodymium	144.27
Americium	241	Neptunium	237
Antimony	121.76	Neon	20.183
Argon	39.944	Nickel	58.69
Arsenic	74.91	Niobium	92.91
Astatine	211	Nitrogen	14.008
Barium	137.36	Osmium	190.2
Berkelium	243 (?)	Oxygen	16.0000
Beryllium	9.013	Palladium	106.7
Bismuth	209.00	Phosphorus	30.98
Boron	10.82	Platinum	195.23
Bromine	79.916	Plutonium	239
Cadmium	112.41	Polonium	210
Calcium	40.08	Potassium	39.096
Californium	244 (?)	Praseodymium	140.92
Carbon	12.010	Promethium	147
Cerium	140.13	Protactinium	231
Cesium	132.91	Radium	226.05
Chlorine	35.457	Radon	222
Chromium	52.01	Rhenium	186.31
Cobalt	58.94	Rhodium	102.91
Copper	63.54	Rubidium	85.48
Curium	242	Ruthenium	101.7
Dysprosium	162.46	Samarium	150.43
Erbium	167.2	Scandium	45.10
Europium	152.0	Selenium	78.96
Fluorine	19.00	Silicon	28.06
Francium	223	Silver	107.880
Gadolinium	156.9	Sodium	22.997
Gallium	69.72	Strontium	87.63
Germanium	72.60	Sulfur	32.066
Gold	197.2	Tantalum	180.88
Hafnium	178.6	Technetium	99
Helium	4.003	Tellurium	127.61
Holmium	164.94	Terbium	159.2
Hydrogen	1.0080	Thallium	204.39
Indium	114.76	Thorium	232.12
Iodine	126.92	Thulium	169.4
Iridium	193.1	Tin	118.70
Iron	55.85	Titanium	47.90
Krypton	83.7	Tungsten	183.92
Lanthanum	138.92	Uranium	238.07
Lead	207.21	Vanadium	50.95
Lithium	6.940	Xenon	131.3
Lutecium	174.99	Ytterbium	173.04
Magnesium	24.32	Yttrium	88.92
Manganese	54.93	Zinc	65.38
Mercury	200.61	Zirconium	91.22

of oxygen as 15.9994. This simply means that sulfur is twice as heavy as oxygen plus a slight fraction more, the slight fraction being .065.

Slight fractions of variation in the atomic weights can also be explained by the presence of the small percentage of isotope atoms ("off weight" atoms). Since an electron weighs only 1/1800 as much as the lightest atom hydrogen (weight, 1.008), the small difference between the weight of an atom and its ion is neglected.

Molecular weights

The molecular weight of a compound is the sum of its atomic weights. For example, the molecular weight of sodium chloride is found as follows. According

Table 8. 1961 table of relative atomic weights ($^{12}C = 12$)

Element	Symbol	Atomic No.	Atomic Weight	Element	Symbol	Atomic No.	Atomic Weight
Actinium	Ac	89	[227]*	Mercury	Hg	80	200.59
Aluminum	Al	13	26.9815	Molybdenum	Mo	42	95.94
Americium	Am	95	[243]*	Neodymium	Nd	60	144.24
Antimony	Sb	51	121.75	Neon	Ne	10	20.183
Argon	Ar	18	39.948	Neptunium	Np	93	[237]*
Arsenic	As	33	74.9216	Nickel	Ni	28	58.71
Astatine	At	85	[210]*	Niobium	Nb	41	92.906
Barium	Ba	56	137.34	Nitrogen	N	7	14.0067
Berkelium	Bk	97	[247]*	Nobelium	No	102	. . .
Beryllium	Be	4	9.0122	Osmium	Os	76	190.2
Bismuth	Bi	83	208.980	Oxygen	O	8	15.9994^a
Boron	B	5	10.811^a	Palladium	Pd	46	106.4
Bromine	Br	35	79.909^b	Phosphorus	P	15	30.9738
Cadmium	Cd	48	112.40	Platinum	Pt	78	195.09
Calcium	Ca	20	40.08	Plutonium	Pu	94	[242]*
Californium	Cf	98	[249]*	Polonium	Po	84	[210]*
Carbon	C	6	12.01115^a	Potassium	K	19	39.102
Cerium	Ce	58	140.12	Praseodymium	Pr	59	140.907
Cesium	Cs	55	132.905	Promethium	Pm	61	[147]*
Chlorine	Cl	17	35.453^b	Protactinium	Pa	91	[231]*
Chromium	Cr	24	51.996^b	Radium	Ra	88	[226]*
Cobalt	Co	27	58.9332	Radon	Rn	86	[222]*
Copper	Cu	29	63.54	Rhenium	Re	75	186.2
Curium	Cm	96	[247]*	Rhodium	Rh	45	102.905
Dysprosium	Dy	66	162.50	Rubidium	Rb	37	85.47
Einsteinium	Es	99	[254]*	Ruthenium	Ru	44	101.07
Erbium	Er	68	167.26	Samarium	Sm	62	150.35
Europium	Eu	63	151.96	Scandium	Sc	21	44.956
Fermium	Fm	100	[253]*	Selenium	Se	34	78.96
Fluorine	F	9	18.9984	Silicon	Si	14	28.086^a
Francium	Fr	87	[223]*	Silver	Ag	47	107.870^b
Gadolinium	Gd	64	157.25	Sodium	Na	11	22.9898
Gallium	Ga	31	69.72	Strontium	Sr	38	87.62
Germanium	Ge	32	72.59	Sulfur	S	16	32.064^a
Gold	Au	79	196.967	Tantalum	Ta	73	180.948
Hafnium	Hf	72	178.49	Technetium	Tc	43	[99]*
Helium	He	2	4.0026	Tellurium	Te	52	127.60
Holmium	Ho	67	164.930	Terbium	Tb	65	158.924
Hydrogen	H	1	1.00797^a	Thallium	Tl	81	204.37
Indium	In	49	114.82	Thorium	Th	90	232.038
Iodine	I	53	126.9044	Thulium	Tm	69	168.934
Iridium	Ir	77	192.2	Tin	Sn	50	118.69
Iron	Fe	26	55.847^b	Titanium	Ti	22	47.90
Krypton	Kr	36	83.80	Tungsten	W	74	183.85
Lanthanum	La	57	138.91	Uranium	U	92	238.03
Lead	Pb	82	207.19	Vanadium	V	23	50.942
Lithium	Li	3	6.939	Xenon	Xe	54	131.30
Lutecium	Lu	71	174.97	Ytterbium	Yb	70	173.04
Magnesium	Mg	12	24.312	Yttrium	Y	39	88.905
Manganese	Mn	25	54.9380	Zinc	Zn	30	65.37
Mendelevium	Md	101	[256]*	Zirconium	Zr	40	91.22

*Value in brackets denotes the mass number of the isotope of longest known half-life (or a better known one for Po, Pm, and Tc).
^{a}Atomic weight varies because of natural variation in isotopic composition: B, ± 0.003; C, ± 0.00005; H, ± 0.00001; O, ± 0.00001; Si, ± 0.001; S, ± 0.003.
^{b}Atomic weight is believed to have following experimental uncertainty: Br, ± 0.002; Cl, ± 0.01; Cr, ± 0.001; Fe, ± 0.003; Ag, ± 0.003. (For other elements, the last digit given for the atomic weight is believed reliable to ± 0.5.)
[Lawrencium (Lw) has been proposed as the name for element 103, nuclidic mass about 257.]

Reprinted from Pure and Applied Chemistry **5**:255, 1962, by permission of the International Union of Pure and Applied Chemistry and Butterworths Scientific Publications.

to Table 8, the atomic weight of sodium is 22.9898 and the atomic weight of chlorine is 35.453. By adding these atomic weights, we find the molecular weight:

Atomic weight of sodium	= 22.9898
Atomic weight of chlorine	= 35.453
Molecular weight of sodium chloride	= 58.4428

The molecular weight of iron sulfide is found in a similar manner (Table 8):

Atomic weight of iron	= 55.847
Atomic weight of sulfur	= 32.064
Molecular weight of iron sulfide	= 87.911

A molecular of water, H_2O, has 2 atoms of hydrogen, each with an atomic weight of 1.0080. The molecular weight of water is found as follows:

	Atomic	*Atomic*
	Table 7	*Table 8*
Atomic weight of H = 1.0080 and 2 H =	2.0160 or	2.0159
Atomic weight of O = 16.0000 and 1 O =	16.0000	15.9994
Molecular weight of H_2O	= 18.0160	18.0153

Expression of weights

Since the atomic weights are relative weights, they could be expressed in grams (gm.), ounces, pounds, or tons. For example, one atomic weight of sodium (22.9898) reacts with one atomic weight of chlorine (35.453). This could mean that 22.9898 gm. of sodium react with 35.453 gm. of chlorine *or* that 22.9898 tons of sodium react with 35.453 tons of chlorine. The chemist, however, usually expresses the atomic weight in grams. Therefore, in order to avoid a maze of useless terminology, this text will always assume that the atomic weights are expressed in grams. Thus, the atomic weight of oxygen becomes 15.9994 gm.; the atomic weight of sulfur, 32.064 gm.; and the atomic weight of hydrogen, 1.00797 gm.

The molecular weights also are usually expressed in grams, and in order to simplify our discussions, this text will always assume that the molecular weights are expressed in grams. Thus, the molecular weight of sodium chloride becomes 58.4428 gm.; the molecular weight of iron sulfide, 87.911 gm.; and the molecular weight of water, 18.0153 gm.

Strictly speaking, when the atomic weight is expressed in grams, it is called a gram-atomic weight, and when the molecular weight is expressed in grams, it is called either a gram-molecular weight or a mole (mol). However, these terms are rather cumbersome and can be simplified, as mentioned above, by stating that all atomic and molecular weights will be expressed in grams.

Writing basic equations

Chemical equations express chemical reactions. Consequently, the chemist must know exactly what takes place before he writes an equation. The equations of today simply express the experimental facts of yesterday.

In the writing of equations, symbols are used to represent atoms and an arrow is used to represent the word "equals" or "yields." The reacting materials are first written on the left-hand side of the equation and the materials produced on the right-hand side. The manner in which the reacting materials combine, known through experimentation, is then considered and any necessary adjustments are made. Finally the equation is balanced; that is, the number and kind of atoms on one side of the equation are made to equal the number and kind on the other side.

From this discussion, it is apparent that the writing of equations may be broken down into the following three steps:

Step 1: By use of symbols, the reacting materials are written on the left-hand side of the equation and the materials produced, on the right.

Step 2: The manner in which the reacting materials combine is considered next, and any necessary adjustments are made.

Step 3: The number and kind of atoms on one side of the equation are then made to equal the number and kind on the other side.

Using the above three steps, we will now consider the writing of several basic equations. The equation that expresses the reaction between iron and sulfur is derived as follows:

Step 1: By use of symbols, the reacting materials are written on the left-hand side and the materials produced, on the right:

$$Fe \; + \; S \; \longrightarrow \; FeS$$

Step 2: The manner in which iron and sulfur combine is then considered. It is known from atomic structure and also from experimentation that iron and sulfur, both solids, combine, atom for atom, to form iron sulfide. Since the equation already indicates that iron and sulfur are combining in this 1 to 1 ratio, no adjustments are necessary. (If there is no number before an atom, it is understood that the quantity is 1.)

Step 3: The number and kind of atoms on one side of the equation must now be made to equal the number and kind on the other side. Since there are 1 Fe and 1 S on the left and 1 Fe and 1 S on the right, no adjustments are necessary, and the equation is balanced as it stands.

The equation is read: "1 atom of iron combines with 1 atom of sulfur to form 1 molecule of iron sulfide." To the chemist, the equation also means that 1 atomic weight of iron (55.847 gm.) combines with 1 atomic weight of sulfur (32.064 gm.) to produce 1 molecular weight of iron sulfide (87.911 gm.).

Consider the equation which expresses the reaction between sodium and chlorine to form sodium chloride:

Step 1: By use of symbols, the reacting materials are written on the left-hand side and the materials produced, on the right-hand side:

$$Na \; + \; Cl \; \longrightarrow \; NaCl$$

Step 2: The manner in which sodium and chlorine combine is considered next. First, chlorine is a gas and gas atoms have a tendency to react only in pairs. Consequently, the Cl should be indicated as Cl_2:

$$Na \; + \; Cl_2 \; \longrightarrow \; NaCl$$

Note that the pair of gas atoms is written Cl_2 and not 2 Cl. The gas atoms which the technician will meet (hydrogen, oxygen, nitrogen, fluorine, and chlorine) are all written in this manner when they stand alone. Second, it is known from experimentation that 2 atoms of chlorine combine with 2 atoms of sodium. Since the equation now has 2 atoms of chlorine, we need 2 atoms of sodium:

$$2 \, Na \; + \; Cl_2 \; \longrightarrow \; NaCl$$

Step 3: The number and kind of atoms on one side of the equation must now be made to equal the number and kind on the other side. Since there are 2 sodium atoms and 2 chlorine atoms on the left, an equal number must appear on the right. This can be accomplished by simply placing a 2 before the NaCl:

$$2 \text{ Na} + \text{Cl}_2 \longrightarrow 2 \text{ NaCl}$$

The equation is read: "2 atoms of sodium combine with 2 atoms of chlorine to form 2 molecules of sodium chloride." This equation also means that 2 atomic weights of sodium (45.9796 gm.) combine with 2 atomic weights of chlorine (70.906 gm.) to produce 2 molecular weights of sodium chloride (116.8856 gm.):

$$2 \text{ Na} + \text{Cl}_2 \longrightarrow 2 \text{ NaCl}$$
$$(45.9796 \text{ gm.}) + (70.906 \text{ gm.}) \longrightarrow (116.8856 \text{ gm.})$$

Consider the equation which expresses the reaction between hydrogen and oxygen to form water:

Step 1: By use of symbols, the reacting materials are written on the left-hand side and the materials produced, on the right:

$$\text{H} + \text{O} \longrightarrow \text{H}_2\text{O}$$

Step 2: The manner in which hydrogen and oxygen combine is considered next. First, since hydrogen and oxygen are gases, they react only in pairs and the equation must be changed to:

$$\text{H}_2 + \text{O}_2 \longrightarrow \text{H}_2\text{O}$$

Second, it is known from experimentation that 4 parts of hydrogen react with 2 parts of oxygen to form water. Since we already have 2 parts of oxygen (O_2), we need 4 parts of hydrogen. This can be accomplished by multiplying the H_2 by 2:

$$2 \text{ H}_2 + \text{O}_2 \longrightarrow \text{H}_2\text{O}$$

Step 3: The number and kind of atoms on one side of the equation must now be made to equal the number and kind on the other side. There are 4 hydrogen atoms and 2 oxygen atoms on the left. Therefore, an equal number must appear on the right. If we place a 2 before the H_2O, we have the necessary 4 hydrogen atoms and also the necessary 2 oxygen atoms:

$$2 \text{ H}_2 + \text{O}_2 \longrightarrow 2 \text{ H}_2\text{O}$$

Note that the 2 before the H_2O multiplies the H_2 by 2 and also the O by 2.

The equation is read: "4 atoms of hydrogen combine with 2 atoms of oxygen to form 2 molecules of water." The equation also means that 4 atomic weights of hydrogen combine with 2 atomic weights of oxygen to produce 2 molecular weights of water:

$$2 \text{ H}_2 + \text{O}_2 \longrightarrow 2 \text{ H}_2\text{O}$$
$$(4.03188 \text{ gm.}) + (31.9988 \text{ gm.}) \longrightarrow (36.0307 \text{ gm.})$$

IONIZATION

In the laboratory, most substances used or tested are in water solution. The water separates the ions of an acid, base, or salt so that they are free to be more active. It must be kept in mind that particles having unlike electric charges attract each other and that like charges repel. This electrostatic attraction is the force holding ions together. The binding force is loosened when a salt or other ionizable substances come in contact with water. Such separation of ions by water is called ionization. Some acids, bases, and salts separate better than others. We say they have different degrees of ionization, sometimes expressed in the percent (%) ionized, sometimes expressed in the ratios (K's) of their ionized parts to those un-ionized. (Table 9.) The ions loosened move about in their solutions in water. A symbolic expression for the separation of salt is written:

$$\text{NaCl in water} \longrightarrow \text{Na}^+ + \text{Cl}^-$$

Thus water, with its ability to separate the ions, becomes the ionizing agent.

When silver nitrate is dissolved in water, it ionizes into a silver ion and the nitrate ion:

$$\text{AgNO}_3 \text{ in water} \longrightarrow \text{Ag}^+ + \text{NO}_3^-$$

Suppose, now, both sodium chloride and silver nitrate are mixed in water. The solution then contains 4 different ions:

$$\text{NaCl in water} \longrightarrow \text{Na}^+ + \text{Cl}^-$$
$$\text{AgNO}_3 \text{ in water} \longrightarrow \text{Ag}^+ + \text{NO}_3^-$$

The chloride ion, because it has a great attraction for the silver ion, unites to form a molecule of silver chloride. This drops out of solution as a white precipitate:

$$\text{NaCl in water} \longrightarrow \text{Na}^+ + \text{Cl}^-$$
$$\text{AgNO}_3 \text{ in water} \longrightarrow \text{Ag}^+ + \text{NO}_3^-$$
$$\text{AgCl}$$

Thus a new combination or molecule of silver chloride is formed. Water is not only the ionizing agent but also the meeting place for new ionic associations commonly called molecules.

The ions play important parts in the chemistry of life. For example, the ferrous ion (Fe^{++}) carries oxygen to the tissues; the calcium ion (Ca^{++}) aids in the coagulation of blood.

Compounds that ionize can be classified as acids, bases, and salts.

Ionization constants

According to the law of mass action, the rate of a chemical reaction is proportional to the molecular concentration of the reactants. As the concentration of any weak electrolyte becomes less, the percent of ionization becomes greater These changes react proportionally to each other or, in other words, offset each other, and the ionization constant remains the same. These weak electrolyte concentrations are expressed in moles per liter; when applied to an ionization equilibrium is usually defined as the ionization constant or K_i. The law of action does not hold for strong electrolytes. An example would be HCl H$_2$SO$_4$ that have no usable ionization constant.

In solving problems concerning these constants it must be remembered the constant involved is not always known to a precision greater than two or three significant figures. Therefore, in various books you may see examples with the word "approximate" written to the side.

The concentration value of an aqueous solution needed for the calculation of the ionization constant may be obtained by measuring the concentration of ions in the solution, by means of electric current: the more ions there are in a solution, the more current flows through the solution.

The following examples are given to help you understand various reactions that may take place with the weak acids and bases. Acetic acid will be the main example used for calculating various problems. Remember that opposing arrows in the equations indicate reversible reactions—meaning that the reaction will go in both directions, depending upon the conditions of the reaction, which will then reach a point of equilibrium where no further change is apparent. The ions are still in constant motion, separating as rapidly as they are bound together, only there is no change in the balance or equilibrium. The brackets [ ] enclosing the constant factor equations are used as a symbol of molecular concentration.

In relation to their ionization, weak acids may be classified as monobasic (monoprotic), dibasic (diprotic), or polybasic (triprotic, etc.). These are classifications according to the number of positive hydrogen ions (protons) that can be replaced per molecule.

Monobasic acid. A monobasic acid is an acid having 1 replaceable hydrogen atom per molecule. Example—acetic acid:

$$HC_2H_3O_2 \rightleftarrows H^+ + C_2H_3O_2^-$$

$$\frac{[H^+] \times [C_2H_3O_2^-]}{[HC_2H_3O_2]} = K_i$$

Dibasic acid. A dibasic acid is an acid having 2 replaceable hydrogen atoms per molecule. The ionizaton takes place in two steps and each reaction has its own equilibrium constant (K_i), designated K_1, or K_2. Example—carbonic acid:

1. $H_2CO_3 \rightleftarrows H^+ + HCO_3^{-1}$

$$\frac{[H^+] \times [HCO_3^-]}{[H_2CO_3]} = K_1$$

$HCO_3^{-1} \rightleftarrows H^+ + CO_3^{-2}$

$$\frac{[H^+] \times [CO_3^{-2}]}{[HCO_3^-]} = K_2$$

asic acid. An acid having more than 2 replaceable hydrogen atoms per ʰus requiring more than two steps in order to obtain an ionization is termed a polybasic acid. Each step has its K value. Example—d:

$H^+ + H_2PO_4^{-1}$

$$\frac{[H^+] \times [H_2PO_4^-]}{[H_3PO_4]} = K_1$$

$+ HPO_4^{-2}$

$$\frac{[H^+] \times [HPO_4^{-2}]}{[H_2PO_4^-]} = K_2$$

3. $HPO_4^{-2} \rightleftarrows H^+ + PO_4^{-3}$

$$\frac{[H^+] \times [PO_4^{-3}]}{[HPO_4^{-2}]} = K_3$$

Examples

A 0.1 molar (M) solution of acetic acid is 1.34% ionized. This has been estab-
shed by the measurement, mentioned earlier, of electric conductance. Since
4% of the hydrogen acetate is ionized, then the remaining covalent molecules
ld be 98.66%. As has been discussed, the ion and molecule concentrations
in constant although there is a continual reaction taking place. Water is
cluded in the equilibrium constant equation because water concentration
ically unchanged in a dilute aqueous solution. However, because of the
ce of water and its ions, the numerical value of that K_i (constant) should
bered. (Table 9.)

lculate the ionization constant (K_i) for 0.1 M acetic acid at 25° C.

$HC_2H_3O_2$	$\rightleftarrows$	H^+	$+$	$C_2H_3O_2^-$
98.66% of 0.1 M		1.34% of 0.1 M		1.34% of 0.1 M
or		or		or
0.09866 M		0.00134 M		0.00134 M

$$\frac{[H^+] \times [C_2H_3O_2^-]}{[HC_2H_3O_2]} = K_i$$

$$\frac{0.00134 \times 0.00134}{0.1^* - 0.00134} = \frac{0.00000179}{0.09866}$$

$$\frac{00000179}{866} = 0.0000182 \text{ or } 1.8 \times 10^{-5} = K_i$$

ent ionization in a 0.2 M solution of acetic acid at

K_i constant $= 1.8 \times 10^{-5}$

gen concentration in a 0.2 M solution

$$\frac{[C_2H_3O_2^-]}{H_3O_2]} = 1.8 \times 10^{-5}$$

$$\frac{x}{x} = 1.8 \times 10^{-5}$$

000018×0.2

or

$2 - x =$ approximately 0.2

$r \ 3.6 \times 10^{-6}$

9×10^{-3}

0.2 M solution of acetic acid

hat is the ionization

K_i

M solution of acetic

Table 9. Ionization constants at 25° C. (Other temperatures noted in parentheses)

Name	Ionization reaction			K_i
Acetic acid	$HC_2H_3O_2$	$\rightleftarrows H^+$	$+ \; C_2H_3O_2^-$	1.8×10^{-5}
Ammonium hydroxide	$NH_3 + H_2O$	$\rightleftarrows NH_4^+$	$+ \; OH^-$	1.8×10^{-5} $(0°) \; 1.4 \times 10^{-5}$
Arsenic	H_3AsO_4 $H_2AsO_4^{-1}$ $HAsO_4^{-2}$	$\rightleftarrows H^+$ $\rightleftarrows H^+$ $\rightleftarrows H^+$	$+ \; H_2AsO_4^{-1}$ $+ \; HAsO_4^{-2}$ $+ \; AsO_4^{-3}$	$K_1 \; 5 \times 10^{-3}$ $K_2 \; 8.3 \times 10^{-8}$ $K_3 \; 6 \times 10^{-10}$
Arsenious acid	H_3AsO_3	$\rightleftarrows H^+$	$+ \; H_2AsO_3^-$	6×10^{-10}
Benzoic acid	$HC_7H_5O_2$	$\rightleftarrows H^+$	$+ \; C_7H_5O_2^-$	6.3×10^{-5}
Boric acid	H_3BO_3	$\rightleftarrows H^+$	$+ \; H_2BO_3^-$	$5.8 \times 10^{-}$
n-Caprylic alcohol	$HC_8H_{15}O_2$	$\rightleftarrows H^+$	$+ \; C_8H_{15}O_2^-$	1.27×10
Carbonic acid	H_2CO_3 HCO_3^{-1}	$\rightleftarrows H^+$ $\rightleftarrows H^+$	$+ \; HCO_3^{-1}$ $+ \; CO_3^{-2}$	$K_1 \; 4.5 \times 1$ $K_2 \; 5.6 \times 1$
Creatine (anhydrous)	$C_4H_9O_2N_3$	$\rightleftarrows H^+$	$+ \; C_4H_8O_2N_3^-$	$(40°) \; 1.9 \times$
Creatinine	$C_4H_7ON_3$	$\rightleftarrows H^+$	$+ \; C_4H_6ON_3^-$	$(40°) \; 3.7 \times$
Formic acid	$HCHO_2$	$\rightleftarrows H^+$	$+ \; CHO_2^-$	$1.8 \times$
Hydrochloric acid	HCl	$\rightleftarrows H^+$	$+ \; Cl^-$	No cons
Lactic acid	$HC_3H_5O_3$	$\rightleftarrows H^+$	$+ \; C_3H_5O_3^-$	1.387
Phosphoric acid	H_3PO_4 $H_2PO_4^{-1}$	$\rightleftarrows H^+$ $\rightleftarrows H^+$	$+ \; H_2PO_4^{-1}$ $+ \; HPO_4^{-2}$	$K_1 \; 7.5$ $K_2 \; 6.2$
Phosphorous acid	H_3PO_3 $H_2PO_3^{-1}$	$\rightleftarrows H^+$ $\rightleftarrows H^+$	$+ \; H_2PO_3^{-1}$ $+ \; HPO_3^{-2}$	$K_1 \; 1.6$ $K_2 \; 7$
Picric acid	$HC_6H_2O_7N_3$	$\rightleftarrows H^+$	$+ \; C_6H_2O_7N_3$	4
Sulfuric acid	H_2SO_4 HSO_4^{-1}	$\rightleftarrows H^+$ $\rightleftarrows H^+$	$+ \; HSO_4^{-1}$ $+ \; SO_4^{-2}$	N K_2
Sulfurous acid	H_2SO_3 HSO_3^{-1}	$\rightleftarrows H^+$ $\rightleftarrows H^+$	$+ \; HSO_3^{-1}$ $+ \; SO_3^{-2}$	K_1 K_2
Trichloroacetic acid	$HC_2O_2Cl_3$	$\rightleftarrows H^+$	$+ \; C_2O_2Cl_3^-$	
Urea	CH_4ON_2	$\rightleftarrows H^+$	$+ \; CH_3ON_2^-$	
Uric acid	$C_5H_4O_3N_4$	$\rightleftarrows H^+$	$+ \; C_5H_3O_3N_4$	
Water	H_2O	$\rightleftarrows H^+$	$+ \; OH^-$	

3. A normal solution of acetic acid is 0.42% ionized. W
constant? Referring to problem 1, solve as follows:

$$\frac{0.0042 \times 0.0042}{1 - 0.0042} = 0.0000177 \text{ or } 1.8 \times 10^{-5} =$$

4. Sufficient sodium acetate was dissolved in a 0.1

acid to bring the molarity to a 1.5 solution. What is the hydrogen ion concentration of this 1.5 M solution?

$$\frac{[H^+] \times 1.5}{0.1} = 1.8 \times 10^{-5} = K_i$$

$$15\ [H^+] = 0.000018 \text{ or } 1.8 \times 10^{-5}$$

$$[H^+] = 0.0000012 \text{ or } 1.2 \times 10^{-6} \text{ M}$$

Problems

1. Calculate the ionization constant of formic acid, $HCHO_2$, which ionizes 4.2% in a 0.10 M solution.

   Answer: 1.8×10^{-4} or 0.00018.

2. Refer to Table 9 for the ionization constant of ammonium hydroxide at $25°$ C. (a) Determine the degree of ionization. (b) Find the OH^- concentration of a 0.08 M solution of NH_4OH.

   Answers: (a) 1.5%. (b) 1.2×10^{-3} mole/liter.

3. A solution of acetic acid is 1.0% ionized. (a) What is the molarity of the solution? (b) What is the hydrogen concentration of the solution?

   Answers: (a) 0.18 M. (b) 1.8×10^{-3} or 0.0018 mole/liter.

ACIDS, BASES, AND SALTS

Acids, bases, and salts are compounds whose molecules ionize when dissolved in water. The discussion will cover the following:

> Acids
> Bases
> Salts
> Strength of acids and bases
> Titratable acidity of an acid

Acids

An acid is a compound containing a hydrogen atom (H) that is capable of ionizing. The following acids are frequently used by the technician: hydrochloric acid, nitric acid, sulfuric acid, and acetic acid. The composition of these acids and the manner in which they ionize are discussed below.

Hydrochloric acid (HCl). Hydrochloric acid is a water solution of a dense gas, hydrogen chloride. In 100 parts of concentrated hydrochloric acid there are about 38 parts of hydrogen chloride gas, the remainder being water. The acid is ionized as follows:

$$HCl \text{ in water} \longrightarrow H^+ + Cl^-$$

Nitric acid (HNO₃). Nitric acid is a liquid. In 100 parts of concentrated nitric acid there are about 68 parts of nitric acid, the remainder being water. The acid is ionized as follows:

$$HNO_3 \text{ in water} \longrightarrow H^+ + NO_3^-$$

Sulfuric acid (H_2SO_4). Sulfuric acid is a dense, oily liquid. In 100 parts of concentrated sulfuric acid there are about 95 parts of sulfuric acid, the remainder being water. The acid is ionized as follows:

$$H_2SO_4 \text{ in water} \longrightarrow 2 H^+ + SO_4^{--}$$

Acetic acid ($HC_2H_3O_2$). Acetic acid is a colorless liquid. When pure, it is called glacial acetic acid. In 100 parts of glacial acetic acid there are about 99.5 parts of acetic acid, the remainder being water. The acid is ionized as follows:

$$HC_2H_3O_2 \text{ in water} \longrightarrow H^+ + C_2H_3O_2^-$$
$$\text{(HAc)} \qquad\qquad\qquad \text{(Ac)}$$

Bases

A base is a compound containing a hydroxyl radical (OH) that is capable of ionizing. Sodium hydroxide and ammonium hydroxide are two commonly used bases. Their composition and method of ionizing are given below.

Sodium hydroxide ($NaOH$). Sodium hydroxide is a white solid commonly known as caustic soda. It is readily dissolved in water. One hundred parts of water will dissolve about 100 parts of sodium hydroxide. The base ionizes as follows:

$$NaOH \text{ in water} \longrightarrow Na^+ + OH^-$$

Ammonium hydroxide (NH_4OH). Ammonium hydroxide is a water solution of ammonia gas. One volume of water at 20° C. dissolves 200 volumes of ammonia gas. Ammonium hydroxide ionizes as follows:

$$NH_4OH \text{ in water} \longrightarrow NH_4^+ + OH^-$$

Salts

When an acid and a base react, a salt and water are formed. The reaction is called neutralization. Three neutralization reactions are given below:

$$HCl + NaOH \longrightarrow NaCl + H_2O$$
$$\text{(acid)} + \text{(base)} \longrightarrow \text{(salt)} + \text{(water)}$$

$$H_2SO_4 + 2 NaOH \longrightarrow Na_2SO_4 + 2 H_2O$$
$$\text{(acid)} + \text{(base)} \longrightarrow \text{(salt)} + \text{(water)}$$

$$HAc + NaOH \longrightarrow NaAc + H_2O$$
$$\text{(acid)} + \text{(base)} \longrightarrow \text{(salt)} + \text{(water)}$$

In the first reaction, hydrochloric acid is neutralized by sodium hydroxide to form water and sodium chloride. In the second reaction, sulfuric acid is neutralized by sodium hydroxide to form water and sodium sulfate.

Sometimes, to emphasize the weak ionization of the acetic acid, the arrow is written very short or the symbols are recorded in small print. The hydrogen ion of an acid (H^+) in water is loosely held to a water molecule by the free electrons on the oxygen atom. In other words, the hydrogen ion shares a pair of electrons with the oxygen as shown:

$$H:\overset{..}{\underset{..}{O}}:H^+$$
$$H$$

These H_3O^+ ions are named hydronium ions. The hydroxyl (OH^-) ions of an added base more strongly attract the H^+ to form another molecule of water. We shall use the simpler expression, hydrogen ion, rather than hydronium H_3O^+ ion.

Strength of acids and bases

With the acids and bases, the degree of ionization is the factor that determines their strength. For example, if acetic acid is put in water, only about 1% of the molecules ionize into hydrogen ions and acetate ions. Since this is a very small degree of ionization, acetic acid is a weak acid.

On the other hand, when hydrochloric acid is put in water, about 92% of the molecules ionize into hydrogen ions and chloride ions. Since this is a high degree of ionization, hydrochloric acid is a strong acid.

The above facts are illustrated in the following equations, where the percent that ionizes is indicated above the arrow:

$$HC_2H_3O_2 \text{ in water} \quad \xrightarrow{1\% \text{ ionization}} H^+ + C_2H_3O_2^-$$
$$HCl \text{ in water} \quad \xrightarrow{92\% \text{ ionization}} H^+ + Cl^-$$

Ammonium hydroxide does not ionize to any great extent. Therefore, ammonium hydroxide is a weak base. Sodium hydroxide, however, ionizes almost completely. Consequently, sodium hydroxide is a strong base.

By nature, each acid and base has its own particular degree of ionization. Those with a high degree of ionization are strong, whereas those with a small degree are weak.

It should be understood, however, that a strong acid or base can be diluted with water and thereby lose its strength. For example, if we take a beaker of the strong acid, hydrochloric acid, and pour it into a gallon of water, the diluted acid may become as weak as acetic acid.

Most salts ionize to a high degree, and thus we do not speak of strong or weak salts, but rather of salt concentrations.

Titratable acidity of an acid

The total strength of an acid is known as the titratable acidity. For example, acetic acid ionizes about 1%. This means that 99% of the potential hydrogen ions are bound in the acetic acid molecule. These bound ions plus the free ions make up the titratable acidity.

HYDROGEN ION CONCENTRATION

The exact ionic strength of dilute acid and basic solutions may be expressed by their hydrogen ion concentration. This, however, entails the use of extremely small numbers, and the chemist prefers to express the hydrogen ion concentration by a symbol. This symbol is known as the pH value. A brief discussion follows.

Water ionizes to a very slight degree ($H_2O \longrightarrow H^+ + OH^-$). Consequently, water contains both hydrogen ions and hydroxyl ions.

All dilute acid and basic solutions contain water. Therefore, all dilute acid and basic solutions contain both hydrogen ions and hydroxyl ions.

These solutions differ, however, in their respective concentrations of ions.

In dilute acid solutions, the hydrogen ions outnumber the hydroxyl ions. In dilute basic solutions, the hydroxyl ions outnumber the hydrogen ions.

It has been shown that the following condition exists in all dilute acid and basic solutions: the hydrogen ion concentration times the hydroxyl ion concentration equals the extremely small number 0.000,000,000,000,01. This condition may be expressed by the following equation, in which the brackets around the hydrogen ion and hydroxyl ion indicate that the concentrations are given in moles per liter:

$$[H^+] \times [OH^-] = 0.000,000,000,000,01$$

Thus, in any dilute acid or basic solution, the hydrogen ion concentration times the hydroxyl ion concentration equals 0.000,000,000,000,01.

One tenth normal hydrochloric acid is a dilute acid solution. The concentrations of the ions have been found by experimentation and are written below their respective symbols:

$$[H^+] \times [OH^-] = 0.000,000,000,000,01$$
$$0.1 \times 0.000,000,000,000,1 = 0.000,000,000,000,01$$

Note that the hydrogen ion concentration is much greater than the hydroxyl ion concentration. (One tenth of a dollar is much more than one trillionth of a dollar.)

One tenth normal sodium hydroxide is a dilute basic solution. The concentrations of the ions have been found by experimentation and are given below:

$$[H^+] \times [OH^-] = 0.000,000,000,000,01$$
$$0.000,000,000,000,1 \times 0.1 = 0.000,000,000,000,01$$

This time, note that the hydrogen ion concentration is much less than the hydroxyl ion concentration. The number 0.000,000,000,000,1 is much smaller than 0.1.

Extremely small numbers such as those used above may be expressed by the mathematical shorthand given in Table 10. In this table, 10^{-3} equals 0.001. The -3 is known as the exponent in the number 10^{-3}. Also, as shown, 10^{-13} equals

Table 10. Mathematical shorthand

$$10^{0} = 1.0$$
$$10^{-1} = 0.1$$
$$10^{-2} = 0.01$$
$$10^{-3} = 0.001$$
$$10^{-4} = 0.000,1$$
$$10^{-5} = 0.000,01$$
$$10^{-6} = 0.000,001$$
$$10^{-7} = 0.000,000,1$$
$$10^{-8} = 0.000,000,01$$
$$10^{-9} = 0.000,000,001$$
$$10^{-10} = 0.000,000,000,1$$
$$10^{-11} = 0.000,000,000,01$$
$$10^{-12} = 0.000,000,000,001$$
$$10^{-13} = 0.000,000,000,000,1$$
$$10^{-14} = 0.000,000,000,000,01$$

0.000,000,000,000,1. The −13 is known as the exponent in the number 10^{-13}. Note that the exponent simply tells how many places the decimal point has been moved from unity (1.0). For example, in $10^{-2} = 0.01$, the exponent is −2. This −2 means that the decimal point has been moved two places to the left of unity (from 1.0 to 0.01).

Using this mathematical shorthand, a hydrogen ion concentration of 0.001 may be written as 10^{-3}, and a hydrogen ion concentration of 0.000,000,000,000,1 may be written as 10^{-13}.

From the above discourse, we can draw the following conclusion: when discussing the hydrogen ion concentration, it is much simpler to use mathematical shorthand such as 10^{-3}, 10^{-13}, etc.

The chemist, however, in order to simplify matters still further, expresses the hydrogen ion concentration by the symbol pH. *The symbol pH stands for the exponent of the hydrogen ion concentration with the minus sign dropped.* A few examples follow:

If the hydrogen ion concentration is 10^{-3}, the exponent is −3. Dropping the minus sign gives 3, and the pH becomes 3.

If the hydrogen ion concentration is 10^{-13}, the exponent is −13. Dropping the minus sign gives 13, and the pH becomes 13.

These and a few other examples are listed below:

Hydrogen ion concentration	*pH value*
10^{-1}	1
10^{-3}	3
10^{-7}	7
10^{-10}	10
10^{-13}	13

To repeat, the pH value of a solution is simply the exponent of the hydrogen ion concentration with the minus sign dropped.

The relationship between the hydrogen ion concentration and the pH value is indicated in Fig. 4. In the figure, the letter N stands for the word normal. This is a term which is used to express the strength of a solution. The greater the normality (N), the stronger the solution.

The student should carefully study Fig. 4 and make certain that he understands the following four points.

1. Neutral solutions, such as pure water, have a pH of 7. Acids have pH values between 0 and 7; the larger the pH number, the weaker the acid. Bases have pH values between 7 and 14; the larger the pH number, the stronger the base.
2. There is a seesaw relationship between the hydrogen ion concentration and the pH value. When one goes up, the other goes down. For example, as the hydrogen ion concentration *increases* from 10^{-2} to 10^{-1}, the corresponding pH values *decrease* from 2 to 1.
3. Only *dilute* solutions, such as 0.1 N or 1 N, can be measured on the pH scale. Concentrated solutions, such as 10 N or 12 N, exceed the limits of the scale. Therefore, they cannot be measured.
4. It might be well to remember that in such water solutions of acids the hydroxyl (OH^-) ion is also present in lesser amounts than the hydrogen (H^+) ion. So we could use the expression pOH. Since $H^+ \times OH^-$

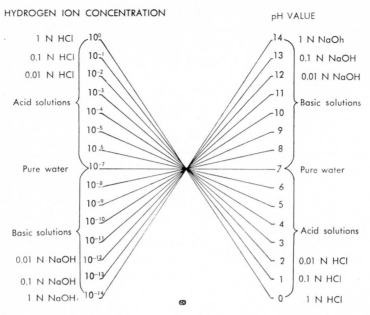

Fig. 4. Seesaw relationship between the hydrogen ion concentration and pH value. When one goes up, the other goes down.

$= 10^{-14}$ (known ionic product for water), the pOH can always be found whenever the pH is known (or vice versa) by subtracting the known value from 14.

After you have studied Fig. 4, answer the following questions before you continue. The answers may be derived from the figure and the four points discussed above.

1. A solution has a pH of 13. Is it acid or basic?
2. An acid solution has a hydrogen ion concentration of 10^{-1}. What is the corresponding pH value?
3. A solution of hydrochloric acid has a pH of 2, and a solution of sulfuric acid has a pH of 4. Which solution is more acid?
4. A solution has a pH of 7. Is it acid, basic, or neutral?
5. Suppose the hydrogen ion concentration of the blood increases. Does the pH value increase, decrease, or remain the same?
6. Suppose the hydrogen ion concentration of the blood decreases. Does the pH value increase, decrease, or remain the same?
7. The gastric juices of a patient have a pH value of 5. Are they acid or basic?
8. A basic solution has a pH of 10. What is the corresponding hydrogen ion concentration?

CHEMICAL INDICATORS

Indicators are substances that show color changes according to the concentration of the hydrogen (hydroxyl) ion. These are used to determine the strength of solutions and the end points of reactions. Here are a few types of indicators you may become acquainted with in the field of chemistry:

1. Achromatic—a mixture of indicators chosen for their complementary colors so that at the end of the reaction, the end point is colorless.

2. Absorption—an indicator that shows the end point of a titration by changing the indicator's colloidal condition, so that the precipitate, which has been colored by the indicator, will either lose or gain the color.

3. External (outside)—an indicator that is used outside the solution being titrated, with the indicator placed in a small beaker while the solution being titrated is added dropwise into the beaker to obtain the end point.

4. Fluorescent—an indicator that shows the end point of a reaction by either an increase or a decrease in fluorescence.

5. Internal—an indicator that is added to the solution being analyzed.

6. Neutralization—the indicator that undergoes a distinct color change at the equivalence point where the acid and base solutions are neutralized in titrations.

7. Oxidation-reduction—an indicator that undergoes a distinct color change at a definite state of oxidation of a solution.

8. Turbidity—indicators of a type that shows the end point by an increase in turbidity or precipitation; usually colloidal solutions.

9. Universal—a selected mixture of indicators giving a wide range of pH values.

Five common indicators

This section deals with five indicators that are frequently used by the technician. Following the discussion, the reasons for the reactions of indicators are considered.

> Litmus paper
> Nitrazine paper
> Töpfer's reagent
> Phenolphthalein
> pHydrion

Litmus paper. Litmus paper is a strip of chemically treated paper. It turns red in an acid solution and blue in a basic solution. Litmus paper is generally used to determine the acidity or alkalinity of urine.

Nitrazine paper. Nitrazine paper is also a strip of chemically treated paper. This indicator turns from green to yellow in an acid solution and blue in a basic solution. It is also used to test urine for acid or basic properties.

Töpfer's reagent. Töpfer's reagent is a dye dissolved in alcohol. It is red up to a pH of 2.8. As the pH value increases, it turns light orange and finally yellow at pH 4.0. Töpfer's reagent is used to test gastric juices for hydrochloric acid and to determine the strength of weak acid and basic solutions.

Phenolphthalein. Phenolphthalein is an organic salt dissolved in alcohol. It is colorless up to pH 8.3. As the pH value increases beyond 8.3, it turns pink and finally bright red at pH 10.0. Phenolphthalein is used to test the strength of weak acid and basic solutions.

pHydrion. pHydrion is a chemically treated paper strip that gives specific pH values. The color of the paper is compared to the color chart in the container.

Reason for the color change of indicators

Indicators are usually organic dyes whose color in a solution changes according to the degree of ionization of the indicator. In a basic indicator there will be

Table 11. Indicators

Indicator	Color change		pH range	Preparation	
	Acid	*Alkaline*			
Thymol blue					
Acid	Red	Yellow	1.2-2.8	Thymol blue (thymolsulfonphthalein)	40.0 mg.
Alkaline	Yellow	Blue	8.0-9.6	Absolute ethyl alcohol	100.0 ml.
Bromphenol blue	Violet	Blue	3.0-3.6	Tetrabromophenolsulfonphthalein	0.1 gm.
				Ethyl alcohol (20%)	100.0 ml.
Töpfer's reagent	Red	Yellow	3.0-4.0	p-Dimethylaminoazobenzene	0.5 gm.
				Ethyl alcohol (95%)	100.0 ml.
Congo red	Blue	Red	3.0-5.0	Congo red	0.5 gm.
				Distilled water	90.0 ml.
				Ethyl alcohol (95%)	10.0 ml.
Methyl orange	Orange-red	Yellow	3.1-4.4	Methyl orange	100.0 mg.
				Distilled water	100.0 ml.
Bromcresol green	Yellow	Blue	3.8-5.4	Tetrabromometacresolsulfonphthalein	40.0 mg.
				Absolute ethyl alcohol	100.0 ml.
Methyl red	Red	Yellow	4.2-6.3	Methyl red	1.0 gm.
				Ethyl alcohol (95%)	300.0 ml.
				Dilute to 500 ml. with distilled water	
Chlorphenol red	Yellow	Red	4.8-6.4	Chlorphenol red	40.0 mg.
				Absolute ethyl alcohol	100.0 ml.
Alizarin red	Yellow	Red	5.5-6.8	Sodium alizarin monosulfonate	1.0 gm.
				Distilled water	100.0 ml.
Bromthymol blue	Yellow	Blue	6.0-7.6	Dibromthymolsulfonphthalein	40.0 mg.
				Absolute ethyl alcohol	100.0 ml.
Neutral red	Red	Yellow	6.8-8.0	Neutral red	0.5 gm.
				Ethyl alcohol (95%)	300.0 ml.
				Dilute to 500 ml. with distilled water	
Phenol red	Yellow	Red	6.8-8.4	Phenol red (phenolsulfonphthalein)	20.0 mg.
				Ethyl alcohol (95%)	100.0 ml.
Phenolphthalein	Color-less	Red	8.3-10.0	Phenolphthalein	1.0 gm.
				Ethyl alcohol (95%)	100.0 ml.

more negative ions than in a solution that is neutral. The weak acid indicator
has even fewer ions. In the case of the indicator methyl red, since the negative
ion differs from the molecule, the acid color of red changes to the base color of
yellow according to the ionization taking place. In water solution these indicator
ions are in balance (equilibrium) with the molecule. This is symbolized as
follows:

$$\text{H Ind} \rightleftarrows \text{H}^+ + \text{Ind}^-$$
$$\text{Color A} \qquad \text{Color B}$$

If acid with more H^+ is added, the equilibrium will be pushed to the left;
color A is dominant. If base is added, uniting with the H^+ ions, the equilibrium
will move to the right; color B is dominant.

In such an equilibrium there is always a constant ratio between the product of the ions and the molecule:

$$\frac{[H^+] \times [Ind^-]}{[H\ Ind]} = K \text{ (constant)}$$

or

$$[H^+] \times [Ind^-] = K\ [H\ Ind]$$
$$\text{Color A} \qquad \text{Color B}$$

At the end point of a reaction, the two color forms will be in equal concentrations, and the amount of $[H^+]$ will equal the ionization K of the indicator.

•   •   •

Since each indicator has its own K value, the indicator that is to be used must be selected to fit the ionization value of the mixture being measured. A list of indicators and their pH range is given in Table 11.

Chapter 2

Basic techniques

The basic techniques that the student should know are as follows:

Methods of measuring liquids
Methods of weighing solids
Methods of separating solids from liquids

After reading this material, the student should perform all the exercises given at the end of the chapter.

METHODS OF MEASURING LIQUIDS

The vast majority of chemical tests call for the measurement of liquids. The measuring vessels most frequently used are pipets, graduated cylinders, and volumetric flasks. These are discussed below.

Measures

A liter (L.) is the unit of measure. It is slightly larger than a quart. The word "milli" is Latin for 1/1000. And 1/1000 part of a liter is called a milliliter (ml.).

Since for all practical purposes a milliliter and a cubic centimeter (cc.) measure the same volume, they are used interchangeably. Actually, 1 L. contains 1000.000 ml. or 1000.028 cc. The measures and abbreviations used by the technician are given in Table 12.

Table 12. Measures

Measure	Abbreviation	Equivalent
Milliliter	ml.	1/1000 of a liter
Cubic centimeter	cc.	1/1000 of a liter
Liter	L.	1000 ml. or cc.
Fluid ounce	fl. oz.	29.57 ml. or cc.

Pipets

Volumes up to 25 ml. are usually measured by pipets. A pipet is an expensive, calibrated glass tube resembling a soda straw. The pipet is the most abused equipment in the laboratory. No matter how elaborate the equipment of the laboratory or how simple or complex the analysis, the result is worth nothing if the pipetting has been inaccurate. Use the correct pipet according to the demands of the analysis. Do not use serological pieces for exacting volumetric work. The badge of a fine technician is not how many instruments he can use but how accurate he is in manual methods and how reproducible is his work.

To use a pipet, the technician places the lower end in the liquid and the upper end in his mouth. Fluid should be drawn up past the mark, the tip of the pipet wiped carefully with tissue and then lowered to the mark by gradually easing the pressure of the finger. The markings or graduations are indicated on the sides of the pipet.

By covering the upper end of the pipet with the tip of the index finger, the technician holds the fluid in the pipet. To transfer to another container, the pipet is held in a vertical position with the tip touching the side of the container at a slight angle. The fluid is allowed to drain into the container by a releasing of finger pressure on the mouth of the pipet. The technique, which is illustrated in Fig. 5, can be acquired with a little practice.

There are two general types of pipets: serological and volumetric.

Serological pipets are used to measure various volumes. For example, a 1

Fig. 5. Technique of pipetting.

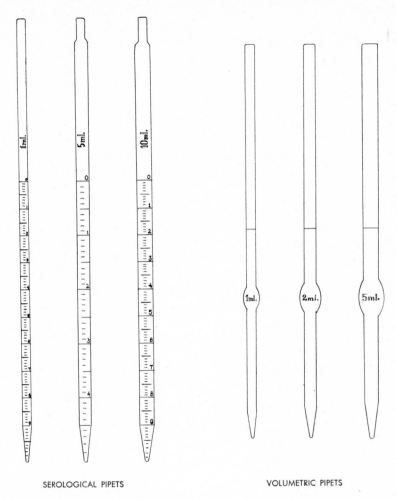

SEROLOGICAL PIPETS   VOLUMETRIC PIPETS

Fig. 6. Serological and volumetric pipets.

ml. serological pipet may measure 0.2, 0.5, or 0.7 ml. The volumes are denoted by markings on the sides of the pipet. The most frequently used serological pipets are the 1, 5, and 10 ml. sizes. These are illustrated in Fig. 6.

Each volumetric pipet is used to measure one fixed volume. For example, a 1 ml. volumetric pipet will measure only 1.0 ml. The volume is denoted by a line or circle on the stem of the pipet. The most frequently used volumetric pipets are the 1, 2, and 5 ml. sizes. These are illustrated in Fig. 6.

When volumetric pipets are used, and the fluid is allowed to drain into a container, there is a tiny portion which remains in the tip of the pipet. This portion should *not* be blown out. If it were blown out, an error would be introduced, for all volumetric pipets are calibrated to deliver (TD) the specified volume.

Ostwald-Folin pipet

The pipet generally used for delivering whole blood or viscous material is called the Ostwald-Folin pipet. This type of pipet has a relatively large oval bulb and a short delivery tip. The pipet is usually calibrated to deliver a fixed volume, and the last drop of material *is* blown out the delivery tip. The "blow-out" pipet is indicated by an etched band at the mouthpiece. There will be many references to this pipet in the following chapters. This type of pipet is not to be confused with the volumetric pipet described above.

Graduated cylinders and volumetric flasks

Volumes above 25 ml. are often measured by graduated cylinders and volumetric flasks.

Graduated cylinders are commonly referred to as graduates. They are used to measure various volumes. For example, a 50 ml. graduate measures volumes such as 15, 32, or 48 ml. These volumes are denoted by markings on the sides of the graduate. The most frequently used graduates are the 50 and 100 ml. sizes.

When a liquid is poured into a graduate, the uppermost portion of the liquid forms a curve or meniscus. In measuring, the reading is always taken from the bottom of this meniscus (Fig. 7).

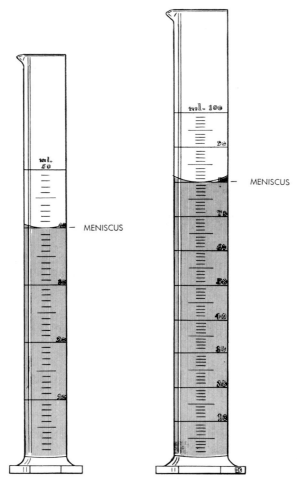

Fig. 7. Graduates.

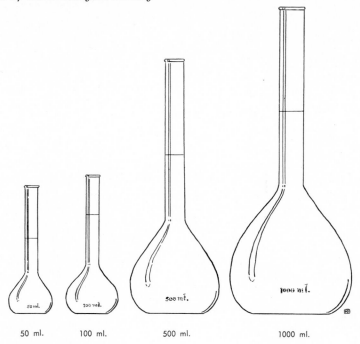

50 ml.   100 ml.   500 ml.   1000 ml.

Fig. 8. Volumetric flasks.

The volumetric flask, also, is used to measure one fixed volume. For example, a 50 ml. volumetric flask will measure only 50 ml. The volume is denoted by a line or circle on the neck of the flask. The most frequently used volumetric flasks are the 50, 100, 500, and 1000 ml. sizes. These are illustrated in Fig. 8.

Fluids expand with heat. When a solution is hot, it may measure 100 ml. Upon cooling to room temperature, however, it may measure only 98 ml. To avoid error, all fluids should be adjusted to room temperature before they are measured. Room temperature, for the average laboratory, is about 25° C. (77° F.).

METHODS OF WEIGHING SOLIDS

The rough balance and the analytical balance are used to weigh chemical reagents. The operation of the rough balance is quite simple. The operation of the analytical balance, however, requires a bit of technique.

The rough balance weighs accurately to one tenth of a gram. This balance is used for weighings that do not call for extreme accuracy.

The analytical balance weighs accurately to one thousandth of a gram. This balance is used for weighings that require the utmost in accuracy.

The type of balance to be employed is specified with each weighing procedure.

This section discusses the following:

Weights
Rough balance
Analytical balance

Table 13. Weights

Weight	Abbreviation	Equivalent
Microgram	γ (gamma) or μg	1/1000 of a milligram
Milligram	mg.	1/1000 of a gram
Gram	gm.	1/1000 of a kilogram
Kilogram	kilo. or kg.	1000 grams

Weights

A gram is the unit of weight. One thousandth part of a gram is called a milligram (mg.). (A large pea weighs about 1 gm. and an eyelash weighs about 1 mg.) The word "kilo" is Greek for 1000. It follows that a kilogram (kilo. or kg.) is 1000 gm. This is equivalent to 2.2 pounds. The weights and abbreviations used by the technician are given in Table 13.

Rough balance

A rough balance that is widely used is illustrated in Fig. 9. It is operated in the following manner.

1. Place a piece of paper on the right-hand pan and another piece of equal size on the left-hand pan.
2. By moving the weights on the two sliding scales, find the desired weight. For example, if you wish to weigh 35 gm., the weight on the lower sliding scale is put on the 30 gm. mark and the weight on the upper sliding scale is put on the 5 gm. mark.
3. Add the reagent to the left-hand pan until the pointer comes to rest at the midpoint of the scale.
4. Transfer the reagent to a container. Discard the papers. Replace the weights to the zero points on their sliding scales.

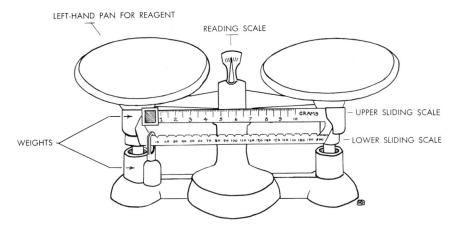

Fig. 9. Rough balance.

Analytical balance

An analytical balance is a highly sensitive instrument. It can weigh such objects as an eyelash or even a few grains of salt. With each analytical balance

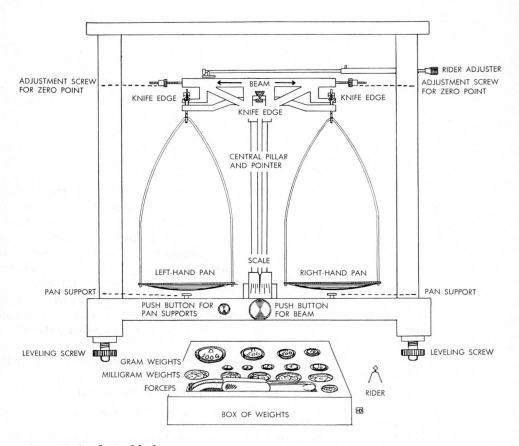

Fig. 10. Analytical balance.

there is a set of weights. Both the balance and the weights should be handled with the utmost care.

A typical set of weights is illustrated in Fig. 10. There are both gram weights and milligram weights. These weights are placed on the right-hand pan of the balance.

In the box of weights, there is also a small piece of bent wire that is known as a rider. When the rider is properly adjusted on the beam of the balance, it enables the technician to weigh to the fourth decimal place. For example, the technician could weigh 5.1001 gm. of substance. The chainomatic balances and the new automatic balances enable a technician to weigh easily to the fourth decimal place. However, the analytical balance in Fig. 10 does just as well. The following discussion concerns mainly the balance shown in Fig. 10.

In any given weighing, such as 5.1001 gm., the numbers on the left side of the decimal point represent grams, whereas the numbers on the right-hand side of the decimal point represent milligrams. Thus, in weighing 5.1001 gm., we would use a 5 gm. weight and a 100 mg. weight. Step 5 explains how the fourth decimal place is obtained.

In weighing 6.155 gm., we would use the following weights:

Gram weights	*Milligram weights*
1 gm.	100 mg.
5 gm.	50 mg.
	5 mg.
6 gm.	155 mg.

An analytical balance is so sensitive that a 1 mg. weight will cause a deflection of the pointer. The degree of deflection produced by the 1 mg. weight is called the sensitivity of the balance. For example, if the pointer moves 3 units on the scale when a 1 mg. weight is added to either pan, the sensitivity of the balance is 3.

This instrument should be placed where there is controlled temperature and there are no drafts, corroding fumes, dust, or vibrations. Be sure to set up away from ovens, radiators, or cold, damp areas, for this temperature change sets up a convection current within the balance, affecting the swings of the beam and giving what is called an irregular falling off. Some laboratories have temperature and humidity controlled rooms as "weighing rooms." Although the "weighing room" is ideal, it is not practical for the average hospital laboratory or doctor's office. Place the balance in the cleanest and most draft-free area of the room, the part having the least vibration and temperature change. Extreme caution and observation should be made to eliminate errors caused by the above factors.

Before operating an analytical balance, the student should study the parts of the balance as illustrated in Fig. 10.

During all weighing procedures, keep the following rules in mind.

1. *Always* handle the weights with a pair of forceps. This keeps them free from moisture and dirt.
2. *Never* put anything on or take anything off the pans unless they are resting on the pan supports. This preserves the knife edges on which the beam and stirrups rest and thus helps to maintain the accuracy of the balance.
3. Close the glass door of the balance before the actual weighing. This prevents drafts from moving the pans of the balance.

The steps outlined below for the operation of an analytical balance have been followed with good results by many technicians. However, they are by no means the final word, as the technique of weighing varies considerably. The student should get firsthand instruction from the chemist or technician in charge of the department.

1. Check to see if the balance is resting in a level position. The "level indicator" is usually located near the central pillar. If the balance is not level, adjust the leveling screws. (This adjustment of the level indicator rarely needs to be made.)
2. Carefully note which push button is used to lower the beam and which push button is used to lower the pan supports. Now check the zero point by *carefully* lowering the beam onto the knife edges and then *slowly* lowering the pan supports. The pointer should come to rest at the midpoint (zero point) on the scale. If it does not, ask the chemist to adjust the screw at the end of the beam. Now raise the pan supports and beam. (This adjustment of the zero point also rarely needs to be made.)

3. Many have a problem at first with parallax in reading the indicator on the index scale. It is difficult to find the exact midpoint of the scale. The technician will look at the indicator while squinting with one eye. Then he will "take bead" on the indicator with the other eye, and of course the exact midpoint moves. Next comes squirming in the chair, and the line of sight is definitely off. To obtain a consistent technique in weighing, place a permanent mark or dot on the balance door window, and always take your readings with the eye level so located that the "midpoint" appears directly behind this mark. This is a suggestion once made by Christian Becker, the maker of torsion balances.

4. At some time in your work, you may have to calibrate a set of weights for your own use. The simplest method is to compare the test set against a standard set (certified from the Bureau of Standards). Make a chart and record plus or minus weights of the test set against those of the control set. The tolerances of the weights shown are for Class S_1 weights, which are used for general routine laboratory work. These are tolerances allowed by the National Bureau of Standards.

Weight	Tolerance
100 gm.	1.0 mg.
50	0.6
20	0.35
10	0.25
5	0.18
2	0.13
1	0.10
500 mg.	0.080
200	0.060
100	0.050
50	0.042
20	0.035
10	0.030
5	0.028
2	0.025
1	0.025

5. When a student is learning to weigh a sample, the fourth decimal place is sometimes avoided because of a lack of confidence. If the balance has a calibrated beam and rider, as previously mentioned, and if this is a 5 mg. rider, the third and fourth decimal places may be obtained. With the 5.1001 gm. quantity the rider would be placed as in Fig. 11. (*Note:* Detach the rider adjuster from the rider before releasing the beam and pan supports to obtain the weight of specimen.) For 5.1021 gm. you could either use a 2 mg. weight for the 2 and set the rider as illustrated in Fig. 11 or set the rider at 2.1, giving the .0021 weight needed. If no rider is available, a method is recommended whereby the fourth decimal place is found by calculation from the known sensitivity of the balance.

6. The sensitivity must first be determined. This is a more or less stable characteristic so the sensitivities are done only at intervals or when the balance is moved to a new location. The zero point in practical weighing need not be the exact zero on the scale, but it should be determined each day when beginning the balance work for the day.

7. Sensitivity means the number of points of swing equivalent to 1 mg. A scale for the pointer numbered 0 to 20 from left to right will simplify calculations. Those that are not numbered may be marked for the individual who has difficulty in recording swings. (Fig. 12.) A beginner should determine the "rest-point" several times until the final point is reproducible. Due to friction, each swing is somewhat shorter than the preceding one. With the pans empty set the beam in motion

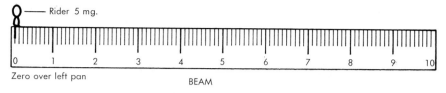

Fig. 11. Beam of the analytical balance.

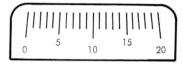

Fig. 12. Scale of the analytical balance.

by slowly releasing the beam arrest and the pan arrest to get the desired amplitude of swing. The beam may be set into motion by placing the rider on the beam momentarily and then removing it. Do not start the oscillations by tapping the pans or by blowing air into the balance. The first few swings will be erratic due to vibrations caused in releasing the beam and pan arrests. The pointer should swing about ten divisions on the scale. Average the readings of the three consecutive swings on the left and the readings of the two consecutive swings on the right. Average these two results to obtain the midpoint. This is called the equilibrium point of the balance under zero load. Example:

	Left ← Swings → Right	
	5	15
	6	14
	7	
Totals	18	29
Average	6 (18 ÷ 3)	14.5 (29 ÷ 2)
Total	20.5 (6 + 14.5)	
Midpoint or equilibrium	10.2 (20.5 ÷ 2)	

8. Now place the rider on 1 mg. notch of the beam. Again find the equilibrium or midpoint in the same way. Of course, it will be less than 10.2. Say, for illustration, the midpoint calculates 6.2. Subtracting the 6.2 from the 10.2 gives a sensitivity of 4.0 for the empty balance. Therefore, four points of the swing will equal 1 mg. The sensitivity of the balance is the tangent of the angle through which the equilibrium position of the pointer is displaced by an excess load (usually, 1 mg.) on one of the pans. The angle is so small the sensitivity may be taken as the number of scale divisions displaced by the overload of the 1 mg. on the pan. The technician should determine the sensitivity of the balance at 0, 1, 5, 10, 20, and 50 gm. Plot the sensitivity in scale divisions against the load and draw a smooth curve through the points. This will give a chart in which sensitivity may be read directly for any given load. Each of the midpoints is obtained as explained in the directions given above.

9. Practice weighing a small beaker and a small rubber stopper together and then separately until you can check with accuracy to the fourth place. For example, if the actual weight of the two articles is 5.1001 gm, and you have on the pan a 5 gm. weight and a 100 mg.

weight the swing of the pointer is light. Now determine the equilibrium or midpoint. It should average 10.6. The midpoint of the empty balance was 10.2. Using the sensitivity of 4.0, you found that 4 points of the swing = 1 mg. (step 8). Therefore, 0.4 of a point of swing = 0.1 mg. or 0.0001 gm. The total weight would then be 5.1001 gm.

10. Watchglasses, weighing bottles, or 3 by 5 glassine weighing paper may be used as containers for reagents. *Never* put any reagent directly on the pans. Now determine which is the heavier by lowering the beam and very *gently* partially lowering the pan supports. The heavier container, of course, will be the one that drops lower. After raising the supports and the beam, transfer the lighter containers to the right-hand pan of the balance.

11. Balance the pans by adding weights to the right-hand pan of the balance. The pointer will come to rest at *exactly* midpoint of the scale. Using the forceps, place the desired weights on the right-hand pan.

12. With a clean dry spatula add small portions of reagent to the left-hand pan of the balance. When it appears to the naked eye that an amount equal to the weights has been added, lower the beam and very gently *partially* lower the pan supports. Note whether too much or too little has been added and then raise the pan supports and beam. Using a clean dry spatula, add or remove the reagent from the pan until the pointer can be made to come to rest *exactly* at the midpoint of the scale. When you add or remove the reagent, *make certain* that the pan supports are raised so that the "shock" is taken off the knife edges of the beam. *(Note: Never* place excess reagent back into the bottle.)

13. Check the weights to see if you have weighed the amount desired. Check the reagent to see if you have weighed the reagent desired.

14. Place a clean dry funnel in a volumetric flask of the desired volume. Carefully transfer the reagent into the funnel, making certain not to lose any. Wash the reagent down the funnel and into the flask with the solvent.

15. Using forceps, place the weights back in the box.

16. Clean the balance, using a small camel's-hair brush for the pans. Close the door of the balance.

METHODS OF SEPARATING SOLIDS FROM LIQUIDS

In many instances, it is necessary to separate solids from liquids. For example, in the analysis of urine, we must obtain and examine the urinary sediments. Solids may be separated from liquids by centrifuging or by filtering. A discussion of each follows.

Centrifuging

A centrifuge is an instrument that spins fluid suspensions at a high rate of speed. This forces the solid material to the bottom of the container. The solid material is called the precipitate, and the upper liquid portion is known as the supernatant fluid (Fig. 13).

A centrifuge may operate at various rates of speed. There is the hand-driven model, holding two or four tubes, which can be cranked to 2500 revolutions per minute (RPM). At the other extreme, a new high-speed centrifuge can be purchased that will go to 19,000 RPM. For the average centrifuge, the speed is about 3000 RPM.

If the tubes to be centrifuged are of different weights or sizes use a centrifuge tube balance for equalizing the weight. These balances are small, cheap,

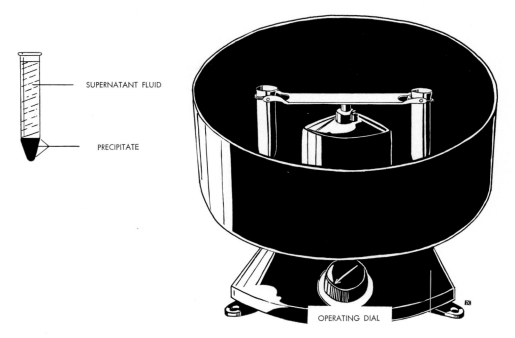

Fig. 13. Centrifuge, supernatant fluid, and precipitate.

and worth their weight in gold if you have a group of tubes that are of all weights and sizes. However, if you have uniform tubes the following procedure is quite adequate.

To operate a centrifuge, proceed as follows:

1. Pour the fluid to be centrifuged into a test tube or centrifuge tube.
2. Obtain another tube of *equal* size.
3. Fill this tube with water until it is *exactly* equal to the fluid level in the other tube.
4. Now place these tubes in the centrifuge holders (Fig. 13) so that they are *directly* opposite each other. This balances the centrifuge.
5. Slowly turn the operating dial to the RPM recommended.
6. Allow the fluids to spin for about 5 minutes. Spin 10 minutes for viscous material.
7. Turn the operating dial in the reverse direction. This shuts off the power.
8. When the test tubes stop spinning, remove them from their holders. The precipitate will be in the bottom of the centrifuge tube and the supernatant fluid will lie above.
9. To separate the precipitate from the supernatant fluid, simply pour off the fluid.

Filtering

Another method of separating solids from liquids is known as filtering. To filter, proceed as follows:

1. Obtain a piece of filter paper and fold it in half as indicated in Fig. 14, illustration *1*.
2. Again fold the filter paper in half, as indicated in illustration 2.

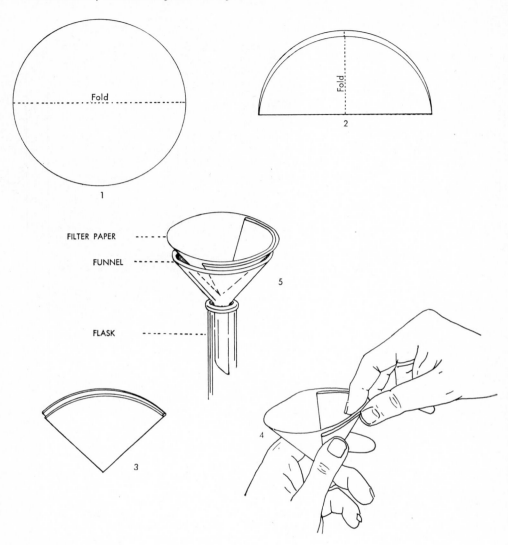

Fig. 14. Technique of folding a filter paper.

3. This will then form a V as shown in illustration *3*.
4. Make a cone-shaped figure, as indicated in illustration *4*. Keep the fingers *out* of the cone.
5. Place the cone-shaped figure in a funnel, as shown in illustration *5*.
6. Put the funnel in a flask.
7. Hold the filter paper in place and carefully add the fluid to be filtered.
8. The precipitate of solid material will collect on the filter paper. The clear fluid, which is known as the filtrate, will drip into the flask below.

   Acid or basic solutions too strong for filter paper may be filtered through a funnel containing glass wool. Be careful in handling, for if you get this in your fingers it is quite annoying. These are very basic exercises but they are to help the beginner in manipulating equipment and in developing dexterity.

STUDENT EXERCISES

The following pages contain exercises in measuring liquids, weighing solids, and separating solids from liquids.

Exercises in measuring liquids

In the laboratory, ordinary water from the faucet is known as tap water. This water contains salts and minerals. Since these substances interfere in many chemical tests, tap water is never used in chemical analysis.

When the salts and minerals have been removed from tap water, it is known as distilled water. All chemical tests call for the use of distilled water.

The following preliminary exercises deal with the identification and manipulation of laboratory glassware (Fig. 15).

1. Fill a large Erlenmeyer flask with distilled water.
2. Using a 1.0 ml. serological pipet, transfer 0.5 ml. of water to an empty beaker.
3. Using a 2.0 ml. volumetric pipet, transfer 2.0 ml. of water to the beaker.
4. Using a 5 ml. serological pipet, transfer 4.0 ml. of water to the beaker.

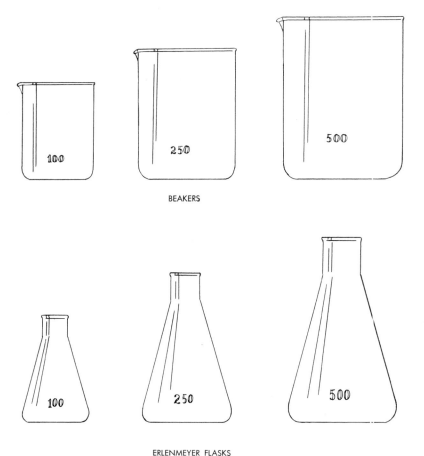

Fig. 15. Beakers and Erlenmeyer flasks.

5. Using a 100 ml. graduate, measure 100 ml. of water and pour into the beaker.
6. Using a 100 ml. graduate, measure 70 ml. of water and add to the contents of the beaker.
7. Using a 250 ml. graduate, measure the amount of water in the beaker. You should have 176.5 ml.

After developing finger-tip control of the pipet, the student technician should concentrate on breath control or suction during the process of pipetting. Using a carbonated beverage, practice carefully avoiding bubbles within the pipet. Mastering this technique will eliminate unnecessary accidents.

Exercises in weighing solids

In using the analytical balance, you should remember that it is a very sensitive instrument. Therefore, handle it carefully!

The following exercises deal with the operation of the rough balance and the analytical balance.

If the sodium chloride used in these exercises is lumpy, loosen it with a spatula. Methods of removing a reagent from a bottle are illustrated in Fig. 16.

1. Using the rough balance, weigh out 5.0 gm. of sodium chloride. Transfer to a small beaker.

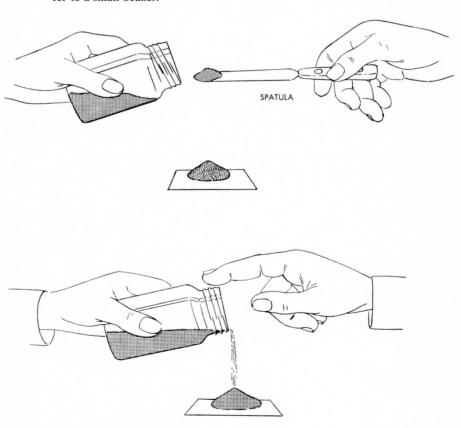

Fig. 16. Methods of removing reagent from bottle.

2. Using the rough balance, weigh out 8.5 gm. of sodium chloride. Transfer to a small beaker.
3. Using the rough balance, weigh out 11.8 gm. of sodium chloride. Transfer to a small beaker.
4. Using the analytical balance, weigh out 2.0053 gm. of sodium chloride. Using a funnel, transfer to a small Erlenmeyer flask.
5. Using the analytical balance, weigh out 0.3214 gm. of sodium chloride. Using a funnel, transfer to a small Erlenmeyer flask.

Exercises in separating solids from liquids

A Kahn tube is a small test tube, measuring about 75×100 mm.

The following exercises deal with the techniques of centrifuging and filtering.

1. Fill a Kahn tube about ¾ full with urine.
2. Fill a second Kahn tube with the same amount of water.
3. Centrifuge both tubes about 5 minutes.
4. Pour off and discard the supernatant in the tube of urine.
5. Note the small amount of grayish white precipitate in the bottom of the tube. This is the urinary sediment that is examined in the analysis of urine.
6. Obtain a piece of filter paper and a funnel and filter about 50 ml. of urine into a flask. Observe the precipitate on the filter paper.

Chapter 3

Preparation of solutions

T̲he student should prepare all the solutions discussed on the following pages. This experience will be of considerable help on student examinations, enable him to gain some degree of dexterity with laboratory glassware, and teach him the technique of using chemical balances. In schools and hospitals where instructors do not allow students to use the analytical balance, the rough balance may be substituted—with the understanding, of course, that the results may not be absolutely accurate.

The discussion covers the following:

> Saturated solutions
> Percent solutions
> Molar solutions
> Molal solutions
> Normal solutions

SATURATED SOLUTIONS

When a solid is dissolved in a liquid, the solid is known as the solute and the liquid is known as the solvent. For example, if you add sugar to coffee, the sugar is the solute and the coffee is the solvent.

A saturated solution is one that contains as much solute as it can hold in solution. To illustrate, if you were to add 25 teaspoons of salt to a glass of water, some salt would remain undissolved. The supernatant would then be a saturated solution.

Prepare a saturated solution of sodium chloride in the manner given below.

1. Add about 40 ml. of distilled water to a 125 ml. Erlenmeyer flask.
2. Using a teaspoon, add about 2 teaspoons of sodium chloride to the flask.
3. Swirl the flask in order to mix (Fig. 17).
4. Continue adding sodium chloride and mixing until no more dissolves.
5. Pour into a clean bottle.
6. Add a little extra sodium chloride to the bottle.
7. Label the bottle: Saturated Solution of Sodium Chloride. Also put your name and the date of preparation on the bottle.

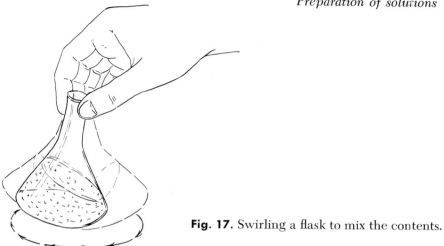

Fig. 17. Swirling a flask to mix the contents.

Now repeat the above procedure, using benzoic acid in place of sodium chloride. You will notice that benzoic acid appears to be insoluble. Actually it dissolves very slowly and requires only a very small amount to make a saturated solution. For this reason a solvent with an excess of solute should be allowed to stand, with frequent agitation, for at least an hour before you can be sure that the solution is saturated.

PERCENT SOLUTIONS

A percent solution contains a measured amount of the solute in a specified volume of solution. The solute may be either a solid or a liquid. For example, sodium chloride is a solute that is a solid, whereas acetic acid is a solute that is a liquid.

In most percent solutions, distilled water is used as the solvent. However, in some instances, alcohol or another liquid may be used.

For the preparation of percent solutions, the student should remember the following "rule of thumb": the number before the percent sign indicates the amount of solute needed for 100 ml. of solution. For example, in preparing 5% sodium chloride, 5 gm. of sodium chloride are needed for 100 ml. of solution, and in preparing 10% acetic acid, 10 ml. of acetic acid are needed for 100 ml. of solution.

The procedures for preparing the following percent solutions are given below.

> 5% sodium chloride
> 0.85% sodium chloride
> 5% acetic acid

Preparation of 5% sodium chloride

In preparing this solution, you should carefully observe the technique of mixing the contents of a volumetric flask.

1. Using the analytical balance, weigh out 5 gm. of sodium chloride.
2. Place a funnel in the neck of a 100 ml. volumetric flask.
3. Being careful not to lose any, transfer the sodium chloride to the funnel (Fig. 18).

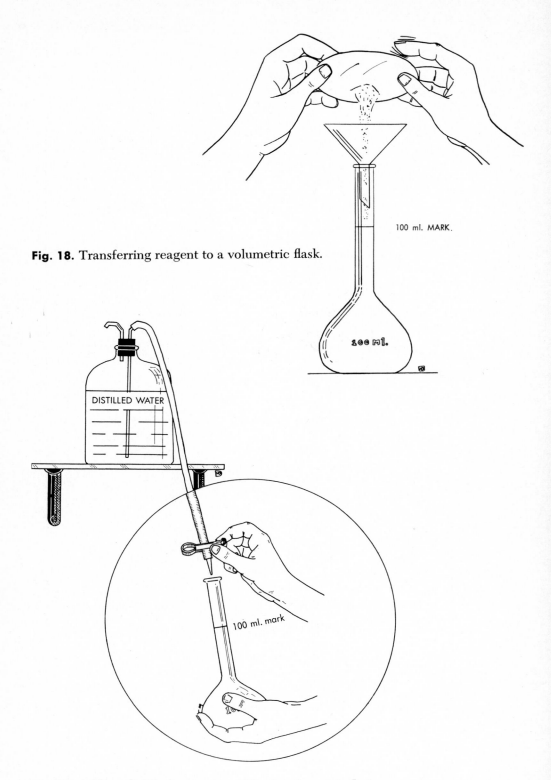

100 ml. MARK.

100 ml.

Fig. 18. Transferring reagent to a volumetric flask.

DISTILLED WATER

100 ml. mark

Fig. 19. Adding distilled water to a 100 ml. volumetric flask.

4. Wash the sodium chloride through the funnel and into the flask with distilled water.
5. Continue adding distilled water to the 100 ml. mark (Fig. 19).
6. Mix as illustrated in Fig. 20, making certain that all the sodium chloride dissolves.
7. Get a clean bottle.
8. Pour 5 to 10 ml of the sodium chloride solution into the bottle. Shake and discard. This rinses the bottle.
9. Pour the remaining sodium chloride solution into the bottle.
10. Label: 5% Sodium Chloride. Also put your name and the date of preparation on the bottle.

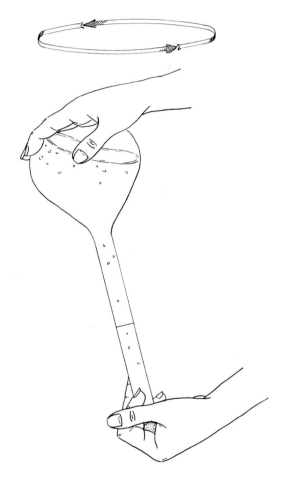

Fig. 20. Mixing the contents of a volumetric flask.

1. Stopper the flask and place the palm of your left hand on the stopper.
2. Now grasp the bottom of the bulblike portion with your right hand and invert the flask.
3. Hold your left hand in a fixed position and, using your right hand, rotate the bulblike portion in a circular motion.
4. Make about ten circular motions and then place the flask in an upright position for a few seconds.
5. Repeat mixing process at least five times.

Preparation of 0.85% sodium chloride

An 0.85% solution of sodium chloride is often referred to as physiological saline or "normal saline." This solution has the same osmotic pressure as normal blood. Physiological saline is used for injections intravenously to restore lost body fluids or is sometimes used as a conveyance for drugs. Another solution used for the same purpose—one that contains both sodium and potassium chlorides—is called Ringer's solution.

Physiological saline prevents the red cells of the blood from swelling or shrinking; that is, water neither enters nor leaves the cells. Such a solution is said to be isotonic. A solution that is less concentrated than physiological saline is called hypotonic, whereas a solution that is more concentrated is called hypertonic.

If the red cells were placed in a hypotonic solution, water would pass through the cell membrane and enter the cells. This would cause the cells to swell. On the other hand, if the red cells were placed in a hypertonic solution, water would leave the cells and cause them to shrink.

The student will recall from his previous studies that the above is simply an illustration of the principle of osmosis: when two liquids of different densities are separated by a semipermeable membrane, the flow of water is always toward the greater density.

Prepare 100 ml. of 0.85% sodium chloride in the following manner.

1. Use the analytical balance to weigh out the sodium chloride. Since 0.850 gm. is required, select the weights listed below. Next, place the weights on the right-hand pan of the balance. Finally, weigh out the 0.850 gm. of sodium chloride.

500 mg. weight
200 mg. weight
100 mg. weight
 50 mg. weight
—————————
850 mg.

2. Place a funnel in the neck of a 100 ml. volumetric flask.
3. Being careful not to lose any, cautiously transfer the salt to the funnel.
4. Wash the salt through the funnel and into the flask with distilled water. Continue adding distilled water to the 100 ml. mark.
5. Mix as illustrated in Fig. 20.
6. Get a clean bottle.
7. Pour from 5 to 10 ml. of the salt solution into the bottle. Shake and discard. This rinses the bottle.
8. Transfer the remaining salt solution to the bottle.
9. Label: 0.85% Sodium Chloride. Also put your name and the date of preparation on the bottle.

Preparation of 5% acetic acid

If water is added to concentrated acid, a reaction may occur which splatters the acid. The splattered acid could result in a severe burn. If, however, the acid is added to water, little danger is incurred. Therefore, in mixing concentrated acids and water, *always add the acid to the water.*

Prepare 100 ml. of 5% acetic acid in the following manner.

1. Add approximately 85 ml. of distilled water to a 100 ml. volumetric flask.

2. *Cautiously* add 5 ml. of glacial acetic acid, using a volumetric pipet with a large rubber bulb.
3. Mix by swirling.
4. Fill to 100 ml. mark with distilled water, stopper, and invert about six times to mix.
5. Pour this into a clean bottle.
6. Label: 5% Acetic Acid. Also put your name and the date of preparation on the bottle.

MOLAR SOLUTIONS

A molar (M) solution contains 1 gram-molecular weight per liter of solution. The procedure for preparing 1 M sodium chloride is given below.

Preparation of 1 M sodium chloride

Since a molar solution contains 1 gram-molecular weight per liter (1000 ml.) of solution, we must find the molecular weight of sodium chloride. Sodium has an atomic weight of 22.9898 gm., and chlorine has an atomic weight of 35.4530 gm. The molecular weight of sodium chloride is found by adding the atomic weights:

$$
\begin{array}{ll}
\text{Atomic weight of sodium} = & 22.9898 \text{ gm.} \\
\text{Atomic weight of chlorine} = & 35.4530 \text{ gm.} \\
\hline
\text{Molecular weight of NaCl} = & 58.4428 \text{ gm.}
\end{array}
$$

The molecular weight of sodium chloride is therefore 58.4428 gm. To make a 1 M solution, 58.4428 gm. are needed for 1000 ml., or 5.844 gm. are needed for 100 ml.

Make 100 ml. of 1 M sodium chloride as follows:

1. Use the analytical balance to weigh out the sodium chloride. Since 5.844 gm. are required, select the weights listed below. Next, place the weights on the right-hand pan of the balance. Finally, weigh out the 5.844 gm. of sodium chloride.

Gram weights	Milligram weights
5 gm.	500 mg.
	200 mg.
	100 mg.
	20 mg.
	10 mg.
	10 mg.
	4 (two 2 mg.)
5 gm.	844 mg.

2. Place a funnel in the neck of a 100 ml. volumetric flask.
3. Being careful not to lose any, transfer the salt to the funnel.
4. Wash the salt through the funnel and into the flask with distilled water. Continue adding distilled water to the 100 ml. mark.
5. Mix as illustrated in Fig. 20, p. 49. Make sure that all the salt dissolves.
6. Get a clean bottle.
7. Pour about 5 ml. of the salt solution into the bottle. Shake and discard.
8. Transfer the remaining salt solution to the bottle.
9. Label: 1 M Sodium Chloride. Also put your name and the date of preparation on the bottle.

MOLAL SOLUTIONS

Whereas the *molar* solution contains 1 mole (molecular weight in grams) of solute in 1000 ml. of solution, the *molal* solution contains 1 mole of solute in 1000 gm. (1 kg.) of solvent. A more technical definition of molal solution states that it contains 1 gram-molecular weight of solute dissolved in 1 kg. of solvent.

An easy way to remember the difference is to note that the molar solution is always on a solute per solution basis and the molal solution is always on a solute per solvent basis.

The student and technician should become familiar with the term "molal." This is used with osmometry (Chapter 15), which is one of the newer diagnostic tools for the routine laboratory.

NORMAL SOLUTIONS

Normal solutions are used extensively by the technician. Therefore, the student should thoroughly master the material of this section. The discussion covers the following:

> Composition of normal solutions
> Equivalent weights
> Use of normal solutions
> Preparation of normal solutions

Composition of normal solutions

The word "normal" is abbreviated with the capital letter N.

The normality of a solution is expressed with numbers. For example, 0.1 N NaOH is one tenth normal sodium hydroxide.

Unfortunately for the student, some chemists write the numbers as fractions. Thus they may write 0.1 N as N/10. Or they may write 0.01 N as N/100. In order to avoid confusion, the student should note the type of labelling used in his particular laboratory.

A replaceable hydrogen atom is one that is capable of ionizing. Hydrochloric acid, HCl, has 1 replaceable hydrogen atom. Sulfuric acid, H_2SO_4, has 2 replaceable hydrogen atoms. Acetic acid, $HC_2H_3O_2$, has 4 hydrogen atoms but only 1 is capable of ionizing. Therefore, acetic acid has only 1 replaceable hydrogen atom. The number of replaceable hydrogen atoms in an acid is an inherent property, which the chemist has found through experimentation and a study of molecular structure.

An equivalent weight of an *acid* is the molecular weight divided by the number of replaceable hydrogen atoms. For example, hydrochloric acid (HCl) has 1 replaceable hydrogen atom. Its equivalent weight is, therefore, the molecular weight divided by 1:

$$\text{Equivalent weight HCl} = \frac{\text{Molecular weight}}{\text{Number of replaceable hydrogen atoms}}$$

$$= \frac{36.461 \text{ gm.}}{1}$$

$$= 36.461 \text{ gm.}$$

Sulfuric acid (H_2SO_4) has 2 replaceable hydrogen atoms, and, consequently, its equivalent weight is the molecular weight divided by 2:

$$\text{Equivalent weight } H_2SO_4 = \frac{\text{Molecular weight}}{\text{Number of replaceable hydrogen atoms}}$$

$$= \frac{98.078 \text{ gm.}}{2}$$

$$= 49.039 \text{ gm.}$$

The equivalent weight of a *base* is the molecular weight divided by the number of replaceable hydroxyl ions. For example, sodium hydroxide (NaOH) has 1 replaceable hydroxyl ion. Therefore, its equivalent weight is the molecular weight divided by 1:

$$\text{Equivalent weight NaOH} = \frac{\text{Molecular weight}}{\text{Number of replaceable hydroxyl ions}}$$

$$= \frac{39.997 \text{ gm.}}{1}$$

$$= 39.997 \text{ gm.}$$

Calcium hydroxide, $Ca(OH)_2$, has 2 replaceable hydroxyl ions. Therefore, its equivalent weight is the molecular weight divided by 2:

$$\text{Equivalent weight Ca(OH)}_2 = \frac{\text{Molecular weight}}{\text{Number of replaceable hydroxyl ions}}$$

$$= \frac{74.0947 \text{ gm.}}{2}$$

$$= 37.047 \text{ gm.}$$

The equivalent weights of *salts,* such as silver nitrate and potassium permanganate, are determined by the number of electrons which they give or take during a reaction. For example, silver nitrate, $AgNO_3$, gives 1 electron. Therefore, the equivalent weight is the molecular weight divided by 1. Potassium permanganate, $KMnO_4$, takes 5 electrons. Therefore, the equivalent weight is the molecular weight divided by 5.

The equivalent weights of the compounds that the technician is likely to meet are given in Table 14.

An equivalent weight is contained in 1 liter of a 1 normal (1 N) solution. For example, 49.039 gm. of sulfuric acid are present in 1 liter of 1 N H_2SO_4, and 39.997 gm. of sodium hydroxide are present in 1 liter of 1 N NaOH.

It follows that 2 equivalent weights are present in 1 liter of a 2 N solution, and 0.1 equivalent weight is present in 1 liter of an 0.1 N solution.

Some chemists prefer to discuss equivalent weights in terms of milliequiva-

Table 14. Equivalent weights of compounds

Compound	Formula	Molecular weight	Equivalent weight
Hydrochloric acid	HCl	36.461	36.461
Sulfuric acid	H_2SO_4	98.078	49.039
Oxalic acid	$H_2C_2O_4 \cdot 2H_2O$	126.067	63.033
Sodium hydroxide	NaOH	39.997	39.997
Potassium hydroxide	KOH	56.109	56.109
Silver nitrate	$AgNO_3$	169.874	169.874
Potassium permanganate	$KMnO_4$	158.038	31.607

lent weights. The prefix "milli" means 1/1000. Consequently, a milliequivalent weight is 1/1000 of an equivalent weight. The word "milliequivalent" is often abbreviated meq. (or mEq.). Milliliter is abbreviated ml. There is 1 meq. in 1 ml. of every 1 N solution. This may be expressed by the following equation:

$$\text{Volume (in ml.)} \times \text{Normality} = \text{Milliequivalent}$$

or

$$V \times N = meq.$$

Equivalent weights

The system of using equivalent weights is a useful tool in chemistry calculations because the differences in the weights (or masses) of various atoms need not be considered. For example, 3 gram atoms of sodium have a combined weight of 69 gm., whereas 2 gram atoms of chlorine have a weight of 71 gm. Even though their weights are nearly the same, it is known that only 2 atoms of sodium can combine with the 2 atoms of chlorine. This, then, leaves an excess of sodium even though there are fewer grams of sodium than there are of chlorine.

On the other hand, if it were stated that there are 3 equivalents of sodium and only 2 equivalents of chlorine it would be readily apparent that there is an excess of sodium.

Another example of the usefulness of the equivalent system is in the neutralization of acids and bases. Keep in mind, however, that the same scheme may be used in any situation where chemical reaction occurs.

By definition 1 ml. of 1 N solution contains 1 meq. of material. Therefore, 2 ml. contain 2 meq., and 10 ml. contain 10 meq. Generally then, volume in milliliters times normality equals milliequivalents. Stated mathematically, $V \times N = meq.$ If one has, for example, 10 ml. of a 1 N acid, it will contain 10 meq. of acid. This amount of acid will exactly neutralize 10 meq. of any alkali. If one wants to calculate the normality of an alkali and it is found that 5 ml. of the alkali are required to neutralize the 10 ml. of 1 N acid, it is known that there must be 10 meq. of alkali in the 5 ml. volume. The normality of the alkali must then be 2, since 5 ml. of a 2 N alkali would contain 10 meq. Examples that follow will illustrate this principle of $V \times N = meq.$

Since the equivalent weight of acid is the same as that of alkali, volume of acid × normality of acid = volume of base × normality of base.

This same system applies to many other types of calculation. For example, for a mixture of 10 ml. of 1 N HCl with 5 ml. of 2 N NaOH the following calculations may be made:

$$10 \times 1 = 10 \text{ meq. of HCl}$$

and

$$5 \times 2 = 10 \text{ meq. of NaOH}$$

Therefore, the alkali exactly neutralizes the acid.

In addition, the amount of NaCl that could be produced in such a combination is easily determined. Since 1 meq. of HCl and 1 meq. of NaOH produce 1 meq. of NaCl, the mixture just described would yield 10 meq. of NaCl. Since 1 meq. requires 58.5 mg., 10 meq. would represent 585 mg. of NaCl.

At this point it might be brought out that all quantities need not necessarily be discussed in terms of specific volumes. For example, if one had a flask that contained exactly 40 mg. of NaOH, the amount of water in which it was dissolved would not alter the absolute quantity. When titrating this amount of NaOH with a standard acid it would not matter whether the NaOH was dissolved in 5 ml. or 500 ml. of water. Consider the following examples:

1. Assume that 40 mg. of NaOH are dissolved in 5 ml. of H_2O. Therefore, there is 1 meq. in a volume of 5 ml. Since $V \times N = $ meq., you can calculate that the value of N will be 0.2. It would require 1 meq. of acid to to neutralize the NaOH. Suppose that 0.1 N HCl is used. Then:

$$V_A \times N_A = V_B \times N_B$$

$$V \times 0.1 = 5 \times 0.2$$

$$V = 10$$

Therefore, 10 ml. of 0.1 N HCl would be required to neutralize 40 mg. of NaOH dissolved in 5 ml. of H_2O.

2. If 40 mg. of NaOH are dissolved in 10 ml. of H_2O, $10 \times N = 1$ or $N = 0.1$. Suppose the same HCl solution is used. Then:

$$V_A \times 0.1 = 10 \times 0.1$$

$$V = 10 \text{ ml.}$$

Note that in both cases 10 ml. of the 0.1 N HCl are required. This should be evident, since 10 ml. of 0.1 N HCl constitute 1 meq. In other words, the 1 meq. of HCl neutralizes the 1 meq. of NaOH regardless of the amount of H_2O used to dissolve the NaOH.

The following problem demonstrates the usefulness of the equivalent system. Suppose 20 ml. of 0.2 N HCl are added to 10 ml. of 0.3 N NaOH: (1) Is the resulting solution acid or alkaline? (2) What is the final normality? (3) How much NaCl is produced?

The amounts of the acid and alkali are calculated with the equation $V \times N = $ meq. as follows:

$$20 \times 0.2 = 4 \text{ meq. of HCl}$$

$$10 \times 0.3 = 3 \text{ meq. of NaOH}$$

Since there is more HCl than required to neutralize the NaOH, the resulting solution will be acid. In this situation, 3 meq. of HCl will be utilized to neutralize the 3 meq. of NaOH. Therefore, there will be 1 meq. of HCl in the final solution, which has a volume of 30 ml. There is, therefore, 1 meq. of HCl in a volume of 30 ml., or $30 \times N = 1$. The final N of the HCl is then 1/30. Further, 3 meq. of NaOH with 3 meq. of HCl will produce 3 meq. of NaCl. Since 1 meq. of NaCl weighs 58.5 mg., there would be 3×58.5 (or 175.5) mg. of NaCl produced.

Many other uses of the meq. system, too numerous to itemize, make this an essential tool for use in quantitative chemistry.

By way of summary—an equivalent weight of an acid is the molecular weight divided by the number of replaceable hydrogen atoms, whereas the equivalent weight of a base is the molecular weight divided by the number of replaceable hydroxyl ions. A 1 normal solution of an acid or base contains 1 equivalent weight per liter of solution.

Use of normal solutions

The neutralizing power of a 1 N acid solution is exactly equal to the neutralizing power of a 1 N basic solution ($H^+ = OH^-$). Thus 10 ml. of 1 N HCl will exactly neutralize 10 ml. of 1 N NaOH, or 8 ml. of 0.1 N HCl will exactly neutralize 8 ml. of 0.1 N NaOH. This neutralizing ability of acids and bases enables the chemist to determine the exact normality of solutions of unknown normality. A few examples follow.

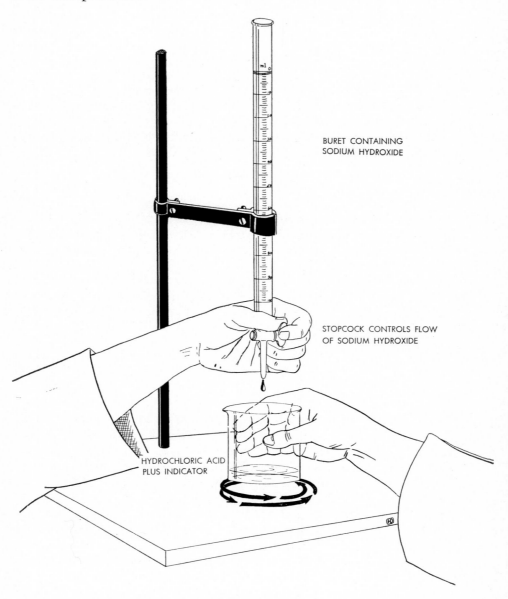

BURET CONTAINING
SODIUM HYDROXIDE

STOPCOCK CONTROLS FLOW
OF SODIUM HYDROXIDE

HYDROCHLORIC ACID
PLUS INDICATOR

Fig. 21. Titrating with a buret. Note that the buret must always be left chemically clean and dry, ready for the next titration.

Suppose we have a hydrochloric acid solution of unknown normality, and the problem is to determine the exact normality of this solution. The following two steps are necessary:

Step 1: Titration (Fig. 21), or standardization
Step 2: Calculation

Step 1: Titration. Titration is a volumetric operation measuring the concentration of a solution or a constituent within a solution by measuring the reaction of this unknown against a standard of known concentration. The proper indicator is used to aid in determining the end point. In this discussion hydrochloric acid is the solution to be standardized. First, 10 ml. of the HCl are pipetted into a flask or beaker. A few drops of the indicator phenolphthalein are then added. Next, 0.1 N NaOH is slowly added from a buret until the indicator changes from colorless to a faint pink, thus signifying the completion of neutralization. The number of milliliters required to reach this end point is recorded and used in the calculation given below. Let us assume, for the sake of illustration, that 20 ml. of the 0.1 N NaOH were used. Consequently, from the above titration, we would have the following data:

Volume of acid (HCl) used: 10 ml.
Normality of base (NaOH) used: 0.1 N
Volume of base (NaOH) used: 20 ml.

Step 2: Calculation. The normality of the hydrochloric acid is found by writing down the following equation, filling in the blanks with the available data, and then solving the equation.

Vol. of acid × Norm. of acid = Vol. of base × Norm. of base
(   )   ×   (   )   =   (   )   ×   (   )

For example, we first write down the equation as indicated above and then proceed to fill in the blanks in the following manner. Since we are looking for the normality of the acid, a question mark is put under the Norm. of acid. Because the volume of acid used was 10 ml., a 10 is put below the Vol. of acid. Since the normality of the base was 0.1 N, an 0.1 is put below the Norm. of base. Then, as we are assuming the volume of the base was 20 ml., a 20 is placed below the Vol. of base. Thus, we have:

Vol. of acid × Norm. of acid = Vol. of base × Norm. of base
    10   ×   ?   =   20   ×   0.1

To solve the equation, we must first eliminate the number 10 on the side of the unknown. Since there is a rule in algebra which states that both sides of an equation can be divided by the same number, we divide both sides by 10:

$$\frac{10 \times \text{Norm. of acid}}{10} = \frac{20 \times 0.1}{10}$$

Cancelling the 10's, we have:

Norm. of acid = 2 × 0.1

Multiplying, we have:

Norm. of acid = 0.2

Consequently, the exact normality of the HCl is 0.2 N.

The formula on p. 57 should be learned by each student, as he will use it frequently. You will note that there is a balance in the equation: that is, the volume times normality of the acid equals the volume times normality of the base. Another way to calculate the normality is shown below:

Vol. of acid × Norm. of acid = Vol. of base × Norm. of base
10   ×   x   =   20   ×   0.1

$$10 \times x = 20 \times 0.1$$
$$10 \ x = 2.0$$
$$x = 0.2$$

Ten multiplied by x gives 10 x. Twenty multiplied by 0.1 gives 2.0. Dividing 2.0 by 10 gives a result of x = 0.2.

In algebra this type of equation is called a proportion formula, or an equality of ratios. You are finding x in the proportion of:

$$\frac{x}{0.1} = \frac{20}{10} \quad \text{or} \quad 10 \ x = 20 \times 0.1$$

Suppose we have a sodium hydroxide solution of unknown normality, and the problem is to determine the exact normality. The following two steps are necessary:

Step 1: Titration
Step 2: Calculation

Step 1: Titration. First, 10 ml. of 0.1 N oxalic acid are put in a flask. A few drops of the indicator phenolphthalein are then added. Next, the NaOH is slowly added from a buret until the indicator changes from colorless to faint pink, thus signifying the completion of neutralization. The number of milliliters required to reach this end point is recorded and used in the calculation given below. Let us assume, for the sake of an illustration, that 8 ml. were used. Thus from the above titration, we would have the following data:

Normality of acid (oxalic acid) used: 0.1 N
Volume of acid (oxalic acid) used: 10 ml.
Volume of base (NaOH) used: 8 ml.

Step 2: Calculation. The normality of the sodium hydroxide is found by writing down the following equation, filling in the blanks with the given data, and then solving the equation. You should note that this is the same equation which we used in finding the normality of the acid previously discussed.

Vol. of acid × Norm. of acid = Vol. of base × Norm. of base
(   )   ×   (   )   =   (   )   ×   (   )

In this example we first write down the equation as indicated above and then proceed to fill in the blanks in the following manner. Since we are looking for the normality of the base, a question mark is put under the Norm. of base. Because the normality of the acid was 0.1 N, an 0.1 is put below the Norm. of acid. Since the volume of the acid was 10 ml., a 10 is put below the Vol. of acid. Then, as we are assuming that 8 ml. of the base were used, an 8 is put below the Vol. of base. Thus, we have:

Vol. of acid × Norm. of acid = Vol. of base × Norm. of base
10   ×   0.1   =   8   ×   ?

To solve the equation, we must first eliminate the number 8 on the side of the unknown. Since there is a rule in algebra which states that both sides of an equation can be divided by the same number, we divide both sides by 8:

$$\frac{10 \times 0.1}{8} = \frac{8 \text{ Norm. of base}}{8}$$

Cancelling the 8's, we have:

$$1.25 \times 0.1 = \text{Norm. of base}$$

Multiplying, we have:

$$0.125 = \text{Norm. of base}$$

Consequently, the exact normality of the NaOH is 0.125 N.

It is extremely important that students understand the above calculations. There are just three simple steps:

1. Write down the equation.
2. Fill in the blanks.
3. Solve the equation.

In order to fix these three steps in your mind, solve the four problems given below. The answers follow the problems.

1. Suppose 5 ml. of 1 N NaOH are used to neutralize 10 ml. of HCl. What is the normality of the acid?

    Answer: 0.5 N.

2. Suppose 20 ml. of NaOH of unknown normality are used to neutralize 10 ml. of 0.1 N oxalic acid. What is the normality of the NaOH?

    Answer: 0.05 N.

3. It took 7.5 ml. of 0.1 N NaOH to neutralize 10 ml. of an acid. What was the normality of the acid?

    Answer: 0.075 N.

4. It required 16 ml. of NaOH of unknown normality to neutralize 10 ml. of 1 N oxalic acid. What was the normality of the NaOH?

    Answer: 0.625 N.

Preparation of normal solutions

The normal solutions most frequently used by the technician are 0.01 N, 0.1 N, and 1 N solutions of acids and bases. It is common practice to prepare 1 N solutions and then obtain the 0.01 N and 0.1 N solutions by dilution.

The examples that follow will be used to illustrate the preparation of normal solutions.

Preparation of 1 N oxalic acid
Preparation of 1 N sodium hydroxide
Preparation of 1 N sulfuric acid
Preparation of 0.1 N and 0.01 N solutions
Titration to test accuracy of preparations

Preparation of 1 N oxalic acid

The oxalic acid comes in the form of highly purified crystals. Because of its purity, a 1 N solution may be prepared by simply weighing out an equivalent weight and diluting to 1 liter. This 1 N oxalic acid solution can then be used to determine the strength of basic solutions.

A pure solution, such as 1 N oxalic acid, that is used to find the strength of other solutions is known as a *primary standard*.

The equivalent weight of oxalic acid is 63.033 gm. To make a 1 N solution, 63.033 gm. are needed for 1000 ml., or 6.303 gm. are needed for 100 ml.

Make 100 ml. of 1 N oxalic acid in the following manner.

1. Use the analytical balance for the weighing and use reagent grade or C.P. (chemically pure) oxalic acid. Since 6.303 gm. are required, the weights listed below are needed. Place these weights on the right-hand pan of the balance and weigh out the oxalic acid.

Gram weights	Milligram weights
5 gm.	200 mg.
1 gm.	100 mg.
	2 mg.
	1 mg.
6 gm.	303 mg.

2. Place a funnel in the neck of a 100 ml. volumetric flask.
3. Being careful not to lose any, cautiously transfer the oxalic acid crystals to the funnel.
4. Wash them through the funnel and into the flask with distilled water. Continue adding distilled water to the 100 ml. mark.
5. Mix as illustrated in Fig. 20. Make certain that all the crystals dissolve.
6. Get a clean 4-ounce bottle. Pour about 5 ml. of the solution into the bottle. Shake and discard.
7. Transfer the remaining 1 N oxalic acid to the bottle.
8. Label: 1 N Oxalic Acid. Also put your name and the date of preparation on the bottle.

Preparation of 1 N sodium hydroxide

Because oxalic acid is a pure substance, it was possible to weigh out an equivalent weight. This equivalent weight was then used to prepare a 1 N solution.

Sodium hydroxide, however, is not a pure substance. For example, if we were to weigh out 40 gm. of sodium hydroxide, we might have 35 gm. of sodium hydroxide and 5 gm. of sodium carbonate. The impurities in sodium hydroxide make it impossible to weigh an equivalent weight. Therefore, we must prepare a 1 N solution in a roundabout manner.

To prepare 1 N sodium hydroxide, we first prepare a solution that is slightly stronger than 1 N. Next, we determine the exact normality of this solution. Finally, we dilute this to 1 N.

A 1 N sodium hydroxide solution is prepared by the following three steps:

Preparation of slightly stronger than 1 N NaOH
Determination of exact normality
Dilution to make 1 N NaOH

Preparation of slightly stronger than 1 N NaOH

A solution of sodium hydroxide is very corrosive—handle it carefully! Do not get any on your fingers because it may cause a mild burn. When pipetting do not get any in your mouth, for it will cause a severe burn.

Sodium hydroxide picks up moisture rapidly. Take care, weigh rapidly, and keep the reagent bottle closed when not in use.

The equivalent weight of sodium hydroxide is 39.997 gm. To make a 1 N solution, we would need 8.0 gm. for 200 ml. However, since we want a slightly stronger than 1 N solution, we should use about 9 gm. for 200 ml.

Prepare 200 ml. of the slightly stronger than 1 N solution in the following manner. This method of preparation is sufficiently accurate for student preparations. For more accurate work, however, equal parts of sodium hydroxide and distilled water should be mixed. The solution should then stand for about a week to let the carbonates settle out. This concentrated solution is about 18 N, and the slightly stronger than 1 N solution can be prepared by dilution.

1. Using the rough balance, weigh 9 gm. of sodium hydroxide pellets (use C.P. or reagent grade) into a 500 ml. Pyrex beaker.
2. Using a 100 ml. graduate, add 200 ml. of distilled water.
3. With a glass stirring rod, gently stir the solution until all the sodium hydroxide dissolves. (*Caution:* This solution gets hot.)
4. Transfer to a polyethylene bottle. (The sodium hydroxide is kept in a container of this nature because it attacks the silicates of the glass. The dissolved silicates could alter the strength of the solution.)
5. Label: Slightly Stronger than 1 N NaOH. Also put your name and the date of preparation on the bottle.

Determination of exact normality

In order to determine the exact normality of the slightly stronger than 1 N NaOH, the following two steps are necessary:

> Step 1: Titration, or standardization
> Step 2: Calculation

Step 1: Titration (Fig. 21). (Note: In pipetting the following solutions, be careful not to get any in your mouth.)

1. Get the 1 N oxalic acid solution that you prepared.
2. Using a 10 ml. volumetric pipet, place exactly 10 ml. of this 1 N oxalic acid in a 125 ml. Erlenmeyer flask.
3. Add a few drops of the indicator phenolphthalein (preparation given in Table 11).
4. Fill the 10 ml. buret with the NaOH. Gently swirl the flask and add the NaOH, drop by drop, until the solution becomes a *faint* pink color throughout. The faint pink color must remain when the solution is mixed and must persist for at least 30 seconds. This is the end point.
5. Write down the total number of milliliters used.

Step 2: Calculation. Now we must calculate the exact normality of the sodium hydroxide solution. From the above titration, we have the following data:

Volume of oxalic acid used:	10 ml.
Normality of oxalic acid:	1.0 N
Volume of sodium hydroxide used:	milliliters used in your titration
Normality of sodium hydroxide:	?

Insert this information into the blanks on the following page, and solve the equation for the normality of the sodium hydroxide.

$$\text{Vol. of acid} \times \text{Norm. of acid} = \text{Vol. of base} \times \text{Norm. of base}$$
$$(\quad) \times (\quad) = (\quad) \times (\quad)$$

After you have made the above calculation, label the bottle of NaOH with the exact normality. Also record the exact normality as it is used in the dilution procedure which follows.

Dilution to make 1 N NaOH

Now that we know the exact normality of the NaOH solution, we can prepare a 1 N solution by dilution. This dilution process consists of the following two steps:

Step 1: Calculation
Step 2: Technique

Step 1: Calculation. Suppose we wish to make 100 ml. of 1 N NaOH. How much of our NaOH solution do we need? In this particular case, we have the following:

Normality desired: 1.00 N
Normality on hand: normality of your solution
Volume desired: 100 ml.

With this information, use the formula below to calculate the volume needed. If you have trouble with the calculation, see the sample calculation that follows. Make a record of the volume needed, because it is used in the next step.

$$\frac{\text{Norm. desired}}{\text{Norm. on hand}} \times \text{Vol. desired} = \text{Vol. needed}$$

Sample calculation: The normality desired is 1, and the volume desired is 100 ml. Suppose the normality on hand, which is the normality of your solution, is 1.01. The volume needed is found as follows:

$$\frac{\text{Norm. desired}}{\text{Norm. on hand}} \times \text{Vol. desired} = \text{Vol. needed}$$

$$\frac{1.00}{1.01} \times 100 = 99.0 \text{ ml.}$$

Step 2: Technique. The volume needed is now diluted to 100 ml. To make your measurement and dilution, proceed as follows.

1. Fill a 100 ml. graduated cylinder to the 99 ml. mark with your NaOH solution.
2. Add distilled water to the 100 ml. mark.
3. Mix.
4. Standardize.
5. Transfer to a polyethylene bottle.
6. Label: 1 N NaOH. Also put your name and the date of preparation on the bottle.

Preparation of 1 N sulfuric acid

Sulfuric acid is not a pure substance. For example, if we were to measure out 49 gm. of H_2SO_4, we might have 45 gm. of H_2SO_4, 3 gm of water, and 1 gm. of organic impurities. The water and organic impurities in sulfuric acid make it impossible to measure out an equivalent weight. Consequently, we must prepare

1 N H$_2$SO$_4$ in the same roundabout manner we used in preparing 1 N NaOH.

To prepare 1 N sulfuric acid, we first prepare a solution which is slightly stronger than 1 N. Next, we determine the exact normality of this solution. Finally, we dilute this to 1 N.

A 1 N H$_2$SO$_4$ solution is prepared by the following three steps:

> Preparation of slightly stronger than 1 N H$_2$SO$_4$
> Determination of exact normality
> Dilution to make 1 N H$_2$SO$_4$

Preparation of slightly stronger than 1 N H$_2$SO$_4$

Sulfuric acid is a very corrosive solution—handle it carefully!

The equivalent weight of sulfuric acid is 49.039 gm. To make a 1 N solution, we would need 9.8 gm. for 200 ml. However, since we wish to make a slightly stronger than 1 N solution, we should use about 13 gm. for 200 ml.

We could weigh out the 13 gm. of sulfuric acid. However, because it is a liquid, it is much simpler to measure out the 13 gm.

The weight of 1.00 ml. of sulfuric acid is 1.84 gm. Therefore, 13 gm. measure:

$$13 \times \frac{1.00}{1.84} = 7.0 \text{ ml.}$$

Consequently, we need 7.0 ml. of sulfuric acid. This will make 200 ml. of a slightly stronger than 1 N solution.

Prepare the solution in the manner given below. Use reagent grade or C.P. concentrated sulfuric acid. The concentration is usually about 95%.

1. Using a 100 ml. graduate, pour 193 ml. of distilled water into a clean 200 ml. volumetric Pyrex flask.
2. *Carefully* pipet 7.0 ml. of concentrated sulfuric acid with a serological pipet. (Note: A serological pipet is acceptable at this step, since the solution is not one of *exact* normality.)
3. Slowly add the 7.0 ml of acid to the flask.
4. Place the glass stopper on the flask and invert about ten times to mix. Allow to cool to 20° C. Fill to mark.
5. Label: Slightly Stronger than 1 N H$_2$SO$_4$. Also put your name and the date of preparation on the bottle.

Determination of exact normality

To determine the exact normality, the following two steps are necessary:

> Step 1: Titration, or standardization
> Step 2: Calculation

Step 1: Titration. (Note: In pipetting the following solutions, be careful not to get any in your mouth.)

1. Using a 10 ml. volumetric pipet, *carefully* pipet exactly 10 ml. of the Slightly Stronger than 1 N H$_2$SO$_4$ into a 125 ml. Erlenmeyer flask.
2. Add a few drops of the indicator phenolphthalein.
3. Get the 1 N NaOH that you prepared in the preceding section.
4. Fill a 15 ml. buret with the 1 N NaOH. Gently swirl the flask and add the NaOH, drop by drop, until the solution becomes a *faint* pink color throughout. The faint pink color must not fade. This is the end point.
5. Write down the total number of milliliters used.

Step 2: Calculation. Now we must calculate the exact normality of the sulfuric acid solution. From the above titration, we have the following data.

Volume of sulfuric acid used:	10 ml.
Normality of sulfuric acid:	?
Volume of sodium hydroxide used:	milliliters used in titration
Normality of sodium hydroxide:	1.0 N

Insert this information into the blanks below, and solve the equation for the normality of the sulfuric acid.

$$\text{Vol. of acid} \times \text{Norm. of acid} = \text{Vol. of base} \times \text{Norm. of base}$$
$$(\quad) \times (\quad) = (\quad) \times (\quad)$$

After you have made the above calculation, label the bottle of H_2SO_4 with the exact normality. Also record the exact normality, as it is used in the dilution procedure, which follows.

Dilution to make 1 N H_2SO_4

Now that we know the exact normality of the H_2SO_4, we can prepare a 1 N solution by dilution. This dilution consists of the following two steps:

Step 1: Calculation
Step 2: Technique

Step 1: Calculation. Suppose we wish to make 100 ml. of 1 N H_2SO_4. How much of our H_2SO_4 solution do we need? In this particular case, we have the following:

Normality desired:	1.00
Normality on hand:	normality of your solution
Volume desired:	100 ml.

Using this information in the formula below, calculate the volume needed. Make a record of the volume needed, because it is used in the next step.

$$\frac{\text{Norm. desired}}{\text{Norm. on hand}} \times \text{Vol. desired} = \text{Vol. needed}$$

Step 2: Technique. The volume needed is now diluted to 100 ml. To make your dilution, proceed as follows:

1. **Subtract the volume needed (obtained from your calculation in Step 1) from 100 and add this volume of distilled H_2O to a 100 ml. volumetric flask.**
2. **Measure the volume of H_2SO_4 needed into the volumetric flask.**
3. **Add distilled water to the 100 ml. mark.**
4. **Mix, standardize, and transfer to a clean bottle.**
5. **Label: 1 N H_2SO_4. Also put your name and the date of preparation on the bottle.**

Preparation of 0.1 N and 0.01 N solutions

One tenth (0.1) N and 0.01 N solutions are prepared by dilution. For example, if you wish to prepare 0.1 N NaOH, proceed as follows: Get a 10 ml. volumetric pipet. Pipet exactly 10 ml. of the 1 N NaOH into a 100 ml. volumetric flask. Add distilled water to the 100 ml. mark. Mix, standardize, and transfer to a polyethylene bottle. Label: 0.1 N NaOH.

To prepare 0.01 N NaOH, proceed as follows: Get a 10 ml. volumetric pipet. Pipet exactly 10 ml. of the 0.1 N NaOH into a 100 ml. volumetric flask. Add distilled water to the 100 ml. mark. Mix, standardize, and transfer to a polyethylene bottle. Label: 0.01 N NaOH.

Titration to test accuracy of preparations

To test the accuracy of the first three normal solutions which you have prepared, proceed as follows: Using a 10 ml. volumetric pipet, place 10 ml. of your 1 N H_2SO_4 in a small flask. Add a few drops of the indicator phenolphthalein. Now titrate with your 1 N NaOH until the solution in the flask becomes a *faint* pink color throughout. If your solutions have been accurately prepared, it should require 10.0 ml. of the 1 N NaOH.

Calculate the exact normality of the solution and record this on the bottle. Unstable reagents must be restandardized before using or, if the reagent has not been used for a week, be sure that nothing has happened to it. Restandardizing a reagent will save a lot of time when done promptly before using, instead of going through a whole analysis and then wondering what happened.

Chapter 4

Operation of colorimeters

The concentration of a substance in solution is usually determined by a color reaction, the general principle being the greater the concentration, the more intense the color. For example, in the analysis of glucose, the solution is treated to produce a blue color. The greater the concentration of glucose, the more intense the blue color. The depth of color is then measured in an instrument called a colorimeter.

There are two general types of colorimeters: visual and photoelectric. These instruments are considered in this chapter.

VISUAL COLORIMETERS

The Duboscq visual colorimeter (Fig. 22) is a more refined instrument among the visual colorimeters. It consists of an optical system and a light source. The view through the eyepiece displays a round light field divided in half. The object of this is to adjust the cup of the unknown until the color matches that of the reference sample. The source of error with this method depends upon the technician's eyesight. One technician can obtain good reproducibility, but it is difficult for different people to match colors identically. With the blue color developed in the glucose test, the technician would see only blue because that is the predominant color. Standards similar to the concentration of the unknown must be run with each group of analyses.

The operation of a typical visual colorimeter and the calculations involved are discussed below.

Operation of visual colorimeter (Fig. 22)

1. Remove cover or protective housing from colorimeter. Plug in light source and turn on light switch. Place colorimeter so that mirror is directly in front of light source. As you face the source of light, the cup on the left is for the standard and the cup on the right is for the unknown.
2. Fill both cups about ¾ full with the standard solution. Place cups on racks. Using adjustment dial, move cup on left to reading of 20; fix by

tightening setscrew. Move cup on right to reading of 20. Now look through eyepiece and adjust either the mirror, instrument, or source of light so that the two color fields match.

3. Discard solution in cup on right, rinse with unknown, and fill about ¾ full with unknown.

4. Place on rack and, using adjustment dial, move cup up until glass plunger is in solution. Look through eyepiece and match colors by moving cup containing unknown. When colors match, take reading of unknown and write it down.

5. Discard solutions. Rinse cups and plungers several times with tap water and twice with distilled water. Dry glass plungers with soft tissue paper.

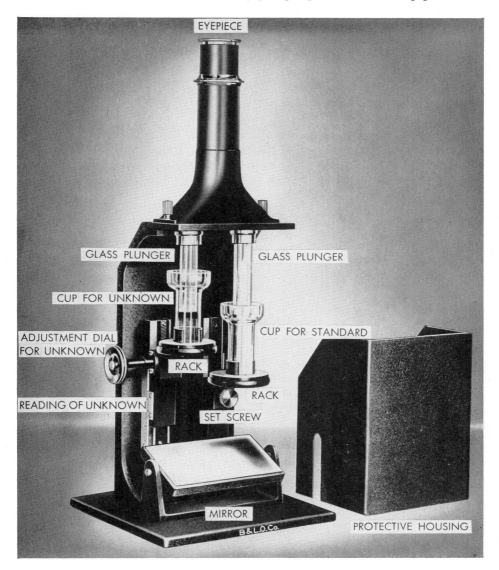

Fig. 22. Visual colorimeter. (Courtesy Bausch & Lomb Optical Co., Rochester, N. Y.)

Clean and dry outside glass bottoms of cups. Replace cups and colorimeter cover or protective housing. Turn off light.
6. With reading of unknown, determine concentration of unknown by using the formula that is given with the test procedure. The formula is discussed below.

Calculations with visual colorimeters

As illustrated above, the depth of color in the unknown solution is compared with the depth of color in the standard solution. This comparison gives us a ratio of their difference. For example, the standard is always set at 20. Suppose the reading of the unknown is 16. Then the ratio is 20/16.

Another example: The standard is set at 20. The reading of the unknown is 22. Therefore the ratio is 20/22.

When the ratio is multiplied by the concentration of the standard, we have the concentration of the unknown:

$$\frac{\text{Reading of standard}}{\text{Reading of unknown}} \times \frac{\text{Concentration}}{\text{of standard}} = \frac{\text{Concentration}}{\text{of unknown}}$$

To illustrate, suppose we are making a glucose determination and have the following data: Reading of the standard is 20; reading of the unknown is 16; and the concentration of the standard represents a glucose concentration of 100 mg./100 ml. of blood. The concentration of glucose is found as follows:

$$\frac{\text{Reading of standard}}{\text{Reading of unknown}} \times \frac{\text{Concentration}}{\text{of standard}} = \frac{\text{Concentration}}{\text{of unknown}}$$

$$20/16 \qquad \times \qquad 100 \qquad = 125 \text{ mg./100 ml. of blood}$$

This is another way to understand the above calculations. Beer's law may be stated as follows: the optical density (O.D. or D) of any colored solution is equal to the product of concentration (C) of the color-producing substance $\times$ the depth (L) of solution through which the light travels $\times$ a constant (K). Therefore:

$$D = C \times L \times K$$

The optical density is proportional to the concentration or depth of the solution being measured. If the blue color is increased then the amount or depth of color and the O.D. would naturally be increased.

In matching the colors in the round light field, D_u (or $C_u \times L_u \times K$) equals the density of the unknown, and D_s (or $C_s \times L_s \times K$), that of the standard. When $D_u = D_s$ they will cancel out of the equation:

$$D_u = C_u \times L_u \times K \text{ (unknown) equals } D_s = C_s \times L_s \times K \text{ (standard)}$$

Since K is on both sides of the equation, it also cancels out. Thus:

$$C_u \times L_u = C_s \times L_s$$

$$\frac{C_s \times L_s}{L_u} = C_u$$

or

$$\frac{100 \times 20}{16} = 125 \text{ mg./100 ml. of blood}$$

PHOTOELECTRIC COLORIMETERS

Discussion here covers the operating principle of photoelectric colorimeters and directions for using the more popular instruments.

Principle of operation

In order to determine the concentration of a substance in solution, the technician takes two major steps.

First, he treats the solution to produce a color. The concentration is related to the color. Usually, the greater the concentration, the deeper the color.

Second, he determines the depth of color by passing a light through the solution. The deeper the color, the less the transmittance of light.*

In the above steps, the technician has created a relationship between three factors: the concentration of the substance in solution, the depth of color produced, and the amount of transmitted light:

$$\text{Concentration of substance} \longleftrightarrow \text{Depth of color} \longleftrightarrow \text{Amount of transmitted light}$$

This three-link chain—concentration, depth of color, and transmitted light—becomes our key to the concentration of a substance in solution.

If we start at the end of the chain and work back, we have the following: the transmitted light is proportional to the depth of color, which in turn is proportional to the concentration of the substance.

Therefore, after we have treated the solution to produce a color, we must find the amount of light transmitted by the solution. The amount of light transmitted by a colored solution is found with a photoelectric colorimeter.

The colorimeter using a colored glass or gelatin filter to obtain a certain wavelength is called a filter photometer. The number on the filter indicates the wavelength of the filter at its optimum transmittancy. For example, filter No. 40 transmits light over the range of 380 to 430 millimicrons ($m\mu$) with its optimum transmittancy at 400 $m\mu$. Table 15 gives various wavelength filters. In the Klett-Summerson manual, a suggestion is made for choosing a proper filter for a procedure when the filter needed is unknown. Refer to Table 15 and choose a filter according to the color of the solution to be read. Set up several known concentrations of this solution, and if the highest reading is not above 400 to 500 on the colorimeter scale, the filter is correct. When the concentrations and readings are plotted on regular (linear) graph paper there should be a straight

---

*The relationship between the depth of color and the transmitted light holds true only within the limits of the Bouguer-Beer law, which is expressed by the following equation:

$$C = -\frac{1}{K} \log \frac{I}{I_0}$$

where C is the concentration of the colored substance in solution, I_0 is the intensity of light that is focused on the solution, I is the amount of light that is able to get through, and K is an absorption constant that is characteristic of the substance. In effect, the law says that the relationship between the depth of color and the transmitted light holds true only within certain limits. For example, if the solution is extremely pale or extremely dark, the transmitted light may not be a true indication of the depth of color. The technician, however, need not worry about this. It is a problem that confronts the clinical chemist when he devises a test.

Table 15. Wavelength and filter range

Filter no. (for optimum transmittancy)	Color	Wavelength range (in millimicrons)	Color of solutions (for filter used)
40		380–430	
42	Blue	400–465	Red, orange, yellow, green, blue, turbidities
44		410–480	
47		445–505	
50		470–530	
52		485–550	
54	Green	500–570	Red, yellow, purple, orange, blue
55		520–600	
56		540–590	
59		565–630	
60		580–640	
62		590–660	
64		620–680	
66	Red	640–700	Blue, green, yellow
69		660–740	

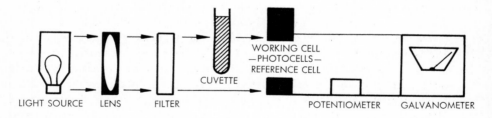

Fig. 23. Diagram of a single-cell photometer.

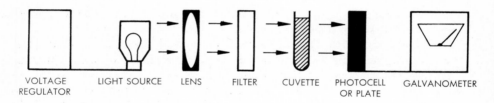

Fig. 24. Diagram of a double-cell photometer.

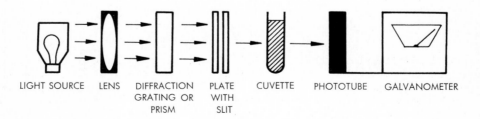

Fig. 25. Diagram of a spectrophotometer.

line. The Klett-Summerson readings are proportional to optical density instead of percent transmittancy (% T).

Photometers may have one or two photocells. The single-cell instrument must have a voltage regulator to minimize voltage fluctuations reaching the instrument. The single-cell instrument is dependent on the effectiveness of the regulator, since the light striking the photocell is a function not only of the solution in the light path but also of the intensity of the light source. (Fig. 23.)

Double-cell instruments are not affected by fluctuations in the line current because the cells are balanced, with either water or a reagent blank, before photometric measurements are made. When the test or unknown solution is placed in the light path, the cells become electrically unbalanced, deflecting the galvanometer needle. By adjusting the needle back to zero, the cells are brought back into balance. The potential difference between the photoelectric cells remains constant despite line voltage variations. (Fig. 24.)

Spectro (spectrum) photo (light) meters (measure) have a prism or a diffraction grating to split the light into spectral bands of light of various wavelengths. By the accurate measurement of the spectral light transmission of the sample, the amount of unknown in the sample can be quantitated. (Fig. 25.) The advantages of the spectrophotometer are appreciated when we consider that all wavelengths are obtainable on this type of instrument whereas the colorimeter wavelength is limited to the filters produced for that instrument. In some analyses, the wavelength is chosen not so much for increasing sensitivity as for eliminating interference. With the colorimeter, the filter needed for this problem is not always available. Some spectrophotometers may also be used for both ultraviolet and infrared analysis. This is made possible by the use of proper phototubes in conjunction with the prism. It is also generally considered that spectrophotometers yield a better quality of monochromatic light than can be obtained with filters. The cost of the spectrophotometer is usually greater than that of the colorimeter, and the prism type is even more expensive than the unit with the diffraction gratings.

Calibrating the instrument

Even though many manufacturers have a calibration chart delivered with the instrument, the new piece of equipment should be calibrated in the laboratory. No matter how well packed the instrument is for shipping, it receives abuse enough to demand recalibration. The basic equation for calibrating instruments is O.D. = K × C.

A series of standards are run at various concentrations so the optical density (O.D.) is known at any given concentration. The K factor may be calculated by dividing the O.D. by the mg.% concentration of the standards. The K factor is a constant for a particular procedure done in a particular way. If K is known and the O.D. is measured, then the concentration of the unknown may be calculated:

$$K = \frac{O.D.}{mg.\%} \quad \text{or} \quad mg.\% = \frac{O.D.}{K}$$

Example:

50 mg.% sugar reads 71% T
71% T is equal to an O.D. of 0.148
Divide 0.148 by the 50 mg.%, giving a K factor of 0.00298
Refer to Table 19 for converting % T to O.D.

For the series of standards and their calculations for the K factor make up a work sheet similar to this sample:

Concentration of sugar (mg.%)	Reading (% T)	O.D. (Refer to Table 19)	$K = \dfrac{O.D.}{mg.\%}$
0	100	0.000	0.00000
25	85	0.070	0.00280
50	72	0.142	0.00284
75	62	0.207	0.00276
etc.	etc.	etc.	etc.

C_u = Concentration of unknown

Total this column and divide by the total number of standards run. The 0 mg.% concentration is the reagent blank:

$C_u = \dfrac{O.D.}{0.00280}$ or $280 \times$ O.D. (unknown)

$0.00840 \div 3 = 0.00280$ K

The terms % T and O.D. are used without a true understanding of what they really mean. Other terms used in photometry are used with a "half-understanding."

Definitions and formulas used in colorimetry

Absorbance The amount of light that is absorbed by a solution and expressed as optical density. This is the negative logarithm of percent transmittance. O.D. = 2 − log % T or O.D. = − log T.

Fluorescence The event of absorbing light on one wavelength and radiating a part of this absorbed light on some other wavelength.

Frequency Vibrations per second (v).

Linear Relating to a straight line or a dimension of length. This term is often used in describing graph paper as either plain or linear paper.

Monochromatic light Light of a narrow range of wavelength.

Monochromer A device for producing monochromatic light.

Nephelometry Quantitative measurement of substances in suspension by means of scattered light, or the determination of the degree of turbidity of a solution.

Optical density The same as absorbance. As the concentration of a color solution increases, the optical density increases. Values range from 0 to 2.0000.

Photometer An instrument used to measure the light-transmitting power of a solution.

Photometric relationships The Beer-Lambert laws, showing the two important principles of photometry:

    Beer's law (Absorption law) the absorption of light by a solution is directly proportional to the concentration of the solute. The principle of this law is applicable only when a monochromatic light is employed.

    Lambert's law the absorption of light is independent of the intensity of radiant energy passed through a solution containing a solute. As the light passes through the solution it is subjected to a logarithmic reduction in its intensity as the concentration of the solution increases.

Photometry Measurement of light-transmitting power of a solution in order to determine the concentration of light-absorbing material present.

Relationship The greater the frequency, the shorter the wavelength.

Spectrometer A device for producing light of selected wavelengths.

Spectrophotometer A photometer that permits selection of wavelength through use of prisms or grating, rather than filter.

Transmittance or transmission (% T) The ratio of light passing through a colored solution compared to the ratio of light passed through a solution or water blank. It may be expressed as percent of original light. Values range from 100 to 0.

Turbidimetry Refer to Nephelometry. Quantitative measurement of substances in suspension by means of scattered light.

Wavelength Distance between the crests of adjacent waves expressed as millimicrons.

Operation of photoelectric colorimeters

There is no point in learning the operational procedures of all the various colorimeters. The student should first note the type of instrument that is being used in his school or laboratory. He should then carefully study the operating directions for that particular instrument.

This section contains the operating procedures for five colorimeters. These directions have been taken verbatim from the respective colorimeter manuals, special permission having been granted by the manufacturers:

> Bausch & Lomb Spectronic 20
> Coleman Spectrophotometer
> Hellige CliniCol
> Leitz Photrometer
> Photovolt Lumetron

Operation of Bausch & Lomb Spectronic 20 (Fig. 26)*
Colorimetry

"For colorimetric use the wavelength control (1) is rotated until the desired wavelength in millimicrons is indicated by the wavelength scale (2). This wavelength is found by referring to the procedure being used. The instrument is turned on by rotating the amplifier control (3) clockwise. After a few minutes warm-up time the amplifier control may be adjusted to bring the meter needle to '0' on the Percent Transmittance Scale (4) or '∞' on the optical density scale. The test tube or cuvette containing water or other solvent is then inserted in the sample holder (5). For best results when using test tubes one should use only Bausch & Lomb selected tubes and be careful to set the index line on the test tube opposite the index line on the sample holder. To avoid any possible scratching of the test tube in the optical path, insert tube with index line at right angles to index line on test tube holder. After test tube is seated, line up the index lines. The light control (6) should now be rotated until the meter reads '100' on the Percent Transmittance Scale or '0' on the optical density scale. The unknown sample may then be inserted in place of the blank and the Percent Transmittance or Optical Density value read directly from the meter.

"Although the meter (4) is electronically protected from burn-out, it is best to turn the light control (6) counter-clockwise before changing to another wavelength where the photocell might be more sensitive.

"For the very utmost in precision, the use of cuvettes is recommended, although excellent results are obtainable by the use of Bausch & Lomb selected test tubes with this instrument."

Spectrophotometry

"The Spectronic 20 Colorimeter makes an excellent spectrophotometer. The method of operation is essentially the same as that for colorimetry, except, of course, the wavelength is reset for each reading and consequently the light control is also readjusted. The amplifier control is adjusted with no light striking the photocell and therefore is independent of the wavelength setting. For determinations above 650 millimicrons (the red part of the wavelength scale) the

---

*Courtesy Bausch & Lomb Optical Co., Rochester, N. Y.

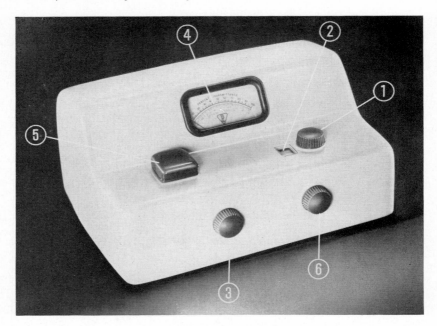

Fig. 26. Bausch & Lomb Spectronic 20. (Courtesy Bausch & Lomb Optical Co., Rochester, N. Y.)

accessory red filter and type 1P40 photocell are used. To insert these, refer to the Bausch & Lomb Reference Manual."

Operation of Coleman Spectrophotometer* (Fig. 27)

1. Mount the Selected Scale Panel in the Galvanometer Window.
2. Insert in the cuvette well a cuvette adapter of the proper size to accept the type of cuvette specified in the contemplated analytical method.
3. Turn on the switch located on back of instrument. The indicated jewel will show that the exciter lamp is lit.
4. Verify the Galvanometer zero setting and readjust if necessary.
5. Adjust the λ dial to that wavelength specified in the contemplated analytical method.
6. WIPE CLEAN and then insert AT THE PROPER ANGLE in the cuvette well a cuvette containing a sufficient volume of the Reference solution.
7. Adjust the COARSE and FINE knobs until the Galvanometer Index reads the correct value for the contemplated analytical method. (Usually this will be 100% T if the black Transmittance scale or 0 if the red Density scale of the 6-401 Scale Panel is used.)
8. Remove the Reference cuvette. WIPE CLEAN and then insert AT THE PROPER ANGLE a similar cuvette containing the Sample solution.
9. Read the position of the Galvanometer Index on the same (red or black) Galvanometer Scale as was used for the initial adjustment (6).
10. Refer to tables, curves or scale reading for the actual concentration of the Sample solution, as directed in the contemplated analytical method.

*Courtesy Coleman Instruments, Inc., Maywood, Ill.

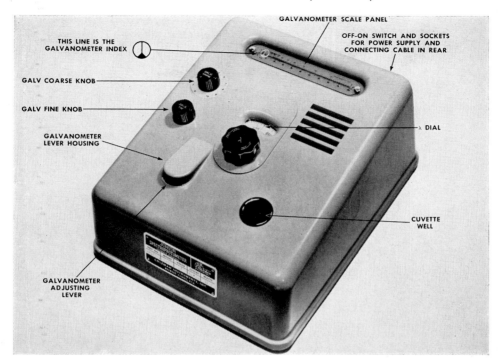

GALVANOMETER SCALE PANEL

THIS LINE IS THE
GALVANOMETER INDEX

OFF-ON SWITCH AND SOCKETS
FOR POWER SUPPLY AND
CONNECTING CABLE IN REAR

GALV COARSE KNOB

GALV FINE KNOB

λ DIAL

GALVANOMETER
LEVER HOUSING

CUVETTE
WELL

GALVANOMETER
ADJUSTING
LEVER

Fig. 27. Coleman Spectrophotometer. (Courtesy Coleman Instruments, Inc., Maywood, Ill.)

Operation of Hellige CliniCol* (Fig. 28)

1. Make certain that the meter needle deflects to zero per cent transmission when the Coarse Control Knob is in the "OFF" position. To adjust, rotate the black screw at the bottom of the cover of the meter faceplate. Tap the housing below the meter and readjust, if necessary.
2. Connect the plug to an electrical outlet supplying the correct voltage and frequency for the model being used. For details, see section on electrical power sources in the Hellige Manual. Models Nos. 900D-90, 900D-66, and 900D-43 operate from two internal dry cell batteries and therefore do not have a plug for connection to an electrical outlet.
3. Revolve the Filter Selector until the value of the color filter specified in the test procedure appears. A click indicates proper alignment of the filter in the light path.
4. Fill a square absorption cell No. 904 with the "blank," prepared as directed in the test procedure. Make certain that the liquid level reaches at least to the graduation on the cell. Insert the cell in the opening at the top of the instrument. ABSORPTION CELLS MUST ALWAYS BE INSERTED WITH ONE FROSTED SIDE FACING THE FRONT OF THE APPARATUS SO THAT THE CLEAR SIDES FACE TO THE LEFT AND RIGHT.
5. Prepare the solution of unknown concentration in accordance with the test procedure and fill a second square absorption cell No. 904 at least to the graduation with the treated sample.

*Courtesy Hellige, Inc. Garden City. N. Y.

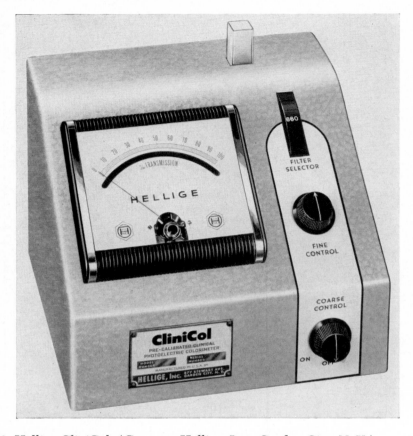

Fig. 28. Hellige CliniCol. (Courtesy Hellige, Inc., Garden City, N. Y.)

6. Rotate the Fine Control Knob until the white arrow points directly upward at the Filter Selector.
7. Turn the Coarse Control Knob clockwise so that the arrow passes the word "ON," and continue to rotate until the meter needle deflects to approximately 98 or 99 on the scale. Then rotate the Fine Control Knob until the needle deflects to exactly 100. Tap the housing below the meter and readjust the knob if necessary.
8. Replace the square absorption cell containing the blank with the one containing the solution of unknown concentration. Tap the housing below the meter. Read and record the meter deflection.
9. Turn the Course Control Knob to the "OFF" position. The instrument should be on only while actual readings are being made.
10. Obtain the concentration value of the unknown solution from the calibration chart for the particular test, as directed in the test procedure.

IMPORTANT—Cleanliness is of utmost importance in all photoelectric measurements. Before placing an absorption cell into the housing, make certain that its outside surface is dry and spotlessly clean. Dirt of any kind, even finger marks, absorb light and will cause inaccurate readings. Do not allow the liquid to dry out in the cells. Always wash and dry absorption cells immediately after use and store them protected from dust and damage.

Fig. 29. Leitz-Photrometer. **A,** Cell holder; **B,** needle setting screw; **C,** absorption cell; **D,** lamp house plate; **E,** setscrew; **F,** filter disk; **S,** light switch; **N,** name plate; **K,** control knob. (Courtesy E. Leitz, Inc., New York, N. Y.)

Operation of Leitz Photrometer* (Fig. 29)

1. RUN ALL DETERMINATIONS IN STRICT ACCORDANCE WITH THE DIRECTIONS GIVEN WITH THE LEITZ PHOTROMETER PROCEDURES. Even slight changes in procedure may change the color produced thus giving inaccurate results.

2. Before using the Photrometer, make sure that the needle on the micro-ammeter scale is at zero (0) when the light is off. The small screw-head (B) may be turned to set the needle at zero. This adjustment is rarely needed. It is inadvisable to place the photrometer in a position where strong light shines directly into the cell-holder (A) while the instrument is in use, since the readings may be affected.

3. Give knob (K) about three complete turns counter-clockwise. This prevents possible damage caused by the meter needle swinging violently beyond "100" when the light is switched on.

4. Set the filter disc (F) by turning it until the number of the filter required by the method becomes visible, and it clicks into position.

5. At least 5 minutes before a sample is ready to be measured, turn on the light switch (S). This is done while the sample is being prepared, so that no time is lost.

6. When ready to make a measurement insert the absorption cell containing distilled water into the cell-holder (A), pushing it down gently as far as it will go. The frosted glass sides of the cell should be parallel to the long sides of the Photrometer.

---

*Courtesy E. Leitz, Inc., New York, N. Y.

7. Turn knob (K) until the needle comes to exactly "100" on the scale.
8. Remove the absorption cell (C) containing water, and IMMEDI-ATELY replace it with an absorption cell containing the unknown.
9. Note the reading on the scale. From the calibration table, determine the concentration of the unknown.
10. When work is finished, follow step 3. Turn off the light switch (S) when the Photrometer is not in use.
11. Steps 6 and 7 should be carried out *each* time a reading of the unknown is made (step 8). While the Photrometer is in use, the position of the needle will tend to shift slowly, but after the instrument is well warmed up, only slight readjustments of the needle to 100 will be necessary.
12. When measuring the color of a solution it must be free of haze or turbidity, since the latter will also absorb light, causing an error in the reading.
13. The full capacity of the square cells for the Leitz Photrometer is 9 cc.

Operation of Photovolt Lumetron* (Fig. 30)

1. Place selected color filter in light beam as indicated by white lines.
2. Insert tubes containing blank and sample into corresponding openings of sliding tube carrier.
3. Slide carrier toward operator to bring blank into light beam.
4. Set needle on 100 of lower scale (0 of upper scale) by means of coarse and fine control knobs.
5. Slide carrier away from operator to bring sample into light beam and take reading.

FLAME PHOTOMETERS

Practically everyone has spilled ordinary table salt onto a burning gas stove and seen the yellow flame produced by the burning sodium. If it were possible to measure the intensity of this yellow color, we would have an indication of the amount of sodium present. The more intense the color, the greater the concentration of sodium. This principle is used in the flame photometer.

In the flame photometer, dilutions of serum, plasma, or urine are vaporized and burned. Various colors are produced. These are filtered to isolate the color that is characteristic of the substance being determined. The intensity of the color is then compared, by means of a photoelectric cell, with standards of known concentration.

Because of its speed and accuracy the flame photometer is now one of the most used instruments in the diagnostic laboratory. There are many excellent instruments, some that are capable of analyzing lithium, magnesium, and the controversial calcium ions.

The flame photometer has the following basic parts: (1) atomizer; (2) burner; (3) spectrophotometer or abridged spectrophotometer, either single photocell or double photocell; and (4) galvanometer or recorder.

There are two general types of atomizers used with the flame photometer. The upfeed and the gravity-feed types are described below. The function of the atomizer is to create a fine spray of the solution and feed this into the flame. The spray is obtained by a stream of compressed air or oxygen blowing across

---

*Courtesy Photovolt Corporation, New York, N. Y.

Fig. 30. Photovolt Lumetron. (Courtesy Photovolt Corporation, New York, N. Y.)

the top or tip of the capillary tube. The average atomizer siphons at a rate of about 1 ml. in 10 to 15 seconds, which allows time to take readings. A faster siphoning, of course, lessens the reading time because the fluid level of the container is changed rapidly. A tendency of the technician to hold the sample container up to the atomizer for too long changes the fluid level of the container, causing erratic readings.

With the upfeed burner system (Fig. 31) the atomizer, *1*, siphons the dilute sample from the container and dispenses a fine spray into the flame, *2*. For a constant and controlled temperature, the gas and oxygen are mixed within the burner. This adjustment is done manually according to the directions for the specific instrument used. As the mist enters the flame at a constant rate, the light and color produced are transmitted through the lens, filter, and photocell, *3*, and the light intensity is recorded either by a galvanometer or by a recorder, *4*. Those students of qualitative analysis who have done the "bead tests" will recognize the following metals and their colors:

Sodium (Na)	Yellow
Potassium (K)	Violet
Lithium (Li)	Dark red
Calcium (Ca)	Red
Magnesium (Mg)	Colorless

The burner heat is important. A "hot" flame is generally preferred for greater sensitivity, since a higher degree of heat causes a greater action of molecules, which in turn gives off more light. A slow-feeding atomizer does not affect the burner heat by lowering the temperature, because of the smaller volume of spray introduced into the burner, whereas a faster-feeding atomizer introduces more solution into the burner, lowering the temperature and thus affecting the sensitivity.

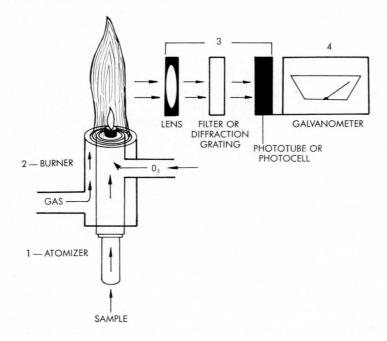

Fig. 31. Upfeed atomizer system.

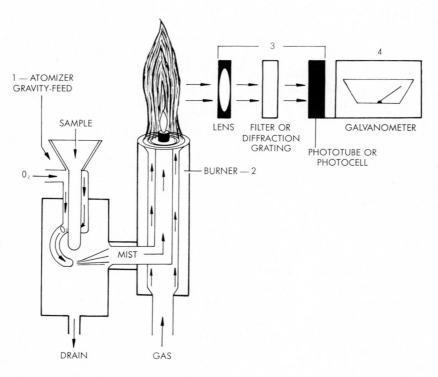

Fig. 32. Gravity-feed atomizer system.

The gravity-feed burner (Fig. 32) functions in a different way. The sample is poured into the funnel, *1*. By gravity, this sample flows to the funnel exit where it is dispensed as a fine mist into the flame. Compressed air at the base of the funnel acts at a constant rate to disperse the liquid into a fine mist. The sample then follows the same basic pattern as the "upfeed" burner.

Flame photometers use either the direct-reading method or the internal standard method of analysis, according to the electrical system of the instrument. With the direct-reading method, emitted light from the salts (sample) sprayed into the flame is measured by a photometer or recorder. The internal standard system is more complex, utilizing the double photocell. With this system, the serum is diluted with a known amount of lithium and water. As the diluted sample is sprayed into the flame, the light is split into two beams with the lithium filter transmitting the lithium light to one photocell. The light of the element being analyzed is transmitted through its respective filter to the other photocell. The current from the lithium photocell is adjusted by a potentiometer (with a calibrated dial) until it exactly equals the current of the other photocell. The readings obtained by the potentiometer are compared with standards of known concentration for the values of the element being analyzed.

Even though each instrument has its trouble-shooting chart, the main problems the technician has with a flame photometer are the following:

1. Allowing the sample to aspirate too long, drastically lowering the sample volume in the container.
2. Not cleaning the atomizer after a day's run of samples.
3. The screens, chimney, and surrounding parts of the burner being allowed to collect salts of the various elements, interfering with the constant flow of the spray into the burner.

Before purchasing a flame photometer, all the various types of units should be investigated. Available space in the laboratory, ventilation, fire laws, and the availability of parts and service should be thoroughly looked into. Manufacturers recommend a specific gas for their instrument. The various gases recommended are natural gas, acetylene, propane, and butane. Since fire laws vary in different localities, this factor should be checked before purchase of an instrument.

FLUOROMETRY

Fluorometry is the quantitative measurement of fluorescence in a compound. Under certain conditions the molecules of some compounds absorb radiant energy. After an extremely short time interval (10^{-7} or 10^{-8} second), the excited electrons return to a lower level of energy, which is then emitted as visible light or fluorescence. The difference in fluorescence and phosphorescence is that the fluorescence ceases when the exciting energy is removed but with the phosphorescence, the emission of light persists for some time after the exciting radiation is stopped. Ultraviolet radiation is usually the most efficient exciting energy because of its relatively long wavelength. Molecules emit groups of spectral bands and, if large or complex enough, the spectrum may be continuous. However, some compounds are not fluorescent or are very weak in fluorescence. These may be adapted to fluorometery by chemical reactions of condensation, substitution, or dehydration. The sensitivity of this method of analysis depends upon the intensity of the incident radiant energy and the sensitivity of the instrument used in measuring the fluorescence.

Quantitative measurements may be made of quinidine, porphyrins, catecholamines, vitamins, antibiotics, and estrogens that are difficult to measure by other methods.

There are many available instruments for this type of analysis. Each varies somewhat from the others, and it is the demands of the laboratory and the purchaser that indicate which instrument is the proper one to use. The instruments operate on the general principles of the photometers, with the exception that they utilize the ultraviolet light and measure the intensity of fluorescence at right angles to the incident light. They have phototubes, barrier layer photocells, and photomultiplier tubes with known spectral response characteristics. There are fluorometric attachments for the photometers, spectrophotometers, and the AutoAnalyzer.

Part 2

Quantitative analysis of blood, cerebrospinal fluid, and urine

The composition of blood often varies in disease. For example, the blood sugar rises in diabetes and the uric acid increases in gout. Different diseases produce different variations. As a result, numerous tests have been developed to assist the physician in diagnosing disease. These tests are presented in the following chapters:

Chapter 5

Collection of blood

The average man has about five quarts of blood. This can be separated into nearly two quarts of cells and three quarts of plasma. The cells are suspended in the fluid medium of the plasma. They are classified as red cells, white cells, and platelets.

The plasma is made up of water and dissolved materials. Among these materials are food and metabolic substances traveling to the tissues, and waste products going to the kidneys to be eliminated. The major components of blood are illustrated in Fig. 33.

After a meal, food substances are absorbed into the bloodstream. This alters the composition of the blood. Consequently, blood drawn after a meal should not be used for chemical tests. The usual practice is to secure the specimen before the patient has breakfast. And it is a good policy for the technician—before he starts the procedure—to ask the patient if he has eaten.

With children and adults, the blood is usually secured from the finger or ear and veins of the forearm, wrist, or ankle. With infants, the blood is generally taken from the heel or toe and veins of the forearm, neck, or head. Since the usual practice is to obtain blood from the finger or veins of the forearm, these two methods will be considered and discussed in detail. Before the actual procedure is started, however, the technician should reassure the patient and endeavor to relieve any apprehension that may be present.

Procedure for capillary puncture of finger or ear

An extremely old technique for obtaining blood is the puncture wound of the capillaries. Although the finger puncture is the most used, the technician should be familiar also with the ear puncture and its good points and drawbacks. While the difference in chemistry values between the capillary blood of the ear and that of the finger are insignificant, the following notations must be taken into consideration if blood from the ear is used for hematology work.[1]

Unless the patient has been in the cold or under undue stress, the red cell counts and hemoglobin values are essentially the same as values obtained from a finger stick or from venous blood.

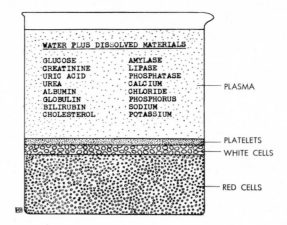

Fig. 33. Composition of the blood.

It has been found that the white cell count from the ear is slightly higher than the count from the finger. Also, larger white cells may be present in greater numbers.

There is a striking difference in results of earlobe blood, versus that from finger or vein, in certain pathological conditions. The difference is seen in the white cell counts and the differential counts of infectious mononucleosis, leukemias, and bacterial endocarditis. The increase of white cells from the earlobe involves all types of white cells, especially the large cells such as monocytes and histiocytes that are seen in large numbers in bacterial endocarditis. This has been explained largely by the greater filtering capacity of the vascular bed of the earlobe in comparison to that in the tip of the finger.

In preparation of blood films for the study of leukemias, leukopenias, and certain infections, the earlobe is the most desirable source of blood. After an earlobe puncture, the first two drops may contain more large cells. After several drops, the cells are similar to those from the finger stick or the venipuncture.

The finger or ear is cleansed with an alcohol sponge, incision is made with a disposable sterile lancet, and drops of blood are available for examination. A detailed procedure of each step follows.

Preparing the finger or earlobe

The fingertip is cleansed with a sterile gauze pad moistened with 70% alcohol, leaving no moisture. The blood will form full rounded drops. If the patient has been outdoors in cold weather, the earlobe is gently warmed to enhance circulation. An alcohol sponge is used to cleanse the area, leaving no moisture.

Puncturing the finger or earlobe

By means of a loose wrist motion the finger is punctured with a sterile disposable lancet. The puncture is made by firmly grasping the finger and making a quick deliberate stab to a depth of about 3 mm. into the finger. It is better to induce a good puncture rather than make the patient apprehensive by having to do a repeat. A deep puncture is no more painful than the superficial one.

Eliminating the first drop

The first drop of blood, containing tissue juices and foreign matter, is always wiped off. The diluted and contaminated drop of blood would give unreliable results.

Withdrawing the blood

Free-flowing blood should be used for examination, although gentle pressure may be applied if needed to enhance the flow of blood. *Never* exert heavy pressure, because that may cause the flow of tissue juices in the blood.

Preventing further bleeding

After the required amount of blood has been taken, an antiseptic pad (70% alcohol pad) is placed on the puncture. The patient may be instructed to apply pressure to the wound until the bleeding has ceased.

The previously described steps in the finger puncture are illustrated in Fig. 34.

Summary of the finger puncture

1. Prepare the finger.
2. Puncture the finger.
3. Eliminate the first drop.
4. Withdraw the blood.
5. Prevent further bleeding.

Procedure for the venipuncture

Larger volumes of blood needed for chemical analyses are obtained from the veins of the forearm, wrist, or ankle. Because of convenience and the larger size of the veins in the forearm, this area is usually chosen for a venipuncture. With good technique and sharp needles, the same vein may be used many times with little discomfort to the patient or damage to the vein. However, bandages, soreness, obesity, or scar tissue formed from poor techniques may sometimes make it necessary to use the veins of the wrist or ankle.

Obtaining a venipuncture is an art which demands compassion, knowledge, and skill to minimize discomfort to the patient. If the patient is not confined to a bed, have him seated comfortably in a chair with his arm placed upon a table, counter, or some other solid form. The chair and table should be on a level such that the arm will be extended downward at an angle and not raised above the shoulder level. Avoid low chairs and high tables. If the patient has a tendency to bend his arm, place a support under the elbow. Use books, a package of paper towels, or anything solid enough to hold the arm straight. A patient may feel faint from apprehension. Keep a fresh bottle of smelling salts available or moisten a piece of cotton with *dilute* ammonium hydroxide. Wave this under the nose and if you do not get immediate response, *call a physician.*

If a patient is in bed, place the blood-collecting tray where it will not be upset by either yourself or the patient. Try not to disturb the patient any more than is absolutely necessary. Take the arm available and gently place it toward you. If the patient shows apprehension, calmly explain what you are going to do and what you would like him to do. If there is still a slight pulling away of the arm, there are two things you may do. Fold a towel about four times and place it under his elbow to keep it from bending; then very gently place your elbow upon the patient's hand and wrist. The second suggestion is to hold the patient's elbow gently with your left hand and introduce the needle with the right—or vice

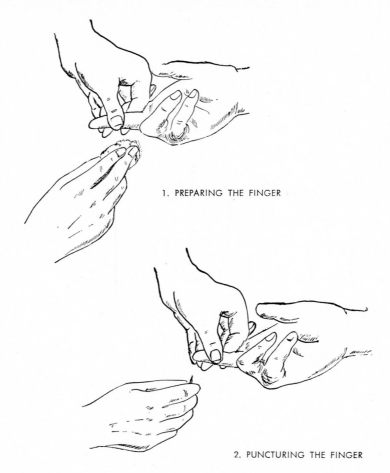

1. PREPARING THE FINGER

2. PUNCTURING THE FINGER

Fig. 34. Steps in the finger puncture. (From Seiverd, C. E.: Hematology for medical technologists, ed. 2, Philadelphia, 1958, Lea & Febiger.)

versa if you are left-handed. A combination of the two steps is also successful. The object of this is to obtain blood without upsetting the patient.

The actual technique of obtaining venous blood is given in the following steps.

Preparing the needle and syringe

The diameter or bore of the needle is indicated by its gauge number. The smaller the number, the greater the diameter. Gauges 20 and 21 are usually used for the forearm and 25 is used for the veins of the wrist and the ankle. The size of the needle chosen is regulated by the size of the vein to be entered.

The choice in size of a syringe is regulated by the amount of blood needed for analysis. (Fig. 35.) Usually, a 10 ml. syringe is most frequently used. The syringe and needle *must be sterile*. If there is any dampness in the syringe because of incomplete drying in the autoclave—do *not* use it. This will hemolyze the blood.

When the needle and syringe have been removed from their sterile pack-

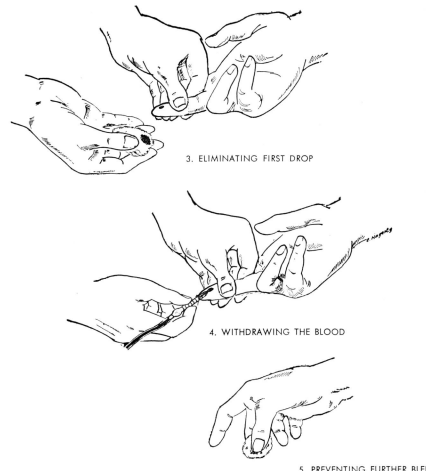

3. ELIMINATING FIRST DROP

4. WITHDRAWING THE BLOOD

5. PREVENTING FURTHER BLEEDING

Fig. 34—cont'd. For legend see opposite page.

ages, carefully place the needle firmly onto the syringe. Do not handle the cannula of the needle or the plunger of the syringe. Use the hub of the needle and the head of the plunger. (Fig. 36.)

Applying the tourniquet

It is most desirable to enlarge the veins of the forearm so that they may become more prominent. With the area for puncture located, utmost care must be used for the proper distention of the vein. Let the arm hang down for a while. The veins will become more apparent.

A piece of soft rubber tubing is most commonly used for a tourniquet although types of tourniquets may range from pieces of cloth to elaborate mechanisms. A blood pressure cuff is a very excellent tourniquet.

The tourniquet is placed above the elbow. The patient then continually opens and closes his hand to aid in filling the vein. During the time that the blood is being drawn the hand is kept closed.

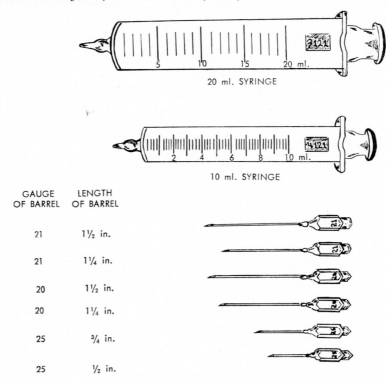

GAUGE OF BARREL	LENGTH OF BARREL
21	1½ in.
21	1¼ in.
20	1½ in.
20	1¼ in.
25	¾ in.
25	½ in.

Fig. 35. Needles and syringes used for the venipuncture. (Redrawn from Seiverd, C. E.: Hematology for medical technologists, ed. 2, Philadelphia, 1958, Lea & Febiger.)

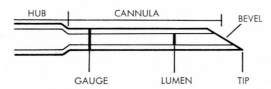

Fig. 36. Diagram of the needle.

Selecting a vein

After the arm has been hanging down until the veins are prominent, the most visible one is selected. If the veins are poorly dilated, even after pumping the hand, release the tourniquet, place a hot wet towel over the arm and cover with a dry towel. Keep this heat pack on the arm for ten or fifteen minutes. Electric blankets, heating pads, and hair dryers have been used successfully to dilate the veins. A word of caution: do not use the hair dryer around any explosives. When the circulation is improved, reapply the tourniquet.

Applying the antiseptic

Many antiseptic solutions are available, but the one most commonly used is 70% ethyl alcohol.

Lundy[2] has expressed the necessity of warming the sponge and antiseptic solution, at least to body temperature, before applying to the area of injection. Because the arm is warm it is more sensitive to the cold, and contact with a cold antiseptic will cause the vein to contract.[2,3]

Inserting the needle

Normally, when the size of the vein to be entered is sufficiently large in relation to the needle size, place the bevel of the needle upward. If a large needle is all that is available for a small vein, however, place the needle into the vein with the bevel facing down. This will prevent a hematoma that might occur from puncturing the wall of the vein. Occasionally a small vein will collapse, covering the opening of the needle, and the technician in attempting to adjust the needle to clear the passage may puncture the wall and cause a hematoma. Many veins have a tendency to "roll" when stuck with a needle. The technician may hold or "fix" the vein either by holding the vein with his thumb or by grasping the patient's arm below the elbow and pulling the skin taut. The needle is held at an angle of approximately 25 degrees and no higher, for there is the possibility of going through the vein.

Withdrawing the blood

When the arm has been prepared with antiseptic and the tourniquet tightened, the needle is aimed in line with the long axis of the vein. Never approach the vein from the side. Holding the syringe by both the plunger and the barrel, pierce the skin. After the blood has entered the syringe, the plunger of the syringe is slowly pulled back. Should the blood start to enter the syringe and then cease, the needle has either slipped out of the vein or gone through it. If it has slipped out, carefully reinsert it. If it has gone through the vein, slowly withdraw the needle until it is once again in the vein. This ability comes with experience. In remedying the above problems, be sure to avoid pushing the plunger forward in the syringe. In the case of a collapsed vein, if little or no blood has been obtained but there is a large air space within the syringe, obtain a new syringe and connect to the needle. This, of course, is unpleasant for the patient, but it must be done.

Releasing the tourniquet

Before the needle is withdrawn from the vein, the tourniquet must be released. Have the patient relax his fist before you release the tourniquet. Otherwise, you will still obtain a blood flow through the puncture.

Withdrawing the needle

Withdraw the needle after the tourniquet has been removed or released. Place a dry, sterile pad or adhesive bandage over the puncture wound immediately.

Preventing bleeding

The patient may gently apply pressure to the sterile pad covering the wound. Folding the arm up toward the shoulder, combined with the finger pressure, will aid in stopping the flow of blood. Sometimes a hematoma will be formed by the blood seeping into subcutaneous tissue. This, of course, leaves a large black and blue mark that may be painful to the patient.

• • •

Hematomas may be caused by several factors: (1) using too large a needle for the vein, therefore puncturing the wall; (2) failure to have the needle com-

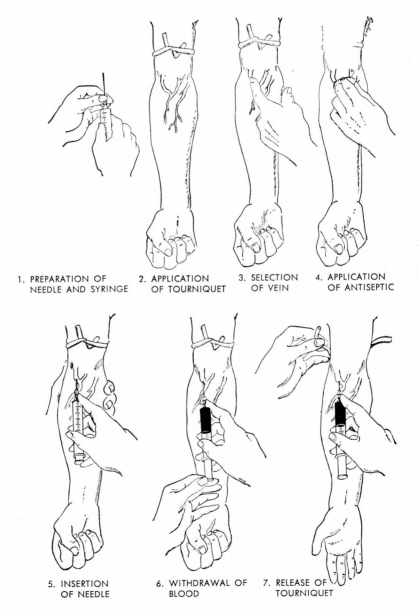

1. PREPARATION OF NEEDLE AND SYRINGE

2. APPLICATION OF TOURNIQUET

3. SELECTION OF VEIN

4. APPLICATION OF ANTISEPTIC

5. INSERTION OF NEEDLE

6. WITHDRAWAL OF BLOOD

7. RELEASE OF TOURNIQUET

Fig. 37. Steps in the venipuncture. (From Seiverd, C. E.: Hematology for medical technologists, ed. 2, Philadelphia, 1958, Lea & Febiger.)

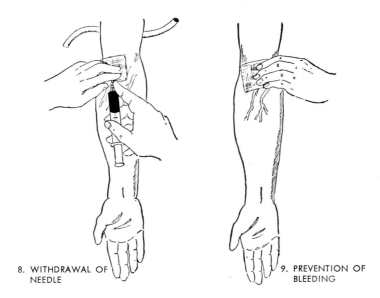

8. WITHDRAWAL OF NEEDLE

9. PREVENTION OF BLEEDING

Fig. 37—cont'd. For legend see opposite page.

pletely in the vein, thus allowing blood to enter into the tissues; (3) forgetting to release the tourniquet before withdrawing the needle, with the result that the pressure expels blood from the vein puncture into the tissues; (4) failure to apply finger pressure to the wound for a sufficient time; and, last but not least, (5) not taking the time and care to do a good job the first time and then having to do repeated punctures of the vein.

The steps in the venipuncture are illustrated in Fig. 37.

Summary of the venipuncture

1. Prepare the needle and syringe.
2. Apply the tourniquet.
3. Select a vein.
4. Apply the antiseptic.
5. Insert the needle.
6. Withdraw the blood.
7. Release the tourniquet.
8. Withdraw the needle.
9. Prevent bleeding.

REFERENCES

1. Page, L. B., and Culver, P. J.: Syllabus of laboratory examinations in clinical diagnosis, rev. ed., Cambridge, Mass., 1961, Harvard University Press.
2. Lundy, J. S.: Suggestions to facilitate venipuncture in blood transfusion, intravenous therapy and intravenous anesthesia, Proc. Staff Meet. Mayo Clin. **12:**122, Feb. 24, 1937.
3. Abbott Laboratories, Medical Department: Parenteral administration, Chicago, 1959.

Chapter 6

Preparation of blood

The blood usually requires some preparation before examination. The specimens may be centrifuged to separate the serum or plasma from the cells. Many procedures require a protein-free filtrate. This may be prepared by using either whole blood (anticoagulated), serum, or plasma.

SERUM

The reaction in blood clotting is the conversion of the soluble protein fibrinogen to the insoluble fibrin. This may be simply described as progressing in steps or phases. In the first phase, ionized calcium and thromboplastic factors (cephalin, tryptases, thromboplastins) activate prothrombin, forming thrombin. In the second phase, the thrombin converts fibrinogen into fibrin. This is the actual formation of the clot.

1. Obtain a test tube and materials for a ventipuncture.
2. Make a venipuncture and withdraw the amount required.
3. Remove the needle from the syringe and gently force the blood into the test tube.
4. Let clot. This takes about 30 minutes.
5. Centrifuge. A clear yellow fluid will be above the clot. This is serum. It is used for the majority of blood examinations, as indicated in Fig. 38.

PLASMA

In order to obtain plasma, the blood must be kept from clotting. Substances that prevent clotting are called anticoagulants. Some chemical anticoagulants remove the ionized calcium from the blood. Heparin prevents clotting by inactivating prothrombin. The more popular anticoagulants and the amounts required per milliliter of blood are given below:

Anticoagulant	*Amount per milliliter of blood*
Sodium oxalate	2 mg.
Potassium oxalate	2 mg.
Sodium fluoride	2 mg.
Heparin	0.2 mg.
Lithium oxalate	1 mg.

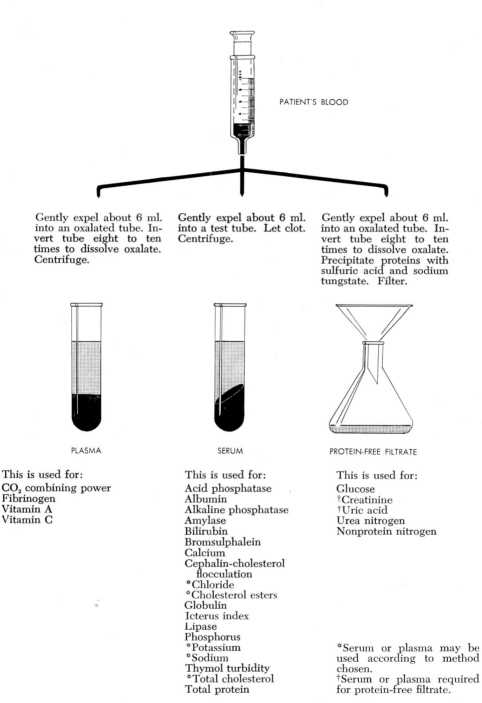

PATIENT'S BLOOD

Gently expel about 6 ml. into an oxalated tube. Invert tube eight to ten times to dissolve oxalate. Centrifuge.

Gently expel about 6 ml. into a test tube. Let clot. Centrifuge.

Gently expel about 6 ml. into an oxalated tube. Invert tube eight to ten times to dissolve oxalate. Precipitate proteins with sulfuric acid and sodium tungstate. Filter.

PLASMA

SERUM

PROTEIN-FREE FILTRATE

This is used for:
CO_2 combining power
Fibrinogen
Vitamin A
Vitamin C

This is used for:
Acid phosphatase
Albumin
Alkaline phosphatase
Amylase
Bilirubin
Bromsulphalein
Calcium
Cephalin-cholesterol
    flocculation
*Chloride
*Cholesterol esters
Globulin
Icterus index
Lipase
Phosphorus
*Potassium
*Sodium
Thymol turbidity
*Total cholesterol
Total protein

This is used for:
Glucose
†Creatinine
†Uric acid
Urea nitrogen
Nonprotein nitrogen

*Serum or plasma may be used according to method chosen.
†Serum or plasma required for protein-free filtrate.

Fig. 38. Preparation of the blood for examination.

A mixture of potassium oxalate and sodium fluoride is usually used as an anticoagulant and preservative for most blood glucose methods. However, since sodium fluoride inhibits enzyme activity it cannot be used as an anticoagulant for any enzyme determination. It may be used in urease method for blood urea nitrogen (BUN) if the amount does not exceed 2 mg./ml. Heparin, a physiological anticoagulant, and EDTA (ethylenediamine tetra-acetate), a chelating agent binding calcium, are very popular anticoagulants used in chemistry and hematology laboratories, since there is no destruction of the cells.

Test tubes containing the proper amount of potassium oxalate are prepared as follows:

1. Using the analytical balance, weigh out 1 gm. of potassium oxalate.
2. Place in a 100 ml. volumetric flask. Add distilled water to the 100 ml. mark. Mix. This is a 1% solution.
3. Place 1 ml. of the 1% potassium oxalate solution in each test tube. Evaporate to dryness in an oven that does not exceed 105° C.

Each of the above tubes contains 10 mg. of potassium oxalate. This will serve as an anticoagulant for 5 ml. of blood. The test tube containing the anticoagulant is commonly referred to as an oxalated tube and, when blood is added, it is called oxalated blood.

To prepare plasma, proceed as follows:

1. Get an oxalated tube and materials for a venipuncture.
2. Make a venipuncture and withdraw the amount required.
3. Remove the needle from the syringe and gently expel the blood into the oxalated tube.
4. Place the cork in the tube and invert eight to ten times to dissolve the oxalate.
5. Centrifuge the oxalated blood. The fluid portion above the cells is plasma. It is used for several tests, as indicated in Fig. 38.

PROTEIN-FREE FILTRATE

If an acid is added to oxalated blood, it precipitates the proteins. The proteins may then be removed by filtration or centrifugation. The three methods listed below employ tungstic acid (formed by the combination of sulfuric acid and sodium tungstate) as the precipitating agent. The clear fluid that remains is known as a protein-free filtrate. It is used for several tests, as indicated in Fig. 38.

A protein-free filtrate may be prepared by any of the three methods listed below. The procedures follow. If it is necessary to prepare any of the reagents, take the number that follows the reagent and refer to Appendix C. (Note: If only 1 ml. of blood is available, divide all the quantities mentioned by 2.)

Folin-Wu method
Haden method
Somogyi method

Folin-Wu method

Reagents needed

Sulfuric Acid, ⅔ N	(C-1)
Sodium Tungstate, 10%	(C-2)

Procedure

1. Place 14 ml. of distilled water in a 125 ml. Erlenmeyer flask.
2. Invert the tube containing the oxalated blood several times in order to mix.
3. Using a 2 ml. volumetric pipet, add 2 ml. of the oxalated blood to the Erlenmeyer flask. Gently swirl the flask to hemolyze the cells.
4. While swirling the flask, slowly add 2 ml. of $2/3$ N sulfuric acid.
5. While swirling the flask, slowly add 2 ml. of 10% sodium tungstate.
6. Let stand for a few minutes. Mix and then filter.

Haden method

Reagents needed

Sulfuric Acid, 1/12 N   (C-3)
Sodium Tungstate, 10%   (C-2)

Procedure

1. Place 16 ml. of 1/12 N sulfuric acid in a 125 ml. Erlenmeyer flask.
2. Invert the tube containing the oxalated blood several times in order to mix.
3. Using a 2 ml. volumetric pipet, add 2 ml. of the oxalated blood to the Erlenmeyer flask. Gently swirl the flask to hemolyze the cells.
4. While swirling the flask, slowly add 2 ml. of 10% sodium tungstate.
5. Let stand for a few minutes. Mix and then filter.

Somogyi method

Reagents needed

Zinc Sulfate, 5%   (C-4)
Barium Hydroxide, 0.3 N   (C-5)

Procedure

1. Invert the tube containing the oxalated blood several times to thoroughly mix the specimen. With an Ostwald-Folin pipet, add 1.0 ml. of blood into a 25 ml. Erlenmeyer flask containing 5.0 ml. of distilled water. The water dilutes the blood and lakes (hemolyzes) the cells.
2. Add slowly with constant agitation 2.0 ml. of 5% zinc sulfate. Mix well.
3. Add slowly 2.0 ml. of 0.3 N barium hydroxide.
4. Insert a rubber stopper and shake vigorously until a metallic click is heard and the absence of foam indicates complete precipitation of the protein. This is called the isoelectric point. Exacting technique must be used to obtain this point of precipitation.
5. Let the flask stand for 5 minutes and then filter or centrifuge.

If the protein-free filtrate is not used the day it is prepared, it should be kept in a refrigerator to prevent decomposition. If it is to be kept several days or sent through the mail, a few drops of toluene or xylene should be added as a preservative.

The protein-free filtrate is used in the determination of glucose, creatinine, uric acid, urea nitrogen, and total nonprotein nitrogen.

In the final calculations for the above tests, a correction is always made for the dilution of the blood that was caused by preparing the filtrate. For example, in preparing the filtrate, the blood is diluted 1 in 10. This means that 10 ml. of filtrate represent 1 ml. of blood.

Chapter 7

Quality control

Although quality control has an ominous sound to the technician, it is actually an excellent tool. The purpose of a quality control program is to produce high-quality analyses, not to frighten the technician or to create a feeling of fear or distrust toward the immediate supervisor or laboratory.

Lack of understanding of the terminology and of what is happening causes apprehension and resistance to the program. Using a system of quality control is a lot of work, it does take time, and it will cost money; but how can this be compared to knowing that the physician has been given an accurate result and the patient will not suffer because of a laboratory error?

A conservative program may be established by recording or charting blanks and standards. Use common sense with the program. Know what you are doing and what is possible with the method in use, and know what you need. Do not run controls even when you are not running the test, just so you can say a control is analyzed daily. Use the quality control (QC) within a group of tests so that you will know if the instruments are functioning adequately, the reagents are pure, and the glassware clean. There are several ways to establish a program. If refrigeration, storage, and mathematics are a problem, this is easily solved by commercial firms that have good standards and fine quality control programs. In alphabetical order are Dade Reagents, of Miami, Florida; Hyland Laboratories, at Los Angeles 39, California; and Warner-Chilcott, in Morris Plains, New Jersey. You may have access to pooled serum and wish to calculate your own results. The American Society of Clinical Pathologists has a manual pertaining to setting up the program with charts and all that is needed.*

A program to suit the needs of your laboratory may be found in one of the above suggestions. Whether the laboratory is large or small, it is a *must* that some form of control be maintained. With the present demands upon the laboratory the technician is obligated to produce the finest quality of work possible at all times.

---

*May be obtained from the Commission on Continuing Education, 2050 North Orleans St., Chicago 14, Ill.

There is no control or standard that is an absolute value. With a hundred analyses of the same sample, the group of results will fall into a pattern that, when plotted, conforms to the shape of a bell. The largest portion of analyses (68%) will hover close to the average value, which is called either the average or the mean value. A lesser amount will be next and finally dwindle to a few results that are borderline or out of range. This normal distribution is called the Gaussian distribution. (See Fig. 39.)

The technician should be familiar with the following terms. The mean is the mathematical average of a group of numbers. Standard deviation (SD) refers to the nature of grouping of individual values around the mean. A deviation of plus or minus 1 standard deviation represents a calculated variation around the mean. A plus or minus 3 standard deviation range represents a wider variation of the values.

Statisticians have established that the three standard deviations are to be considered the "confidence limits." The values that fall within these limits tell the technician the test values are within the normal, expected variation range. This is a reassuring picture, indicating that the test is in control. Any test that is out of this range—and some will be—is a cue to take a look at the reagents, standards, or loss of sensitivity of the instrument used. Three tests out of a thousand (0.3 of 1%) will fall out of range, according to the law of probability. It must be stressed to the technician that this 0.3% is as much a part of the program as the coveted 68%.

If pooled serum or unassayed commercial serum is being used for a quality control program, a series of tests are run, under as nearly identical conditions as possible over a period of several days, utilizing various technicians. The average or mean value is obtained from this series of analyses. The difference of each test from the mean value is determined and squared. The squared values are then totaled. The total of the squared values is next divided by the total number of tests done, minus one. (If 32 tests are run, divide by 31.) The square root of this value is one standard deviation, or 1 SD.

After the standard deviation has been calculated, the values for the confidence limits may be applied graphically to a control chart. The daily values then

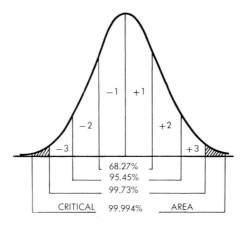

Fig. 39. Bell distribution curve.

may be plotted on the chart so that any fluctuations or trouble areas of the test may become apparent immediately.

It is *most important* that the QC be run as a routine test. Special attention to tube of control destroys the whole purpose of the program. This special attention will not give the true degree of variability of the analysis. The purpose of the program is to measure the degree of accuracy and reproducibility routinely done in the laboratory. The technician desires accuracy and reproducibility; but it may be that he is obtaining reproducibility without accuracy, accuracy without reproducibility, or neither accuracy nor reproducibility. These conditions may result from the use of dirty glassware, a test being done without a standard, using precalibrated curves or a colorimeter or spectrophotometer that is not obtaining the proper sensitivity, or from shortcuts taken in a procedure, with careless attention to the incubation or timing, and last—but definitely not least—poor technique used by the technician.

To assist the technician in calculating the standard deviation and making a control chart for the daily plotting of tests, the following example is given. The tests being calculated are potassium results that were run routinely in the laboratory. The specimens used were obtained from pooled sera prepared and previously assayed. As you will note, the potassium value is above the normal range for potassium. Quality control is needel for elevated and abnormal ranges, as well as for checks within the normal range. Test 25 in Table 16, placed last, shows what cigarette ashes will do to the potassium when a technician is careless with his smoking.

Referring to Table 16, calculate the standard deviation.

Table 16. Sample work sheet for tabulating test results

(A) Number of tests	(B) Test results	(C) Difference from the mean	(D) Difference from the mean squared
1	5.8	0.0	0.00
2	5.6	0.2	0.04
3	5.9	0.1	0.01
4	5.8	0.0	0.00
5	5.7	0.1	0.01
6	5.8	0.0	0.00
7	5.8	0.0	0.00
8	5.8	0.0	0.00
9	5.4	0.4	0.16
10	5.7	0.1	0.01
11	5.7	0.1	0.01
12	5.6	0.2	0.04
13	5.8	0.0	0.00
14	5.7	0.1	0.01
15	5.8	0.0	0.00
16	5.8	0.0	0.00
17	5.8	0.0	0.00
18	5.9	0.1	0.01
19	5.7	0.1	0.01
20	5.8	0.0	0.00
21	5.9	0.0	0.00
22	5.7	0.1	0.01
23	5.7	0.1	0.01
24	5.8	0.1	0.01
25	(9.3)	(Specimen contaminated by cigarette ashes)	
Total	138.0		0.34

Procedure

1. Total column B and divide by the number of tests done. Test **25** is eliminated from the averages because of a technical error.

$$\text{Average or mean value} = \frac{138.0}{24} = 5.8$$

2. Determine the absolute difference of each test from the average value (**5.8**). The difference is recorded in column C, which is *not* added. Do not bother placing plus or minus signs with the differences.
3. In column D, the difference from the mean is squared (multiplied by itself: e.g., $0.4 \times 0.4 = 0.16$). This column is totaled, giving a result of 0.34.
4. With this data, calculate the standard deviation. With n = number of tests done, the formula for calculating SD in this example is as follows:

$$\text{Standard deviation} = \sqrt{\frac{\text{Sum of squared differences (column D)}}{n - 1}}$$

$$\text{SD} = \sqrt{\frac{0.34}{24 - 1}}$$

$$\text{SD} = \sqrt{\frac{0.34}{23}}$$

$$\text{SD} = \sqrt{0.0148}$$

$$\text{SD} = 0.12$$

The symbol "$\sqrt{}$" means taking the square root of a number, 0.0148 in the example shown. Values may be obtained from Table 17 or from Table 24, Chapter 9, for the square roots of small numbers. In order to check the accuracy, multiply the square root by itself. A slide rule may be used to obtain either a square of a number or a square root.

To find the square of a number

Set the hairline to the number on the D scale and read its square under the line on the A scale. The square may also be found by setting the hairline on the C scale and reading the square on the B scale.

To find the square root of a number

Set the hairline on the number of the A scale and read the square root under the line on the D scale. Reading from the B scale to the C scale may also be used.

Note: Use the left half of the slide rule A scale for odd numbers left of the decimal point (1.30). Use the right half of the A scale for the even numbers before the decimal point (24.00).

By the chart, the slide rule, or calculation you will obtain a standard deviation of 0.12. This represents ± 1 standard deviation. In other words, 68% of the tests will vary 0.12 from the average or mean value of 5.8. In view of the fact that controlling a test this closely is highly improbable, 3 deviations have been set as the "confidence limits." With some methods, it is desirable to hold to 2 deviations. A simple multiplying by 2 or by 3 will give the control limits desired:

	Lower	*Average*	Upper
± 1 SD = 0.12 meq./L.	5.7	5.8	5.9
± 2 SD = 0.24 meq./L.	5.6	5.8	6.0
± 3 SD = 0.36* meq./L.	5.4	5.8	6.2

*0.36 is rounded off to 0.4.

Table 17. Squares and square roots

n	n^2	$\sqrt{n}$	n	n^2	$\sqrt{n}$	n	n^2	$\sqrt{n}$	n	n^2	$\sqrt{n}$
1	1	1.000	13	169	3.605	25	625	5.000	37	1369	6.082
2	4	1.414	14	196	3.741	26	676	5.099	38	1444	6.164
3	9	1.732	15	225	3.872	27	729	5.196	39	1521	6.244
4	16	2.000	16	256	4.000	28	784	5.291	40	1600	6.634
5	25	2.236	17	289	4.123	29	841	5.385	41	1681	6.403
6	36	2.449	18	324	4.242	30	900	5.477	42	1764	6.480
7	47	2.645	19	361	4.358	31	961	5.567	43	1849	6.557
8	64	2.828	20	400	4.472	32	1024	5.656	44	1936	6.663
9	81	3.000	21	441	4.582	33	1089	5.744	45	2025	6.708
10	100	3.162	22	484	4.690	34	1156	5.830	46	2116	6.782
11	121	3.316	23	529	4.795	35	1225	5.916	47	2209	6.885
12	144	3.464	24	576	4.898	36	1296	6.000	48	2304	6.928

n = the number.
n² = the number squared.
√n = the square root of the number.

Percent of the mean

It is now understood that standard deviation is the unit variation from an average or mean value. In the case of the example given the unit variation is ± 0.12 meq./L. The percent of the mean or average value called "coefficient of variation" is the percentage variation or ± %. To obtain this coefficient of variation (CV), the standard deviation value is divided by the mean or average value and then multiplied by 100. The following results are obtained by this formula:

$$\frac{SD}{\text{Mean value}} \times 100 = \pm\ \% \text{ or coefficient of variation}$$

±1 Standard deviation of the potassium   = 0.12
Average (mean) value of the potassium = 5.8

$$\frac{0.12}{5.8} \times 100 = 2.06\% \pm 1\ SD$$

$$\frac{0.24}{5.8} \times 100 = 4.13\% \pm 2\ SD$$

$$\frac{0.36}{5.8} \times 100 = 6.20\% \pm 3\ SD$$

Control charts

There are three ways to present a chart for daily plotting of results:
1. The control chart, with the mean and the deviations' boundaries drawn
2. The bell curve, inverted 90 degrees
3. The target control chart, with the rings representing the various deviations

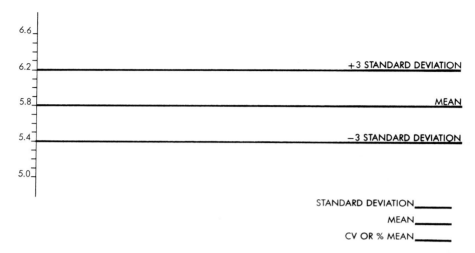

Fig. 40. Quality control chart.

A convenient method of keeping the chart reusable from one month to another is placing the chart with its numerical values under a plastic cover. The average or mean value and the confidence limits are drawn on the plastic cover with a wax pencil. Marks can be wiped off with an alcohol sponge. An example of one of the three charts, the control chart, is given in Fig. 40.

Chapter 8

Glucose

Glucose and glucose tolerance tests aid the physician in diagnosing diabetes and many other disorders. This chapter considers these quantitative tests of glucose in blood, cerebrospinal fluid, and urine. For the convenience of the student, a tabular summary is given at the end of the chapter.

BLOOD GLUCOSE

The discussion covers information significant to the student, procedures for the test, and directions for preparing standards.

Information significant to the student

Glucose, the Greek word for sweet, is one of the simple sugars that are the products of carbohydrate digestion. Upon leaving the small intestine, glucose enters the bloodstream and is carried to the liver. There it may be stored as glycogen, or it may be returned to the blood and oxidized as fuel for bodily activities.

The normal values for glucose depend upon the method of analysis. With the early methods, glucose and saccharoids (nonglucose substances) could not be separated. Consequently, the glucose values included saccharoids.

With the later methods of analysis, however, it was possible to separate glucose from saccharoids and thus determine glucose independently. It was then referred to as true glucose.

The normal values for the early methods of analysis—glucose plus saccharoids—are 80 to 120 mg./100 ml. of blood. The normal values for the later methods of analysis—true glucose—are 65 to 95 mg./100 ml. of blood.

When the glucose level rises above the normal range, the condition is known as hyperglycemia. When the glucose level falls below that range, the condition is referred to as hypoglycemia. Table 18 lists conditions in which an increased or decreased glucose value may be expected. The diseases given in italics are of primary interest to the physician; the others are of somewhat lesser concern.

Insulin, a hormone produced by the pancreas, helps control the glucose level

Table 18. Conditions accompanied by abnormal glucose values

Increased glucose	*Decreased glucose*
Diabetes	*Hyperinsulinism*
Hyperthyroidism	Hypothyroidism
Hyperpituitarism	Hypopituitarism
Nephritis	Hepatic disease
Coronary thrombosis	Addison's disease
Infections	Pernicious vomiting
Pregnancy	Starvation
Uremia	

of blood. In diabetes, sufficient amounts of insulin are not produced, and the glucose level rises and some is excreted in the urine. The presence of excessive glucose in the urine is known as glycosuria.

The blood level at which glycosuria occurs is usually 160 to 180 mg./100 ml. This is known as the renal threshold value.

Some people have a low renal threshold value, and glycosuria occurs in the absence of any pathological condition. This is referred to as renal glycosuria or "renal diabetes." And sometimes glycosuria will occur after a meal that is rich in carbohydrates. This is called alimentary glycosuria.

If glycosuria occurs and the physician suspects diabetes, he may request a glucose tolerance test. The technician gives glucose to the patient and measures glucose levels at specific intervals. The diabetic takes longer to remove the sugar from the blood than a normal individual.

The more commonly used methods for the determination of glucose are listed below. In the brief discussion that follows, special attention has been given to the function of each reagent. It is hoped this will answer many of the questions in the mind of the student.

> Folin-Wu method
> Benedict method
> Somogyi-Nelson method
> Glucose oxidase method (modified)

Folin-Wu method

An alkaline copper solution is added to a protein-free filtrate. The glucose present reduces the copper to cuprous oxide. The cuprous oxide in turn reduces a colorless phosphomolybd*ic* acid solution to blue phosphomolybd*ous* acid. The depth of color is measured in a colorimeter. The normal values for this method are 80 to 120 mg./100 ml. of blood.

Benedict method

A special bisulfite copper solution is used that increases the specificity of the test for glucose at the expense of the saccharoids. This solution is added to a protein-free filtrate and the glucose reduces the copper to cuprous oxide. The cuprous oxide in turn reduces a colorless phosphomolybd*ic* acid solution to blue phosphomolybd*ous* acid. The depth of color is measured in a colorimeter. The normal values are 70 to 100 mg./100 ml. of blood.

Somogyi-Nelson method

A Somogyi protein-free filtrate that removes reducing substances other than sugar is made. A copper tartrate reagent is added to the filtrate and the glucose reduces the copper to cuprous oxide. The cuprous oxide then reacts with an arsenomolybdate reagent to give a blue color. The depth of color is measured in a colorimeter. The normal values are 65 to 95 mg./100 ml. of blood.

Glucose oxidase method (modified)

This is an enzymatic method that will respond to glucose only. No other physiological constituent is measured. Only a Somogyi protein-free filtrate may be used, because it is free of metallic ions. The tungstic acid filtrate cannot be used with this method. The enzyme, glucose oxidase, catalyzes (or promotes) the oxidation of glucose with oxygen to gluconic acid and hydrogen peroxide. The hydrogen peroxide is detected by a chromogenic oxygen acceptor in the presence of peroxidase (horseradish). The normal range is 65 to 95 mg./100 ml.

Procedures for glucose determination

The following general considerations pertain to the procedure for glucose tests:

1. Preparation of patient: must be fasting.
2. Preparation of blood: protein-free filtrate.
3. Preservation of blood: blood may be stored for a few hours in a refrigerator; filtrate may be stored overnight in a refrigerator if a few drops of toluene are added.
4. Precautions: follow the directions *exactly* as given in the procedure.

Measurement of glucose
Somogyi-Nelson method[1,2]

Reagents needed

Alkaline Copper Reagent	(C-6)
Arsenomolybdate Color Reagent	(C-7)
Benzoic Acid, 0.2%	(C-8)
Stock Standard, 1.0 mg./ml.	(C-9)
Working Standard, 0.10 mg./ml.	

Pipet 10.0 ml. of stock standard into a 100 ml. volumetric flask and dilute to mark with 0.2% benzoic acid.

Procedure

Prepare a Somogyi protein-free filtrate. The filtrate *must* be crystal-clear.
Label and prepare Folin-Wu sugar tubes (Fig. 41) as described below:
Blank (1 tube)
1. Pipet 2.0 ml. of distilled water. Use volumetric pipet.
Standards (3 tubes)
1. Pipet 1.0 ml. of working standard and 1.0 ml. of distilled water into three tubes. Use volumetric pipet.
Unknown (1 tube per test)
1. Pipet 1.0 ml. of filtrate and 1.0 ml. of distilled water into numbered sugar tube. Use volumetric pipet.
To all tubes:
1. Add 2.0 ml. of alkaline copper reagent. Shake to mix.
2. Place into boiling water bath for 20 minutes. Time by clock.
3. At the end of 20 minutes, place the tubes into room temperature

25 ml.

Fig. 41. Folin-Wu sugar tube.

water bath to cool. (*Caution:* Do not agitate the tubes when moving from the boiling water bath to the cooling bath. Agitation causes oxidation of cuprous oxide.)

4. When cool, add 2.0 ml. of the arsenomolybdate reagent.
5. Mix well by grasping the top of the tube with the right hand and thumping the bottom of the tube against the palm of the left hand. Allow the tubes to stand for a few minutes and then mix again.
6. Add distilled water to the 25 ml. mark *exactly*. Observe the meniscus! If over the mark, repeat the test!
7. Stopper and invert five times for a thorough mixing.
8. Transfer a portion of the solution to a cuvette and read against the blank at 540 millimicrons (mμ). Read percent transmission and convert to optical density (Table 19, p. 108) or read directly optical density. Average the standards for the calculation of the glucose.

Calculations with an example

$$\frac{\text{O.D. (unknown)}}{\text{O.D. (standard)}} \times \text{Mg. standard} \times 1000 = \text{Mg.\% glucose}$$

Standard readings (O.D.) 0.310
0.310
0.309
$\overline{0.929} \div 3 = 0.3096$ or 0.310

Unknown reading (O.D.) 0.365

$$\frac{0.365}{0.310} \times 0.1 \times 1000 = 117.7 \text{ or } 118 \text{ mg.\% glucose}$$

Table 19. Percent transmission—optical density conversion table

% T		(.25)	(.50)	(.75)	% T		(.25)	(.50)	(.75)
1	2.000	1.903	1.824	1.757	51	.292	.290	.288	.286
2	1.699	1.648	1.602	1.561	52	.284	.282	.280	.278
3	1.523	1.488	1.456	1.426	53	.276	.274	.272	.270
4	1.398	1.372	1.347	1.323	54	.268	.266	.264	.262
5	1.301	1.280	1.260	1.240	55	.260	.258	.256	.254
6	1.222	1.204	1.187	1.171	56	.252	.250	.248	.246
7	1.155	1.140	1.126	1.112	57	.244	.242	.240	.238
8	1.097	1.083	1.071	1.059	58	.237	.235	.233	.231
9	1.046	1.034	1.022	1.011	59	.229	.227	.226	.224
10	1.000	.989	.979	.969	60	.222	.220	.218	.216
11	.959	.949	.939	.930	61	.215	.213	.211	.209
12	.921	.912	.903	.894	62	.208	.206	.204	.202
13	.886	.878	.870	.862	63	.201	.199	.197	.196
14	.854	.846	.838	.831	64	.194	.192	.191	.189
15	.824	.817	.810	.803	65	.187	.186	.184	.182
16	.796	.789	.782	.776	66	.180	.179	.177	.176
17	.770	.763	.757	.751	67	.174	.172	.171	.169
18	.745	.739	.733	.727	68	.168	.166	.164	.163
19	.721	.716	.710	.703	69	.161	.160	.158	.157
20	.699	.694	.688	.683	70	.155	.153	.152	.150
21	.678	.673	.668	.663	71	.149	.147	.146	.144
22	.658	.653	.648	.643	72	.143	.141	.140	.138
23	.638	.634	.629	.624	73	.137	.135	.134	.132
24	.620	.615	.611	.606	74	.131	.129	.128	.126
25	.602	.598	.594	.589	75	.125	.124	.122	.121
26	.585	.581	.577	.573	76	.119	.118	.116	.115
27	.569	.565	.561	.557	77	.114	.112	.111	.109
28	.553	.549	.545	.542	78	.108	.107	.105	.104
29	.538	.534	.530	.527	79	.102	.101	.100	.098
30	.523	.520	.516	.512	80	.097	.096	.094	.093
31	.509	.505	.502	.498	81	.092	.090	.089	.088
32	.495	.491	.488	.485	82	.086	.085	.084	.082
33	.482	.478	.475	.472	83	.081	.080	.078	.077
34	.469	.465	.462	.459	84	.076	.074	.073	.072
35	.456	.453	.450	.447	85	.071	.069	.068	.067
36	.444	.441	.438	.435	86	.066	.064	.063	.062
37	.432	.429	.426	.423	87	.061	.059	.058	.057
38	.420	.417	.414	.412	88	.056	.054	.053	.052
39	.409	.406	.403	.401	89	.051	.049	.048	.047
40	.398	.395	.392	.390	90	.046	.045	.043	.042
41	.387	.385	.382	.380	91	.041	.040	.039	.037
42	.377	.374	.372	.369	92	.036	.035	.034	.033
43	.367	.364	.362	.359	93	.032	.030	.029	.028
44	.357	.354	.352	.349	94	.027	.026	.025	.024
45	.347	.344	.342	.340	95	.022	.021	.020	.019
46	.337	.335	.332	.330	96	.018	.017	.016	.014
47	.328	.325	.323	.321	97	.013	.012	.011	.010
48	.319	.317	.314	.312	98	.009	.008	.007	.006
49	.310	.308	.305	.303	99	.004	.003	.002	.001
50	.301	.299	.297	.295	100	.000	.000	.000	.000

Somogyi-Nelson micromethod[1,2]

This method is the same as the preceding method of glucose determination by Somogyi-Nelson, with the exception that it is scaled down to small quantities so that *extreme accuracy* must be used. This method is mostly used on infants or patients where the veins are difficult to locate. The normal values are 70 to 100 mg.% with capillary blood.

Reagents needed

Same as for the previous Somogyi-Nelson method

Working Glucose Standard (1.0 ml. = 0.05 mg.)

Pipet into a 100 ml. volumetric flask 5.0 ml. of stock standard. Dilute to mark with 0.2% benzoic acid.

Methods of collecting the blood

1. Finger, heel, or earlobe puncture: A pipet rinsed with heparin may be used and blood be pipetted directly from the puncture wound. The filtrate must be made immediately, since there is no fluoride protection. The glucose values run about 3% higher in the normal range than with the venipuncture. The elevated range may differ as much as 20 to 40 mg.%[3]

2. Venipuncture: A venipuncture may be made and the small amount of blood may be placed in a Kahn tube or small beaker containing small amounts of solid oxalate and fluoride.

Procedure

1. Pipet 0.2 ml. of blood into a small test tube containing 1.0 ml. of distilled water.
2. Add 0.4 ml. of zinc sulfate. Mix thoroughly by tapping the tube with the finger.
3. Add 0.4 ml. of barium hydroxide. Mix thoroughly by tapping the tube with the finger.
4. Let the tubes stand for 5 minutes.
5. Centrifuge for 10 minutes.
6. Pipet 0.5 ml. of filtrate and 1.5 ml. of distilled water into a Folin-Wu sugar tube.
7. Pipet 1.0 ml. of standard (0.05 mg./ml.) and 1.0 ml. of distilled water into three Folin-Wu sugar tubes.
8. Pipet 2.0 ml. of distilled water into a sugar tube for the blank.
9. The remainder of the test procedure is the same as that used in the Somogyi-Nelson method.

Calculations

$$\frac{\text{O.D. (unknown)}}{\text{O.D. (standard)}} \times \text{Mg. standard} \times 2000 = \text{Mg.\% glucose}$$

Glucose measurement by the Folin-Wu method[4]

An alkaline copper reagent is heated with a Folin-Wu filtrate. Cuprous oxide produced by the reaction of cupric hydroxide and glucose reduces phosphomolybdic acid to phosphomolybdous acid, which is blue. This blue color is compared to a standard solution of glucose. Values obtained using the Folin-Wu filtrate are about 20 to 30 mg.% higher than those obtained using the Somogyi filtrate. The normal range is 80 to 120 mg.%.

A modification of the Folin-Wu method enables the technician to measure "true glucose." The modification in this method is the use of the Somogyi filtrate to remove the nonglucose reducing substances. A change from the classic Folin-Wu method may be made by changing *only* the preparation of the protein-free filtrate. The normal range is 65 to 95 mg.%.

Reagents needed

Alkaline Copper Reagent	(C-6a)
Phosphomolybdic Acid	(C-10)
Alternate Phosphomolybdic Acid	(C-11)

This reagent may be used to reduce fading, instead of phosphomolybdic acid listed here as C-10; 3.0 ml. should be used instead of 2.0 ml.

Stock Standard, 1.0 mg./ml.	(C-9)
Benzoic Acid, 0.2%	(C-8)

Working Standards (use volumetric flasks):
1. For 0.05 mg./ml. dilute 5 ml. of stock standard to 100 ml. with benzoic acid.

2. For 0.10 mg./ml. dilute 10 ml. of stock standard to 100 ml. with benzoic acid.
3. For 0.20 mg./ml. dilute 20 ml. of stock standard to 100 ml. with benzoic acid.

Procedure

Prepare a Folin-Wu filtrate (or a Somogyi filtrate, if doing a true glucose). The filtrate *must* be crystal-clear. Label and prepare Folin-Wu tubes as described below:

Blank (1 tube)

1. Pipet 2.0 ml. of distilled water into sugar tube.

Standards (3 tubes)

1. Pipet 2.0 ml. of working standard (0.05 mg./ml.) into sugar tube.
2. Pipet 2.0 ml. of working standard (0.10 mg./ml) into sugar tube.
3. Pipet 2.0 ml. of working standard (0.20 mg./ml.) into sugar tube.

Unknown (1 tube per test)

1. Pipet 2.0 ml. of filtrate into each tube.

To all tubes:

1. Add 2.0 ml. of alkaline copper. Mix.
2. Place tubes into boiling water bath for 8 minutes. Time.
3. After 8 minutes, place tubes into room temperature water bath to cool. Do not disturb the precipitate.
4. Add 2.0 ml. of the phosphomolybdic acid. Mix. (*The alternate method:* Add 3.0 ml. of alternate phosphomolybdic acid. Mix. This stabilizes the color, eliminating steps 5 and 6.)
5. To stabilize the color place the tubes into the boiling water bath again for 2 minutes. Time.
6. At the end of 2 minutes, return to the room temperature water bath to cool.
7. Dilute to the 25 ml. mark with distilled water. Stopper and mix thoroughly by inversion.
8. Pour into cuvette and read against the blank at 420 mμ.

Calculations

$$\frac{\text{O.D. (unknown)}}{\text{O.D. (standard)}} \times \text{Mg. standard} \times 500 = \text{Mg.\% glucose}$$

Note: The standards are made so that a 2.0 ml. volume will contain the following mg. concentration:

1. (0.05 mg./ml.) 0.1 mg. equivalent to 50 mg.%
2. (0.10 mg./ml.) 0.2 mg. equivalent to 100 mg.%
3. (0.20 mg./ml.) 0.4 mg. equivalent to 200 mg.%

Calculate the glucose, using the standard that reads closest to the unknown.

SPINAL FLUID GLUCOSE

The normal values for glucose in spinal fluid are approximately two-thirds that of the blood glucose or 40 to 80 mg./100 ml. of fluid. Increased values may accompany brain tumors. Decreased values are seen in most types of meningitis. If the analysis cannot be done within the hour, either a protein-free filtrate must be made or the spinal fluid may be placed in a test tube containing sodium fluoride as a preservative.

Methods

Either the macromethod or the micromethod of Somogyi-Nelson is satisfactory. The spinal fluid glucose may be determined along with the blood glucose, using the same standards, and the calculations are the same.

GLUCOSE IN URINE
Somogyi-Nelson method[5]

A quantitated glucose is occasionally requested for a 24-hour urine specimen. With the following modifications, this may be done by the Somogyi-Nelson method of glucose measurement.

Procedure

1. Measure the 24-hour urine volume.
2. In order to estimate the glucose concentration, do a Benedict semi-quantitative test.
3. Differentiate the glucose from lactose as follows:
   a. Wash approximately a half cake of baker's yeast by placing it into approximately 15 ml. of distilled water and centrifuging for 10 minutes. Decant the supernatant. Repeat the procedure.
   b. Add equal volumes of washed packed yeast and the urine to a test tube. Mix well either by shaking or by using a stirring rod.
   c. Incubate *unstoppered* for 1 hour at 37° C.
   d. Centrifuge the incubated tube for 10 minutes.
   e. Perform the Benedict test on the supernatant.
   f. Results of the second Benedict test:
      (1) If negative, all of the sugar present in the first test is probably glucose. However, in rare cases you may find fermentable reducing sugars such as maltose or fructose.
      (2) If as positive as the first test, all of the sugar is lactose or some other nonfermentable reducing substance such as various preservatives, galactose, or pentose.
      (3) If positive, but lower results than the original test, both glucose and lactose are present and the difference of the two tests represents the glucose.
4. In the same manner used in the Somogyi-Nelson blood glucose method, prepare protein-free filtrates on both the untreated urine and the fermented urine.
5. Perform the glucose method on both filtrates. If the Benedict method shows results of the unfermented urine to be over 2 plus, then use a smaller amount of filtrate. Refer to the directions given for the Somogyi-Nelson method.

Calculations

The calculations are performed in the same way as for the blood glucose. Since other reducing substances may be in the filtrate, in addition to glucose, the value of the fermented sample is subtracted from the value of the untreated urine to obtain the true concentration of glucose.

The 24-hour glucose excretion, expressed in milligrams, is obtained by the following formula:

$$\text{Mg.\% glucose} \times \frac{\text{24-hour urine volume in ml.}}{100} = \text{Mg./24 hour}$$

GLUCOSE TOLERANCE

Discussion here covers information significant to the student and the procedures for the tests.

Information significant to the student

When glucose is given to a normal individual and to a diabetic, the normal individual removes the glucose at a faster rate than the diabetic. This is the principle of the glucose tolerance test. In the diabetic, the delay in reaction is due to lack of insulin. The test is an aid to the physician in diagnosing diabetes.

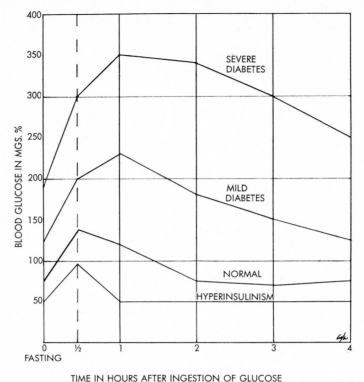

Fig. 42. Typical glucose tolerance curves in the Janney-Isaacson test and the intravenous test.

Three methods for the glucose tolerance tests are listed below, but many other modifications are also used. A brief discussion of each follows.

Janney-Isaacson test
Intravenous test
Exton-Rose test

Janney-Isaacson test

In the Janney-Isaacson test, fasting blood and urine specimens are taken. A known amount of glucose is given orally. Blood and urine specimens are then taken at 1/2, 1, 2, and 3 hours after the ingestion of glucose. Glucose levels are determined on all blood and urine specimens. Normal and abnormal results are indicated in Fig. 42.

Intravenous test

In the intravenous test, the following factors are taken into consideration: When glucose is taken by mouth, it is absorbed into the bloodstream from the small intestine. In health, the rate of absorption is fairly uniform. In diseases of the stomach and intestine, however, the rate of absorption may be altered. This would affect the results of the glucose tolerance test. The situation may be remedied by giving the glucose intravenously.

The intravenous test is performed as follows: Fasting blood and urine specimens are taken. Glucose is given intravenously by a physician. Blood and urine specimens are again taken at 1/2, 1, 2, and 3 hours after the injection. Glucose tests are run on all blood and urine specimens. Normal and abnormal results are indicated in Fig. 42.

Exton-Rose test

In the Exton-Rose test, fasting blood and urine specimens are taken. A known amount of glucose is given. One half hour later, blood and urine specimens are taken. A known amount of glucose is again given. Blood and urine specimens are again taken at 1/2 hour. Glucose levels are determined on all blood and urine specimens.

In a normal person, (1) the fasting blood specimen is normal, (2) the 1/2-hour blood specimen does not exceed the fasting blood specimen by more than 75 mg., (3) the 1-hour blood specimen does not exceed the 1/2-hour specimen by more than 10 mg., and (4) all urines are negative for glucose.

In the diabetic, the 1-hour blood specimen exceeds the 1/2-hour specimen by 10 mg. or more, and the urines are usually positive for glucose.

In renal glycosuria, the blood glucose follows the normal curve, but the urine specimens are positive for glucose.

In alimentary glycosuria, the blood glucose follows the normal curve, the first and second urine specimens are negative for glucose, but the third specimen is positive for glucose.

Procedures for glucose tolerance tests

The procedures for the following tests are given below:

> Janney-Isaacson test
> Intravenous test
> Exton-Rose test

Janney-Isaacson test

1. Instructions to patient: The patient is instructed by the physician to maintain a normal carbohydrate diet (at least 300 gm. of carbohydrate per day) for three days prior to the test. The test is performed in the morning, and the patient is told not to eat or drink anything following the evening meal of the previous day.
2. Prepare the glucose solution as follows: Using the rough balance, weigh 200 gm. of glucose (dextrose) into a container and add 500 ml. of tap water. Stir to dissolve. Place solution in a refrigerator for at least 1 hour in order to chill and thus make more palatable. Just prior to use, add a little lemon juice for flavoring.
3. Make a venipuncture on the patient and collect about 5 ml. of blood. Place in an oxalated tube containing fluoride and invert several times to dissolve the oxalate. Label the test tube: Fasting Blood Sugar, Collect a urine specimen and label: Fasting Specimen. Store this blood specimen and all succeeding blood specimens in a refrigerator until you are ready to run the tests.
4. Obtain the patient's weight. Multiply this number by 2 and give the patient this number in milliliters of the glucose solution. This results in 1.75 gm. of glucose per kilogram of weight. Example: A patient weighs 100 pounds. Multiplying 100 by 2, we get 200. And the patient

	Blood (mg./100 ml.)	Urine
Fasting specimen	75	Neg.
½-Hour specimen	135	Neg.
1-Hour specimen	120	Neg.
2-Hour specimen	75	Neg.
3-Hour specimen	70	Neg.

Fig. 43. Sample report for glucose tolerance test.

gets 200 ml. of the glucose solution. If a patient weighs over 250 pounds, simply give him all the glucose solution.

5. Immediately after giving the glucose, note and record the time.
6. Exactly ½ hour after the ingestion of glucose, take another blood and another urine specimen. Label each: ½-Hour Specimen.
7. Exactly 1 hour after the ingestion of glucose, take another blood and another urine specimen. Label each: 1-Hour Specimen.
8. Exactly 2 hours after the ingestion of glucose, take another blood and another urine specimen. Label each: 2-Hour Specimen.
9. Exactly 3 hours after the ingestion of glucose, take another blood and another urine specimen. Label each: 3-Hour Specimen. If the physician suspects hyperinsulinism, he may request 4- and 5-hour blood specimens. This gives him a more complete picture or curve.
10. Run glucose determinations on all blood specimens. Run *qualitative* glucose tests on the urine specimens.
11. Make the report as indicated in Fig. 43. Normal and abnormal curves are given in Fig. 42.

Intravenous test

1. Instructions to patient: The patient is instructed by the physician to maintain a normal carbohydrate diet (at least 300 gm. of carbohydrate per day) for three days prior to the test. The test is performed in the morning, and he is told not to eat or drink anything after the evening meal of the previous day.
2. Make a venipuncture on the patient and withdraw about 5 ml. of blood. Place in a fluoride oxalate tube and invert several times to dissolve the oxalate. Label the test tube: Fasting Blood Sugar. Collect a urine specimen and label: Fasting Specimen.
3. Obtain the patient's weight. Multiply this by 0.15 to get the dosage in grams (equivalent to 0.3 gm./kg.). Example: Patient weighs 100 pounds. And 100 times 0.15 equals 15 gm.
4. Now the dosage in grams must be multiplied by a glucose concentration factor to get the number of milliliters to inject. If the sterile glucose solution on hand is a 50% solution, the factor is 100/50. If the glucose solution is a 33% solution, the factor is 100/33.
   Example: Patient is to get 15 gm. of glucose. The glucose on hand is a 50% solution. Therefore, the patient gets: 15 × 100/50 = 30 ml. of the 50% glucose solution.
5. Using *sterile* technique, the physician injects the proper amount of *sterile* glucose solution *very slowly* into a vein, taking about 5 minutes to complete the injection.
6. Immediately after giving the glucose, note and record the time.
7. Exactly ½ hour after the injection of glucose, collect another blood and another urine specimen. Label each of them: ½-hour Specimen.
8. Exactly 1 hour after the injection of glucose, collect another blood

and another urine specimen. Label each of them: 1-Hour Specimen.

9. Exactly 2 hours after the injection of glucose, collect another blood and another urine specimen. Label each of them: 2-Hour Specimen.

10. Exactly 3 hours after the injection of glucose, collect another blood and another urine specimen. Label each of them: 3-Hour Specimen.

11. Determine glucose levels of all blood specimens. Run *qualitative* glucose tests on all urine specimens.

12. Make the report as indicated in Fig. 43, noting that it was an intravenous test.

Exton-Rose test

1. Instructions to patient: The patient is instructed by the physician to maintain a normal carbohydrate diet (at least 300 gm. of carbohydrate per day) for three days prior to the test. The test is performed in the morning, and the patient is told not to eat or drink anything after the evening meal of the previous day.

2. Using the rough balance, weigh 100 gm. of glucose (dextrose) into a container. Dissolve in 650 ml. of tap water. Divide the solution into two equal portions and place in a refrigerator for at least 30 minutes in order to chill and thus make more palatable. Just prior to use, add a little lemon juice for flavoring.

3. Make a venipuncture on the patient and withdraw about 5 ml. of blood. Place in a fluoride oxalate tube and invert several times to dissolve the oxalate. Label the test tube: Fasting Blood Specimen. Collect a urine specimen and label: Fasting Specimen.

4. Have the patient drink the first portion of glucose. Note and record the time. Exactly ½ hour later collect another blood and another urine specimen. Label each of them: ½-Hour Specimen.

5. Have the patient drink the second portion of glucose. Note and record the time. Exactly ½ hour later collect another blood and another urine specimen. Label each of them: 1-Hour Specimen.

6. Run glucose determinations on the three blood specimens. Run *qualitative* glucose tests on the three urine specimens.

7. Make the report as indicated by the accompanying chart, simply filling in the blood values and reporting the urine results as positive or negative. Normal and abnormal results are discussed on pp. 111 and 113.

Report of Exton-Rose test

	Blood (mg./100 ml.)	Urine (pos. or neg.)
Fasting specimen	_____	_____
½-hour specimen	_____	_____
1-hour specimen	_____	_____

STUDENTS' SUMMARY FOR GLUCOSE

The significant information consists of the following:

Normal and abnormal values
Methods of analysis and sypnopsis of procedures

Normal and abnormal values

Test	Normal values	When increased	When decreased
Glucose	Folin-Wu: 80-120 mg./100 ml. True glucose methods: 65-95 mg./100 ml.	Diabetes	Hyperinsulinism
Glucose tolerance	Janney-Isaacson: Glucose returns to fasting level within 2 hours	Janney-Isaacson: In diabetes, glucose takes 3 or more hours to return to fasting level	
	Intravenous: Same as for Janney-Isaacson method	Intravenous: Same as for Janney-Isaacson method	
	Exton-Rose: Fasting blood is normal; ½-hour blood specimen does not exceed fasting specimen by more than 75 mg.; 1-hour blood specimen does not exceed ½-hour specimen by more than 10 mg.; all urines negative for glucose	Exton-Rose: In diabetes, 1-hour blood specimen exceeds ½-hour specimen by 10 mg. or more; urines usually positive for glucose	

Methods of analysis and synopsis of procedures

Test	Method	Synopsis of procedure
Glucose	Folin-Wu	1. Make filtrate 2. Add alkaline copper solution and heat; glucose reduces copper to cuprous oxide 3. Add phosphomolybdic acid, which is reduced by cuprous oxide to blue phosphomolybdous acid 4. Measure in colorimeter
	Benedict	1. Make filtrate 2. Add bisulfite copper reagent, which increases specificity of test for glucose 3. Heat; glucose reduces copper to cuprous oxide 4. Add phosphomolybdic acid, which is reduced by cuprous oxide to blue phosphomolybdous acid 5. Measure in colorimeter
	Somogyi-Nelson for: Blood Cerebrospinal fluid Urine	1. Make Somogyi filtrate, which removes interfering substances 2. Add copper tartrate reagent and heat; glucose reduces copper to cuprous oxide 3. Add arsenomolybdate reagent, which reacts with cuprous oxide to give blue color 4. Measure in colorimeter
	Glucose oxidase (modified)	1. Make a Somogyi filtrate 2. Add glucose oxidase (reaction mixture); glucose is oxidized to gluconic acid and hydrogen peroxide 3. Add 4 N HCl; hydrogen peroxide is detected by a chromogenic oxygen acceptor in the presence of peroxidase 4. Read on colorimeter
Glucose tolerance	Janney-Isaacson	1. Collect fasting specimens of blood and urine 2. Give glucose 3. Collect blood and urine specimens at ½, 1, 2, and 3 hours 4. Run glucose tests on blood and urine specimens
	Intravenous	1. Same as for Janney-Isaacson test except inject glucose into vein
	Exton-Rose	1. Collect fasting specimens of blood and urine 2. Give first portion of glucose 3. One half hour later collect blood and urine specimens 4. Give second portion of glucose 5. One half hour later collect blood and urine specimens 6. Run glucose tests on blood and urine specimens

REFERENCES

1. Nelson, N.: Photometric adaptation of Somogyi method for determination of glucose, J. Biol. Chem. **153**:375, 1944.
2. Somogyi, M.: Notes on sugar determination, J. Biol. Chem. **195**:19, 1952.
3. The Upjohn Company: Medical technologist's handbook for the determination of true glucose, Kalamazoo, Mich., 1960.
4. Folin, O., and Wu, H.: A simplified and improved method for determination of sugar, J. Biol. Chem. **41**:367, 1920.
5. Annino, J. S.: Clinical chemistry: principles and procedures, ed. 3, Boston, 1964, Little, Brown & Co.

Chapter 9

Nonprotein nitrogens

Substances containing nitrogen may be divided into proteins and nonprotein nitrogens. This chapter considers the nonprotein nitrogens. In general, they are the waste products of metabolism, being removed from the bloodstream by the kidneys. When they accumulate in the blood, they point to a flaw in the filtering system of the kidneys.

The material in this chapter is arranged as indicated below. At the end of the chapter, there is a students' summary of significant information.

Creatinine: plasma and urine
Creatine: urine
Creatinine clearance
Uric acid
Total nonprotein nitrogen (NPN)
Blood urea nitrogen (BUN)
Urine urea nitrogen (UUN)
Urea clearance

CREATININE

The discussion covers information significant to the student, procedures for the test, and directions for calibrating a colorimeter.

Information significant to the student

Creatinine is a waste product which is removed from the bloodstream by the kidneys. Its normal concentration is 1 to 2 mg./100 ml. of blood and 0.8 to 1.3/100 ml. of plasma. Increased values may be found in nephritis, urinary obstruction, and intestinal obstruction.

For the determination of creatinine, the method of Folin and Wu is commonly used. In this method, sodium picrate in alkaline solution is added to a blood or plasma filtrate. The ensuing reaction is called the Jaffé reaction. It consists of a reaction between creatinine and sodium picrate to form creatinine picrate. The creatinine picrate is red in color. The depth of color is measured in a colorimeter.

Procedure for creatinine[1-3]

The following general considerations pertain to the procedure for creatinine:

1. Preparation of patient: must be fasting.
2. Preparation of blood: either protein-free filtrate or plasma, depending upon method of analysis.
3. Preservation of filtrate: may be stored overnight in refrigerator.
4. Precautions: follow the directions *exactly* as given in the procedure.

Plasma creatinine

Reagents needed

Sulfuric Acid, ⅔ N	(C-1)
Sodium Tungstate, 10%	(C-2)
Saturated Picric Acid	(C-12)
Sodium Hydroxide, 10%	(C-13)
Alkaline Picrate Solution	(See below)

Principle of plasma creatinine method

Creatinine yields a definite color reaction in the presence of picric acid in alkaline solution, due to the formation of a red tautomer of creatinine picrate (Jaffé reaction).

Procedure

1. With a 2.0 ml. Ostwald-Folin pipet, pipet 2.0 ml. of plasma into a 125 ml. Erlenmeyer flask.
2. Add 14 ml. of distilled water.
3. Add 2 ml. of ⅔ N H_2SO_4. Mix by swirling.
4. Add 2 ml. of 10% sodium tungstate. Stopper and shake.
5. Filter.

Alkaline picrate solution

The alkaline picrate solution is made up *just before using*. Set up the blank, standards, and unknowns first. Then make up the alkaline picrate solution and add to the tubes.

Determine the amount of solution needed for the test and mix in the following ratio:

5 volumes of picric acid (saturated)

1 volume of 10% NaOH

Mix well and use immediately.

Either in cuvettes or in test tubes add the following:

Blank

     5.0 ml. of distilled water

     2.5 ml. of alkaline picrate solution

     Mix.

Standards

Two standards of different concentrations are set up to check the calibration curve.

     Standard 2 (from calibration curve)

          1.0 ml. of dilute standard (0.010 mg./ml.)

          4.0 ml. of distilled water

          2.5 ml. of alkaline picrate solution

          Mix.

     Standard 4 (from calibration curve)

          2.0 ml. of dilute standard (0.010 mg./ml.)

          3.0 ml. of distilled water

          2.5 ml. of alkaline picrate solution

          Mix.

Table 20. Blood creatinine calibration chart

Tube no.	Working standard (ml.)	H₂O (ml.)	Alkaline picrate (ml.)	O.D. (520 mμ)	Creatinine equivalent (mg.%)
Blank	0.0	5.0	2.5	0.00	0.0
1	0.5	4.5	2.5		1.0
2	1.0	4.0	2.5		2.0
3	1.5	3.5	2.5		3.0
4	2.0	3.0	2.5		4.0
5	2.5	2.5	2.5		5.0
6	3.0	2.0	2.5		6.0
7	3.5	1.5	2.5		7.0

Unknown
 5.0 ml. of protein-free filtrate
 2.5 ml. of alkaline picrate solution
 Mix.
Allow the tubes to stand for 20 minutes. Read on a colorimeter or spectrophotometer at 520 mμ against the *blank* zero. Read optical density (O.D.) or % transmission and convert to O.D. from Table 19. Calculate values from the calibration curve. The standards should coincide with their values on the curve.

Calibration curve for plasma creatinine

Stock Standard (1 ml. = 1 mg.)
 Weigh on analytical balance 1.0000 gm. of creatinine. If creatinine zinc chloride is used, weigh out exactly 1.6026 gm. of creatinine zinc chloride. Dissolve in 0.1 N HCl and make up to 1000 ml. with 0.1 N HCl.
Working Standard (1 ml. = 0.01 mg.)
 Dilute 10.0 ml. of stock creatinine standard to 1000 ml. with 0.1 N hydrochloric acid.
Prepare a work sheet and set up the standards as shown in Table 20. Allow the color to develop for 20 minutes at room temperature. Read optical density (O.D.) at 520 mμ and record readings in the O.D. column on the work sheet. Plot O.D. readings against the creatinine equivalent (mg.%) on linear graph paper.

Creatinine is the least variable nitrogenous constitutent of the blood, in which it exists to the extent of 1 to 2 mg./100 ml. In early nephritis, values of 2 to 4 mg.% are noted, and in chronic hemorrhagic nephritis with uremia, 4 to 35 mg.% are noted. Creatinine is more readily excreted by the kidneys than urea or uric acid, and an increase of creatinine to 4 to 5 mg.% or more in the blood is evidence of marked impairment of kidney function. Abnormally high creatinine values are accompanied by increased urea content of blood.

Urine creatinine

Procedure

1. Suggested urine dilutions
 Dilution A (For volume less than 1000 ml./ hr.)
 Dilute 1 ml. of urine to 3 ml. with distilled water.
 Multiply the result by 3.
 Dilution B (For volume above 1000 to 1500 ml./24 hr.)
 Dilute 1 ml. of urine to 2 ml. with distilled water.
 Multiply the result by 2.

2. Into 100 ml. volumetric flasks pipet the following. (Note: Upon the addition of the 1.5 ml. of 10% NaOH, start timing for 20 minutes.
   Blank
   > 20.0 ml. of saturated picric acid
   > 1.5 ml. of 10% NaOH

   Standards (two)
   Standard 1
   > 0.5 ml. of creatinine standard (1 mg./ml.)
   > 20.0 ml. of saturated picric acid
   > 1.5 ml. of 10% NaOH

   Standard 2
   > 1.0 ml. of creatinine standard (1 mg./ml.)
   > 20.0 ml. of saturated picric acid
   > 1.5 ml. of 10% NaOH

   Unknown
   > 1.0 ml. of diluted urine
   > 20.0 ml. of saturated picric acid
   > 1.5 ml. of 10% NaOH

3. Swirl flasks to mix.
4. Stand 20 minutes.
5. Dilute to mark with distilled water.
6. Stopper and mix thoroughly.
7. Read on spectrophotometer or colorimeter at 520 mμ against *blank*. Read O.D.

The purpose of the standards is to check the reagents and other conditions of the test. If the reading of the standard varies too much from the curve, the reagents should be checked. It may be necessary to construct a new curve.

Calibration curve for urine creatinine

With the stock standard (1 ml. = 1 mg.) make the following dilutions, using 0.1 N HCl:

Dilution A (1 ml. = 0.25 mg.)
> Mix in a test tube 2.5 ml. of stock standard and 7.5 ml. of 0.1 N HCl.

Dilution B (1 ml. = 0.1 mg.)
> Mix in a test tube 1.0 ml. of stock standard and 9.0 ml. of 0.1 N HCl.

In 100 ml. volumetric flasks, set up the following concentrations according to the work sheet shown in Table 21. Allow the color to develop 20 minutes. Dilute to mark with distilled water and mix well. Pour into proper tubes and read O.D. (optical density) at 520 mμ.

Plot the optical density readings on the vertical (ordinate) of linear graph paper, allowing each division of the graph paper to represent 0.005.

Table 21. Urine creatinine calibration chart

Tube no.	Stock standard (1 ml. = 1.0 mg.)	1:4 dilution (1 ml. = 0.25 mg.)	1:10 dilution (1 ml. = 0.1 mg.)	Picric acid (ml.)	NaOH (10%)	O.D. (520 mμ)	Creatinine equivalent (mg. %)
Blank	0.00	0.00	0.00	20	1.5	0.00	0.00
1	2.00	0.00	0.00	20	1.5		2.00
2	1.50	0.00	0.00	20	1.5		1.50
3	1.00	0.00	0.00	20	1.5		1.00
4		3.00	0.00	20	1.5		0.75
5		2.00	0.00	20	1.5		0.50
6		1.00	0.00	20	1.5		0.25
7			2.00	20	1.5		0.20
8			1.00	20	1.5		0.10

Plot the milligrams per milliliter on the horizontal (abscissa), allowing each
division to represent 0.01 mg./ml.
The curve does not form a straight line.

The daily excretion of creatinine by an adult of medium weight averages about 1.25 gm. The average adult normal range is 1.0 to 1.8 gm./24 hr. The value is nearly constant from day to day for a given individual, being influenced by the diet very little unless the diet consists of a heavy meat diet which contains much preformed creatinine. The excretion of creatinine is, to a certain extent, a measure of muscular efficiency and of the amount of active muscle tissue in the body. Relative to body weight, therefore, less creatinine is excreted by obese persons.

Creatinine excretion is decreased in disorders associated with muscular atrophy and muscular weakness. It increases with increased tissue catabolism as in fever.

Urine creatine

Creatine occurs in only very small amounts in the urine of normal adults, but it is found in larger amounts in the urine of children. Creatine ingestion in adults has little effect on the urinary excretion. In a fasting state, the amount is markedly increased. The normal adult range is 0 to 200 mg./24 hr. Creatine also appears in the urine after high water ingestion. It is found in many pathological conditions associated with malnutrition and disintegration of muscular tissue and in fevers. Large amounts are found in diseases of the muscles.

The method of determining urine creatine is based upon the Jaffé reaction. Creatine, if boiled with acid, is transformed into creatinine. By determining the content of creatinine before and after the acid treatment it is possible to calculate the amount of creatine originally present in the urine.

Procedure

1. Pipet 10 ml. of diluted urine into a Folin-Wu sugar tube.
2. Add 10 ml. of 1 N HCl.
3. Cover top of tube tightly with aluminum foil and put into boiling water bath for 30 minutes. Use timer.
4. Cool in room temperature water bath and dilute to 25 ml. mark with distilled water.
5. Stopper and mix well by inverting tube several times.
6. In 100 ml. volumetric flasks set up the following:

Total creatinine
>2.5 ml. of the above acid-treated urine (2.5 ml. = 1.0 ml. of diluted urine)
>20.0 ml. of saturated picric acid
>2.0 ml. of 10% NaOH
>Swirl to mix.

Preformed creatinine
>1.0 ml. of diluted urine (*not* the acid-treated urine)
>20.0 ml. of saturated picric acid
>1.5 ml. of 10% NaOH
>Swirl to mix.

Blank
>20.0 ml. of saturated picric acid
>1.5 ml. of 10% NaOH
>Swirl to mix.

Standards
Standards are the same as for the urine creatinines; urine creatines may be run with urine creatinines.

7. Swirl flasks to mix.
8. Let stand 20 minutes. Use timer.
9. Dilute to mark with distilled water.
10. Stopper and mix thoroughly.
11. Read optical density at 520 mμ against the *blank*.
12. Calculate the two unknowns *(preformed creatinine and total creatinine)* from the urine creatinine standard curve.
13. The results of the preformed and total creatinine test are then multiplied by the dilution of urine.

Calculations of the creatine

Total creatinine − Preformed creatinine = Mg./ml. creatine

or

(T. creatinine − P. creatinine) × 100 = Mg.% creatine

or

Mg.% creatine × $\dfrac{24 \text{ hr. urine vol.}}{100}$ = Mg./24 hr. creatine

Creatinine clearance

The creatinine clearance test is considered a reliable test of renal function. With diseased kidney the creatinine clearance level will drop before there is an abnormal rise in the serum creatinine or the blood urea nitrogen.

Procedure

One or two hours before the test the patient should be given enough water to ensure a sufficient flow of urine during the test. Complete emptying of the bladder per specimen and timing of the collections are critical.
1. Have patient void; discard first specimen.
2. Start timing and at the end of 1 hour have patient void. Record time. Label: Specimen 1.
3. Draw 6 ml. of clotted blood for the serum creatinine.
4. At the end of the second hour, collect another urine specimen. Record time. Label: Specimen 2.
5. Measure the exact volume of each urine.
6. Determine the creatinine concentration of the two urines and the serum according to the previous methods.

Calculations according to example

	Time	Volume	Creatinine (mg.%)
Specimen discarded	8:00	Beginning of test	——
Urine sample 1, voided	9:05	240 ml.	26.2
Blood drawn	9:20	————	0.8
Urine sample 2, voided	10:10	238 ml.	26.0

Ccr = Creatinine clearance (ml./min.).
U = Urine creatinine (mg./100 ml. or mg.%).
P = Serum creatinine (mg.%).
V = Urine volume ÷ time in minutes.

$$Ccr = \dfrac{UV}{P}$$

Using the data and the formula given, verify the calculations mentioned here.
Urine sample 1, creatinine clearance:
Time = 8:00 to 9:05 = 65 minutes
Urine volume = 240 ml. in 65 minutes
V = 240 ÷ 65 = 3.6 ml./min.

$$\text{Ccr} = \frac{\text{UV}}{\text{P}}$$

$$\text{Ccr} = \frac{26.2 \times 3.6}{0.8}$$

$$\text{Ccr} = 117.9 \text{ ml./min.}$$

Urine sample 2, creatinine clearance:
    Time = 9:05 to 10:10 = 65 minutes
    Urine volume = 238 ml. in 65 minutes
    V = 238 ÷ 65 = 3.6 ml./min.

$$\text{Ccr} = \frac{\text{UV}}{\text{P}}$$

$$\text{Ccr} = \frac{26.0 \times 3.6}{0.8}$$

$$\text{Ccr} = 117.0 \text{ ml./min.}$$

Average of the two urine creatinine clearances = 117.5 ml./min.
Normal range = 100 to 180 ml./min.

Sources of error

1. Incomplete collection of urine.
2. Inaccurate timing.
3. Inaccurate measurement of urine volume.
4. Breakdown of creatinine by bacteria. Specimen must be refrigerated during collections. A few drops of toluol may be added as a preservative.
5. If patient is on a high-meat diet the blood creatinine must be drawn under fasting conditions.

URIC ACID

The discussion covers information significant to the student and procedures for the test.

Information significant to the student

Uric acid is a waste product which is removed from the bloodstream by the kidneys. Conditions in which an increase or decrease may be expected are listed in Table 22. The disorders given in italics are of primary concern; the others are of somewhat lesser interest.

Procedures for uric acid

The following general considerations pertain to the procedures for uric acid:

1. Preparation of patient: must be fasting.
2. Preparation of blood: serum, plasma, or protein-free filtrate, depending upon method of analysis.

Table 22. Conditions accompanied by abnormal uric acid values

When increased		When decreased
Gout	Acute infections	Salicylate therapy
Nephritis	Intestinal obstruction	Atophan therapy
Arthritis	Urinary obstruction	Yellow atrophy of liver
Eclampsia	Metallic poisoning	
Leukemia	Hypertension	
Polycythemia	Following exercise	
Diabetes		

3. Preservation of blood: serum, plasma, or protein-free filtrate may be stored overnight in a refrigerator.
4. Precautions:
   a. Cyanide solutions are *poisonous*. Do not get any in the mouth.
   b. Cyanide solutions should be stored in a refrigerator.
   c. Cyanide solution should be cold (about 12° C.) when added to the test tube.
   d. Follow directions *exactly* as given in the procedure.

The more commonly used methods for the determination of uric acid are listed below. A brief discussion of each follows.

> Folin method
> Brown method
> Newton method
> Archibald method
> Henry method

Folin method

A blood filtrate is treated with urea-cyanide and phosphotungstic acid to form a phosphotungstate complex. The uric acid present reduces the phosphotungst*ate* complex to the blue phosphotungst*ite* complex. The depth of color is measured in a colorimeter and compared with a standard.

Brown method

A blood filtrate is treated with sodium cyanide, urea, and phosphotungstic acid to form a phosphotungstate complex. The uric acid present reduces the phosphotungst*ate* to the blue phosphotungst*ite* complex. The depth of color is measured in a colorimeter and compared with a standard.

Newton method

A special blood filtrate is made to remove interfering substances. The filtrate is treated with a urea-cyanide solution and lithium arsenotungstate to form an arsenotungstate complex. The uric acid present reduces the arsenotungst*ate* complex to the blue arsenotungst*ite* complex. The depth of color is measured in a colorimeter and compared with a standard.

Archibald method[4]

The uric acid in serum or plasma reduces phosphotungstate acid in an alkaline solution, thus producing a blue color. This method may also be used for urine without any modifications of the procedure. The phosphotungstate is not only a color-developing agent. It also precipitates the proteins. Plasma or serum is preferable to whole blood because the glutathione and ergothioneine from the red cells cause interference.[5]

Reagents needed

Uric Acid Stock Standard, 1 mg./ml.	(C-14)
Polyanethol Sodium Sulfonate	(C-15)
Glycerin-Silicate Reagent	(C-16)
Phosphotungstic Acid	(C-17)
Sodium Hydroxide, 0.5 N	(C-18)
Uric Acid Special Reagent	(C-19)
Uric Acid Working Standard, 0.005 mg./ml.	

Pipet 0.5 ml. of stock uric acid standard into a 100 ml. volumetric flask and dilute to the mark with water. Prepare a fresh working standard daily.

Procedure

1. Pipet into a 125 ml. Erlenmeyer flask 2.0 ml. of plasma or serum. With urine make a 1:10 dilution and pipet 2.0 ml. into the flask.
2. Add 16 ml. of distilled water; swirl flask to mix.
3. Add 0.8 ml. of 0.5 N NaOH, swirling the flask for at least 1 minute. For large volumes a mechanical shaker is most helpful.
4. Let the flask stand for 10 minutes.
5. Slowly add 1.2 ml. of the phosphotungstic acid solution to the flask, with constant swirling of the flask to ensure a complete precipitation of protein.
6. Let the flask stand for 5 minutes.
7. Filter through Whatman No. 42 filter paper into large test tubes or flasks.
8. Set up the following tubes:
   Blank

        5.0 ml. of water.

   Standard

        5.0 ml. of working standard.

   Unknown

        5.0 ml. of filtrate.
9. Add 2.5 ml. of glycerin-silicate reagent to each tube. Set timer for 15 minutes. Begin timing upon the addition of 2.0 ml. of uric acid special reagent. Mix immediately. After 15 minutes the color is fully developed.
10. Set zero with blank and read absorbance or O.D. measurements on a spectrophotometer at 700 mμ or, with the aid of a No. 660 red filter, in a photoelectric colorimeter.

Calculations

$$\frac{\text{Absorbance of unknown}}{\text{Absorbance of standard}} \times 5 = \text{Mg./100 ml. of plasma or serum}$$

$$\text{or}$$

$$\text{Mg.\% uric acid}$$

e.g., Urine

Dilution 1:100

Filtrate 5 ml.

$$\frac{\text{Absorbance of unknown}}{\text{Absorbance of standard}} \times 10 \times 5 = \text{Mg.\% uric acid in urine}$$

Normal values[6]

	Men	Women
Serum or plasma	2.5 to 7.0 mg.%	1.5 to 6.0 mg.%
Urine, 24-hour	250 to 750 mg.	250 to 750 mg.

Henry method[7]

The uric acid in serum, plasma, or urine reduces an alkaline phosphotungstate solution to a tungsten blue. The alkali used is sodium carbonate. The depth of color is measured photometrically and compared with a standard.

Serum uric acid (sodium carbonate)

Reagents needed

Phosphotungstic Acid (The directions given in the original publication were in error and were corrected by the authors in a later publication. For this reason the directions for preparing this reagent are given here instead of in Appendix C.)

Weigh 40.0 gm. of reagent grade sodium tungstate and transfer to a 1-liter round-bottom boiling flask containing about 300 ml. of distilled water. Swirl to dissolve. Add 32 ml. of 85% orthophosphoric acid and mix. Attach a reflux condenser to the flask and reflux gently for 2 hours. Cool to room temperature and dilute to 1000 ml. with distilled water. Weigh 32.0 gm. of lithium sulfate monohydrate and add to the above solution. Mix to dissolve. This reagent is stable indefinitely when stored in a refrigerator.

Sodium Carbonate, 14%   (C-20)
Uric Acid, Stock Standard   (C-14)
Working Standard, 0.01 mg./ml.
    Dilute stock standard 1:100 in a volumetric flask.

Procedure

1. Prepare a Folin-Wu protein-free filtrate.
   Avoid: oxalated plasma which may cause a crystalline precipitate.
2. Set up the following tubes:
   Blanks (two tubes)
   Pipet 3.0 ml. of distilled water into each tube.
   Standards (three tubes)
   Pipet 3.0 ml. of working standard into each tube.
   Unknown (one tube per test)
   Pipet 3.0 ml. of unknown filtrate into its numbered tube.
3. *To all tubes:*
   a. Add 1.0 ml. of 14% Na_2CO_3 and mix.
   b. Add 1.0 ml. of phosphotungstic acid and mix.
4. Allow tubes to stand 15 minutes to develop color.
5. Read against the blank at 660 mμ within a 30-minute period. The blank must be colorless.

Calculations

$$\frac{\text{O.D. of unknown}}{\text{O.D. of standard}} \times 10 = \text{Mg.\% uric acid}$$

The three standards are averaged unless they vary a great deal. In that case, repeat the test. The two blanks are used to check against each other.

Urine uric acid

Preparation of the urine

1. If the urine is cloudy, warm it to about 60° C. to dissolve the urates and centrifuge.
2. Dilute 1:10 with distilled water.
3. Proceed with the method given for the serum uric acid. Everything is the same as in the preceding method with the exception of the calculation.

Calculation

$$\frac{\text{O.D. of unknown}}{\text{O.D. of standard}} \times 100 = \text{Mg.\% uric acid}$$

Note: If the O.D. reads less than 0.2 or more than 0.8, repeat the test, using the proper dilution.

TOTAL NONPROTEIN NITROGEN (NPN)

The discussion covers information significant to the student and procedures for the test.

Information significant to the student

The components of total nonprotein nitrogen are the waste products of protein catabolism. These waste products include amino acids, creatine, creatinine, ergothioneine, glutathione, urea, uric acid, and many other components, unknown.

The tungstic acid protein-free filtrate is more commonly used for NPN than barium-zinc sulfate filtrates are. This is partly due to the fact that ergothioneine, glutathione, and uric acid are precipitated by the zinc.

The normal values for the total nonprotein nitrogen are 25 to 35 mg./100 ml. of blood, using a tungstic acid filtrate, and 15 to 25 mg./100 ml. of blood, using the zinc hydroxide filtrate. Higher values indicate faulty elimination and consequently point to a disorder of the kidneys. The conditions accompanied by abnormal NPN values are similar to those for urea nitrogen. These are given in Table 23.

The more commonly used methods for the determination of total nonprotein nitrogen are listed below. A brief discussion of each method follows.

> Folin-Wu method
> Koch-McMeekin method
> Berthelot color reaction (modified)

Folin-Wu method

A protein-free filtrate is made. To this is added a digestion mixture of sulfuric and phosphoric acids, its purpose being to aid in the liberation of ammonia. A few glass beads are added to prevent the solution from bumping, and the mixture is heated with a flame. This decomposes the nitrogen substances and forms an ammonium salt. Nessler's solution is then added to react with the ammonium salt and form the yellow dimercuric ammonium iodide. The depth of color is measured in a colorimeter and compared with a standard.

Koch-McMeekin method

A protein-free filtrate is made. To this is added a mixture of sulfuric acid and hydrogen peroxide, its purpose being to help liberate the ammonia. A few glass beads are added to prevent bumping, and the solution is heated with a flame. This decomposes the nitrogen substances and forms an ammonium salt. Nessler's solution is then added to react with the ammonium salt and form the yellow dimercuric ammonium iodide. The depth of color is measured in a colorimeter and compared with a standard.

The only difference between this method and the preceding one is in the digestion mixture. Folin and Wu use sulfuric and phosphoric acids for the digestion mixture, whereas Koch and McMeekin use sulfuric acid and hydrogen peroxide.

Berthelot color reaction (modified)

A protein-free filtrate (tungstic acid) is made. To this is added 30% sulfuric acid, its purpose being to aid in the liberation of ammonia by oxidizing the organic material. One or two glass beads or boiling stones are added to prevent the solution from bumping and the mixture is heated with flame (Bunsen burner). Phenol color reagent and alkali-hypochlorite reagent are then added.

A blue color is formed by ammonia and phenol in the alkaline oxidizing medium, in the presence of sodium nitroprusside as catalyst. The depth of color is measured in a colorimeter and compared with a standard.

Procedure for total nonprotein nitrogen (NPN)

The following general considerations pertain to the procedure for total nonprotein nitrogen:

1. Preparation of patient: must be fasting.
2. Preparation of blood: protein-free filtrate.
3. Preservation of protein-free filtrate: may be stored overnight in a refrigerator.
4. Precautions:
   a. Digestion must be done in a fume hood.
   b. Contents of tubes must be *cold* before the addition of Nessler's solution; otherwise cloudiness may develop.
   c. Overdiluting with water, excessive heating, causing frothing, or adding hydrogen peroxide (Superoxol) before the tube is cool, resulting in splattering of sample, produces low results.
   d. Extremely elevated sample will cloud. Repeat test, using a smaller amount of filtrate. Calculate accordingly.
   e. If distilled water is not free of nitrogen compounds, the blanks, standards, and unknowns will all read high.
   f. Improper precipitation of the protein-free filtrate or using too much sulfuric acid or sodium tungstate will cause a yellow precipitate to form during the digestion.
   g. Follow directions *exactly* as given in the procedure.

Koch-McMeekin method[2,8]

Reagents needed

Sulfuric Acid, Digestion Mixture, 30%	(C-21)
Hydrogen Peroxide, 30% (refrigerate)	(C-22)
Nessler's Reagent	(C-23)

Standard Solutions:
1. Stock Standard (1.0 ml. = 0.5 mg. of nitrogen)   (C-24)
2. Working Standard: (1.0 ml. = 0.025 mg. of nitrogen)
   a. Using a volumetric pipet, transfer 25.0 ml. of stock standard to a 500 ml. volumetric flask
   b. Dilute to volume with ammonia-free 0.1 N HCl   (C-25)

Procedure

1. Prepare either a Somogyi or a Folin-Wu protein-free filtrate, using 2.0 ml. of oxalated whole blood.
2. Using a volumetric pipet, transfer 5.0 ml. of filtrate to an NPN digestion tube graduated at 35 and 50 ml.
3. Add 1.0 ml. of digestion mixture.
4. Add two or three boiling stones and gently heat the bottom of the tube with a gas flame until it begins to boil.
5. Boil vigorously until the solution begins to turn brown.
6. Continue heating until the tube is filled with dense white fumes.
7. Allow to cool; then add 3 drops of 30% hydrogen peroxide.
8. Cover with a watchglass and continue heating gently for exactly 3 minutes. (Use a timer.)
9. Allow to cool to room temperature and then rinse the underside of the watchglass into the tube, using a small stream of distilled water from a wash bottle.

10. Dilute to the 35 ml. mark with distilled water.
11. Stopper and place the tube, along with a blank and standard tubes, into a cold water bath located in a refrigerator. These remain in the bath for a minimum of 15 minutes. The blanks and standards are not cooked with the unknowns. Set tubes up as follows:

    Blanks (two tubes)
    a. To an NPN tube add 1.0 ml. of digestion mixture.
    b. Dilute to 35 ml. mark with distilled water.
    c. Stopper and mix.

    Standards (three tubes)
    a. To an NPN tube add 5.0 ml. of working standard.
    b. To an NPN tube add 1.0 ml. of digestion mixture.
    c. Dilute to 35 ml. mark with distilled water.
    d. Stopper and mix.

12. *All tubes:*
    a. After cooling for 15 minutes, add Nessler's reagent to the 50 ml. mark.
    b. Stopper and mix by inverting tubes four times. If solution is not absolutely clear repeat the test.
    c. Read O.D. at 540 mμ or Klett units, using a No. 54 filter, against the reagent blank. The blank tubes must be clear and check against each other.

Calculations and dilutions

$$\frac{\text{Reading of unknown}}{\text{Reading of standard}} \times \text{Concentration of standard} \times \frac{100}{\text{Amount of blood used}}$$

$$= \text{Mg.\% NPN}$$

or

$$\frac{\text{RU}}{\text{RS}} \times 0.125 \times \frac{100}{0.5} = \text{Mg.\% NPN}$$

and

$$\frac{\text{RU}}{\text{RS}} \times 25 = \text{Mg.\% NPN}$$

Dilution, instead of using 5.0 ml. of filtrate, use:

A. 3.0 ml. of filtrate. Multiply mg.% NPN by $\frac{5}{3}$.

B. 2.0 ml. of filtrate. Multiply mg.% NPN by $\frac{5}{2}$.

C. 1.0 ml. of filtrate. Multiply mg.% NPN by 5.

Normal range
15 to 25 mg.% (Somogyi filtrate)
25 to 35 mg.% (Folin-Wu filtrate)

UREA NITROGEN

The discussion covers information significant to the student, procedures for the test, and calculations.

Information significant to the student

Urea is the principal waste product of protein catabolism. Its formula is NH_2CONH_2. Since it is difficult to determine urea itself, and a relatively simple matter to analyze for the nitrogen in urea, it has become customary to determine

Table 23. Conditions accompanied by abnormal urea nitrogen values

When increased		When decreased
Nephritis	Dehydration	Acute liver destruction
Intestinal obstruction	Malignancy	Amyloidosis
Urinary obstruction	Pneumonia	Pregnancy
Metallic poisoning	Surgical shock	Nephrosis
Cardiac failure	Addison's disease	
Peritonitis	Uremia	

the urea nitrogen. Most methods depend on the urea being converted to ammonium carbonate:

$$\begin{array}{c} NH_2 \\ / \\ C = O \ + \ 2H_2O \ \xrightarrow[38°]{Urease} \ (NH_4)_2 \ CO_3 \\ \backslash \\ NH_2 \end{array}$$

Urea   Water   Ammonium carbonate

The normal values for the blood urea nitrogen (BUN) are 8 to 20 mg./100 ml. of blood. The corresponding values for urea may be found by multiplying these figures by the factor 2.14. Conditions in which an increased or decreased urea nitrogen value may be expected are given in Table 23. The disorders in italics are of primary concern; the others are of somewhat lesser interest.

The more commonly used methods for the determination of urea nitrogen are listed below. In the discussion that follows, special attention has been given to the function of each reagent. It is hoped that this will answer many of the questions in the mind of the student.

Karr method   Folin-Svedberg method
Van Slyke-Cullen method   Berthelot reaction
Gentzkow method   Urograph

Karr method

A protein-free filtrate is treated with a buffer solution and the enzyme urease. The purpose of the buffer solution is to control the pH of the solution, since the urease reacts better at a certain pH (6.8). Upon incubation, the urease decomposes the urea and liberates ammonia, which forms ammonium carbonate. After incubation, gum ghatti is added to form a protective colloid and keep the solution from becoming cloudy. Nessler's solution is then added. This is an alkaline solution of the double iodide of mercury and potassium ($HgI_2 \cdot 2KI$). It reacts with the ammonium carbonate to form yellow dimercuric ammonium iodide. The depth of color is measured in a colorimeter and compared with a standard.

Van Slyke-Cullen method

In the Van Slyke-Cullen method, oxalated blood is treated with the enzyme urease to form ammonium carbonate. Addition of potassium carbonate liberates the ammonia gas, which is collected in a boric acid solution. This is then titrated with a standard acid solution, and the urea nitrogen found by calculation.

Gentzkow method

Oxalated blood is diluted. To this is added the enzyme urease, which decomposes the urea to form ammonium carbonate. Next, the proteins are precipitated with sulfuric acid and sodium tungstate. The resulting filtrate containing the ammonium carbonate is treated with Nessler's solution to form the yellow dimercuric ammonium iodide. The depth of color is measured in a colorimeter and compared with a standard.

Folin-Svedberg method

A protein-free filtrate is made. To this is added a buffer solution to control the pH. Next, the enzyme urease is added to decompose the urea and form ammonium carbonate. The mixture is incubated to enhance the reaction. Sodium borate is added to the solution to liberate the ammonia gas, which is collected in a weak hydrochloric acid solution. Nessler's solution is then added to convert the ammonium ion to the yellow dimercuric ammonium iodide. The depth of color is measured in a colorimeter and compared with a standard.

Berthelot reaction

The urea in serum, plasma, or urine is split, by the action of urease, into ammonia and CO_2. The ammonia is determined photometrically by the phenol-hypochlorite reaction of Berthelot, using sodium nitroprusside as a catalyst. Because of the very high dilution used, it is not necessary to precipitate and remove proteins.

Urograph*

This method employs strips of chromatography paper (7 by 85 mm.), which are banded with controlled amounts of reagents. As the serum or plasma travels up the Urograph chromatography paper, it first encounters a band of buffered urease. At this position the urea present is converted to an ammonia salt. Upon further migration the sample encounters a potassium carbonate band that produces free ammonia. The free ammonia produces a color change in the uppermost indicator band, which contains bromcresol green in tartaric acid. The height of the blue-green color developed is directly proportional to the amount of urea in the unknown sample.

Results obtained by this method compare well with those obtained by the AutoAnalyzer method when the directions are followed *exactly* as given in the package insert.[11]

Procedure for urea nitrogen

The following general considerations pertain to the procedure for urea nitrogen:

1. Preparation of patient: must be fasting.
2. Preparation of blood: either oxalated blood, plasma, or protein-free filtrate, depending upon method of analysis.
3. Preservation of blood: plasma or filtrate may be stored overnight in a refrigerator.

---

*A preparation of General Diagnostics Division, Warner-Chilcott, Morris Plains, N. J.

4. Precautions:
  a. The following interfere with the urease reaction: excessive anti-coagulant of oxalate or citrate; excessive buffer solution; glassware which contained Nessler's solution or cyanide solution.
  b. Follow directions *exactly* as given in the procedure.

Blood urea nitrogen[9]

Reagents needed

Urease Solution	(C-26)
Sulfuric Acid, ⅔ N	(C-1)
Sodium Tungstate, 10%	(C-2)
Potassium Persulfate, 2.5%	(C-27)
Potassium Gluconate, 1%	(C-28)
Standard Solution (same as for NPN)	(C-24)

Procedure

1. Pipet 2 ml. of oxalated whole blood into a 125 ml. Erlenmeyer flask.
2. Add 13.5 ml. of water.
3. Add 0.5 ml. of urease solution.
4. Mix well. Either stopper the flask or cover with Parafilm.
5. Place the flask in a 38° C. water bath or incubator for 30 minutes.
6. Add 2 ml. of ⅔ N sulfuric acid. Mix well and allow to stand for 5 minutes.
7. Add 2 ml. of 10% sodium tungstate.
8. Stopper the flask and shake vigorously. There should be no frothing. Filter through a Whatman No. 1 filter paper or its equivalent.
9. Prepare the following tubes:
   Blanks (two tubes)
   a. Into an NPN tube pipet 1.0 ml. of 2.5% potassium persulfate.
   b. Into an NPN tube pipet 1.0 ml. of 1% potassium gluconate.
   c. Dilute to 35 ml. mark with distilled water.
   d. Stopper.
   Standards (three tubes)
   a. Into an NPN tube pipet 5.0 ml. of working standard (NPN standard).
   b. Into an NPN tube pipet 1.0 ml. of 2.5% potassium persulfate.
   c. Into an NPN tube pipet 1.0 ml. of 1% potassium gluconate.
   d. Dilute to 35 ml. mark with distilled water.
   e. Stopper.
   Unknowns (one tube per test)
   a. Into an NPN tube pipet 5.0 ml. of filtrate.
   b. Into an NPN tube pipet 1.0 ml. of 2.5% potassium persulfate.
   c. Into an NPN tube pipet 1.0 ml. of 1% potassium gluconate.
   d. Dilute to 35 ml. mark with distilled water.
   e. Stopper.
10. *All tubes*
   a. Cool in ice bath for 15 minutes.
   b. Add Nessler's reagent to the 50 ml. mark.
   c. Stopper and invert four times to mix. Solution must be clear.
   d. Read O.D. at 540 mμ (or Klett units, using a No. 54 filter) against the reagent blank. The blank tubes must be clear and check against each other.

Calculations and dilutions

The same as the NPN calculations and dilutions:

$$\frac{RU}{RS} \times 25 = \text{Mg.\% BUN}$$

Normal range
8 to 20 mg.%

Urea nitrogen
Berthelot reaction[10]

Reagents needed

Buffered Urease Solution*	(C-29)
Phenol Color Reagent*	(C-30)
Alkali-Hypochlorite Reagent*	(C-31)

Urea Standard

    Transfer 0.429 gm. of urea to a 1-liter volumetric flask and dilute to volume with distilled water. Add a few drops of chloroform as a preservative and store in the refrigerator (1 ml. = 0.2 mg. of urea N).

Procedure for serum or plasma

1. Set up the following in test tubes (16 × 125):
   Blanks
       0.2 ml. of buffered urease solution
   Standard
       0.2 ml. of buffered urease solution
       0.02 ml. of urea standard
   Unknown
       0.2 ml. of buffered urease solution
       0.02 ml. of serum or plasma
   The 0.02 ml. aliquots of standard and unknown are added with TC micropipets. Sahli hemoglobin pipets are satisfactory.
2. Incubate the tubes in a water bath at 37° C. for 15 minutes.
3. Then add 1.0 ml. of phenol color reagent to each tube and mix.
4. Add 1.0 ml. of alkali-hypochlorite reagent and mix promptly again.
5. Incubate tubes at 50° to 60° C. for 5 minutes or at 37° C. for 20 minutes.
6. Add 8 ml. of water to all tubes and mix. If mixing must be accomplished by inversion cover the tops of the tubes with clean Saran Wrap or Parafilm and hold with the thumb while inverting the tube.
7. Read O.D. at 625 mμ (or Klett units, using a No. 54 filter). On a Klett photometer, Beer's law is obeyed with a No. 54 filter up to only about 250 Klett units and is not obeyed at all with a No. 62 filter. When specimens read higher than 0.800 O.D. or 250 Klett units, dilute with water, read again, and calculate according to dilution.

Calculation

$$\frac{RU}{RS} \times 0.004 \times \frac{100}{0.02} = \text{Mg. of urea N/100 ml.}$$

$$\frac{RU}{RS} \times 20 = \text{Mg. of urea N/100 ml.}$$

Procedure for urine

1. Since urine normally contains some preformed ammonia, it is necessary to remove this ammonia before proceeding with the test.
2. Measure and record the volume of the urine.
3. Add 5 gm. of Permutit to a 10 ml. aliquot of the urine and shake vigorously for 1 minute. Allow to stand for 10 minutes.
4. Filter.

---

*These reagents are available commercially from Hyland Laboratories in the form of a kit with the trade name UN-Test.

5. Transfer 1 ml. of filtered urine to a 50 ml. volumetric flask and dilute to the mark with water. Stopper and mix.
6. Using an 0.02 ml. aliquot of diluted urine, follow the procedure as with serum or plasma.

Calculation

$$\frac{RU}{RS} \times 20 \times 50 = \text{Mg. of urea N/100 ml. of urine}$$

$$\frac{RU}{RS} \times 1000 = \text{Mg. of urea N/100 ml. of urine}$$

Urine urea nitrogen[9]

The formula for urea is $CO(NH_2)_2$. From the formula it can be seen that nitrogen is a definite fixed portion of urea, and it has become customary to determine the nitrogen present in urine and make the report as urea nitrogen. The normal values for urea nitrogen are 6 to 17 gm. per day. Decreased values may be found in acute nephritis, acidosis, and cirrhosis of the liver. Increased values may be seen in febrile conditions.

Reagents needed

Urease Solution	(C-26)
Sulfuric Acid, ⅔ N	(C-1)
Sodium Tungstate, 10%	(C-2)
Potassium Persulfate, 2.5%	(C-27)
Potassium Gluconate, 1%	(C-28)
Standard Solution (same as for NPN)	(C-24)
Acetate Buffer	(C-32)
Permutit*	

Procedure

1. Measure and record exact volume of urine specimen.
2. Transfer 5.0 ml. of urine to a 125 ml. Erlenmeyer flask.
3. Add 5 gm. of Permutit, stopper, and shake vigorously for 1 minute. This removes any preformed ammonia.
4. Allow to stand for 10 minutes; then filter.
5. Dilute ten times by mixing 1.0 ml. of Permutit-treated urine with 9 ml. of distilled water in a large test tube or flask.
6. Transfer 2.0 ml. of the diluted urine to a 125 ml. Erlenmeyer flask.
7. Add 13.0 ml. of distilled water.
8. Add 0.5 ml. of urease solution.
9. Add 0.5 ml. of acetate buffer.
10. Mix well and stopper or cover with Parafilm.
11. Incubate in a 38° C. water bath for 30 minutes.
12. Add 2.0 ml. of ⅔ N H_2SO_4.
13. Add 2.0 ml. of 10% Na_2WO_4 (sodium tungstate).
14. Shake thoroughly to mix, and filter.
15. Transfer 5.0 ml. of filtrate to an NPN digestion tube.
16. Add about 10 ml. of water (distilled).
17. Add to the filtrate and water:
    1.0 ml. of 2.5% potassium persulfate.
    1.0 ml. of 1% potassium gluconate.
    Dilute to 35 ml. mark with distilled water.
18. *Blanks* and *standards* are set up the same way as the NPN.
19. Place all tubes in ice bath for 15 minutes.

---

*May be purchased from Fisher Scientific Co., Pittsburgh, Pa.

20. Add Nessler's reagent to the 50 ml. mark. Stopper and invert four times to mix.
21. Read O.D. against blank, using a 540 mμ or No. 54 filter for the Klett photometer.

Calculations

$$\frac{RU}{RS} \times 25 \times 10 \text{ (dilution)} = \text{Mg.\% urea nitrogen}$$

or

$$\frac{\text{Mg./100 ml.}}{1000} \times \frac{\text{Ml. volume of 24-hour specimen}}{100} =$$

Gm. urea nitrogen/24 hr.

Normal range

6 to 17 gm./24 hr.

Multiply mg. urea nitrogen/100 ml. urine by 2.14 to obtain mg. urea/100 ml. urine.

Care of equipment

Clean glassware is essential for accuracy in this procedure. It is highly recommended that all glassware used should be washed with concentrated nitric acid, thoroughly rinsed with tap water and finally with distilled water.

Urea clearance

Urea is a waste product which the kidneys remove from the bloodstream and excrete in the urine. The ability of the kidneys to excrete this urea is measured by the urea clearance test. The test is reported in percent of normal. Any value between 60 and 125% is considered normal. Decreased values point to a kidney disorder.

Möller, McIntosh, and Van Slyke method

The discussion covers the collection of specimens and the laboratory procedure.

Collection of specimens

Because exercise interferes with the test, the patient is instructed not to exercise either before or during the test. The patient is requested to eat a light breakfast which may include water but may *not* include coffee or tea. The specimens are then collected in the manner given below. Two urine specimens are obtained so that one may serve as a check on the other. In the collection of urine it is essential that the patient completely empty the bladder and that the exact time interval beween collections be measured.

1. One hour after breakfast, give the patient a glass of water to drink. Ask him to empty the bladder *completely* and to discard the urine. Record the *exact* time at which the urine was voided.
2. *Exactly* 1 hour later, ask the patient to *empty* the bladder *completely* and to save the urine. Record the time at which the urine was collected and label the urine: 1-Hour Specimen. (If the patient cannot void at the prescribed time, the exact period of time which elapses should be recorded on the specimen. For example, if the patient voids 8 minutes after the prescribed time, the specimen should be labelled: 1-Hour 8-Minute Specimen.)
3. Make a venipuncture and collect blood for a blood urea nitrogen determination.

4. Give the patient another glass of water.
5. *Exactly* 1 hour after the collection of the first urine specimen, tell the patient to empty the bladder *completely* and to save the urine. Label: 2-Hour Specimen.

Laboratory procedure

1. Measure the volume of the 1-Hour Specimen of urine.
2. Calculate the milliliters passed per minute and record the results. Example: The urine was collected at the prescribed 1-hour or 60-minute interval. The urine specimen measured 120 ml.; 120 divided by 60 equals 2 ml. per minute.
3. Measure the volume of the 2-Hour Specimen of urine.
4. Calculate the milliliters passed per minute and record the results.
5. Run a urea nitrogen determination on the blood. Record the results.
6. Run a urea nitrogen determination on the two urine specimens. Record the results.
7. Calculations:
   a. The following data, obtained above, must be on hand:
      1-Hr. Urine Specimen, ml. passed per minute and urea nitrogen value
      2-Hr. Urine Specimen, ml. passed per minute and urea nitrogen value
      Blood Sample, urea nitrogen value
   b. If the patient is a child or an unusually small adult, see Note A below before continuing.
   c. The urea clearance of the 1-Hour Urine Specimen and that of the 2-Hour Urine Specimen are calculated separately. The two should not differ by more than 15%.
   d. If the volume of urine excreted is more than 2 ml./minute, use Formula A below and make the calculations. If the volume of urine excreted is 2 ml. or less/minute, use Formula B below and make the calculations.

Formula A:

$$\text{Urea clearance (in percent of normal)} = \frac{\text{Urine urea nitrogen (mg./100 ml.)}}{\text{Blood urea nitrogen (mg./100 ml.)}} \times V \times \frac{100}{75}$$

where V = ml. of urine per minute
and   75 = average normal value

Formula B:

$$\text{Urea clearance (in percent of normal)} = \frac{\text{Urine urea nitrogen (mg./100 ml.)}}{\text{Blood urea nitrogen (mg./100 ml.)}} \times \sqrt{V} \times \frac{100}{54}$$

where V = ml. of urine per minute
and   54 = average normal value

Table 24. Square roots of small numbers

V	$\sqrt{V}$	V	$\sqrt{V}$	V	$\sqrt{V}$	V	$\sqrt{V}$
0.2	0.45	0.7	0.84	1.2	1.1	1.7	1.3
0.3	0.55	0.8	0.89	1.3	1.14	1.8	1.34
0.4	0.63	0.9	0.95	1.4	1.18	1.9	1.38
0.5	0.71	1.0	1.00	1.5	1.23	2.0	1.42
0.6	0.78	1.1	1.05	1.6	1.27	2.1	1.45

e. If Formula B is used, the $\sqrt{V}$ will be needed. For convenience, the square roots of various small numbers are given in Table 24. Thus, if $V = 0.2$, the $\sqrt{V} = 0.45$, etc.

8. Sample calculation:

The following data was obtained from a urine specimen and the blood specimen:

Volume of urine: 138 ml.
Ml. passed per minute: 2.3
Urine urea nitrogen: 244 mg./100 ml.
Blood urea nitrogen: 12 mg./100 ml.

Since the volume of urine excreted per minute is more than 2 ml., Formula A must be used:

$$\text{Urea clearance (in percent of normal)} = \frac{\text{Urine urea nitrogen (mg./100 ml.)}}{\text{Blood urea nitrogen (mg./100 ml.)}} \times V \times \frac{100}{75}$$

$$= \frac{244}{12} \times 2.3 \times \frac{100}{75}$$

$$= 62.3\%$$

ESTIMATION OF SURFACE AREA OF BODY

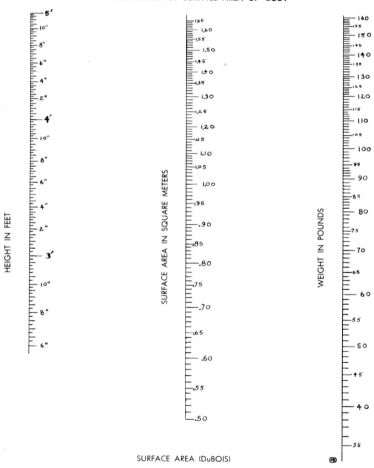

SURFACE AREA (DuBOIS)

Fig. 44. Chart for estimating surface area of body. (DuBois.)

Note A:

a. If the patient is a child or an unusually small adult, a correction for size is essential. In such cases, the milliliters excreted per minute must be multiplied by a size correction factor. This is derived in the following manner:

b. Obtain the patient's height and weight. Refer to Fig. 44 and place a ruler at the height and weight. Read off the surface area from the middle column.

c. Example: Patient is 4 feet tall and weighs 65 pounds. Placing a ruler at these points gives a surface area of 0.97 square meter.

d. To obtain the size correction factor, divide the surface area into 1.73. (The 1.73 is the surface area of the average man.)

e. Example: Patient's surface area is 0.97 square meter:

$$\text{Size correction factor} = \frac{1.73}{\text{Surface area}}$$
$$= \frac{1.73}{0.97}$$
$$= 1.78$$

f. Now multiply this size correction factor by the milliliters of urine passed per minute. Use this corrected value for the milliliters passed per minute and continue with the calculations.

STUDENTS' SUMMARY FOR THE NONPROTEIN NITROGENS

The significant information consists of the following:

Normal and abnormal values

Methods of analysis and synopsis of procedures

Normal and abnormal values

Test	Normal values	When increased
Creatinine Whole blood Plasma Urine	1–2 mg./100 ml. 0.8–1.3 mg./100 ml. 1.0–1.8 gm./24 hr.	Nephritis Urinary obstruction Intestinal obstruction Fever
Creatine, urine	0–200 mg./24 hr.	Malnutrition Fever Disintegration of muscular tissue High water ingestion
Creatinine clearance	100–180 ml./min.	Decrease with diseased kidneys
Uric acid Serum Male Female Urine Male Female	 2.5–7.0 mg./100 ml. 1.5–6.0 mg./100 ml. 250–750 mg./24 hr. 250–750 mg./24 hr.	 Nephritis Arthritis Gout
Total nonprotein nitrogen (NPN)	25–35 mg./100 ml.	Nephritis Urinary obstruction Intestinal obstruction Metallic poisoning Cardiac failure
Urea nitrogen Blood (BUN) Urine (UUN)	 8–20 mg./100 ml. 6–17 gm./24 hr.	Same as NPN Fever
Urea clearance Maximum average Minimum average	 75 ml./min. (64–99) 54 ml./min. (40–68)	Decrease with diseased kidneys

Methods of analysis and synopsis of procedures

Test	*Method*	*Synopsis of procedure*
Creatinine, blood	Folin-Wu	1. Make filtrate 2. Add alkaline sodium picrate to form red creatinine picrate (Jaffé reaction) 3. Measure in colorimeter
Creatinine, urine	Folin-Wu	1. Dilute urine 2. Add alkaline picrate to form red creatinine picrate 3. Measure in colorimeter
Creatine, urine	Folin-Wu	1. Dilute urine 2. Add hydrochloric acid 3. Boil 4. Add alkaline picrate to form red creatinine picrate 5. Measure in colorimeter
Uric acid	Folin	1. Make filtrate 2. Add urea-cyanide and phosphotungstic acid to form phosphotungst*ate* complex, which is reduced by uric acid to blue phosphotungst*ite* complex 3. Measure in colorimeter
	Brown	1. Make filtrate 2. Add sodium cyanide, urea, and phosphotungstic acid to form phosphotungst*ate* complex, which is reduced by uric acid to blue phosphotungst*ite* complex 3. Measure in colorimeter
	Newton	1. Make special filtrate 2. Add urea-cyanide solution and lithium arsenotungstate to form arsenotungst*ate* complex, which is reduced by uric acid to blue arsenotungst*ite* complex 3. Measure in colorimeter
	Archibald	1. Make special filtrate 2. Add glycerol-silicate, polyanethol sodium sulfonate, and phosphotungstic acid to form phosphotungst*ate* complex, which is reduced by uric acid to blue phosphotungst*ite* complex 3. Measure in colorimeter
	Henry	1. Make special filtrate 2. Add sodium carbonate and phosphotungstic acid to form phosphotungst*ate* complex, which is reduced by uric acid to blue phosphotungst*ite* complex 3. Measure in colorimeter
Total nonprotein nitrogen (NPN)	Folin-Wu	1. Make filtrate 2. Add digestion mixture of sulfuric and phosphoric acids to help liberate ammonia 3. Heat to decompose nitrogen substances and form ammonium salt 4. Add Nessler's solution to convert ammonium salt to yellow dimercuric ammonium iodide 5. Measure in colorimeter
	Koch-McMeekin	1. Same as above except use digestion mixture of sulfuric acid and then hydrogen peroxide
	Berthelot color reaction	1. Make filtrate 2. Add sulfuric acid to liberate ammonia 3. Heat to decompose nitrogen substances 4. Add phenol color reagent and alkali-hypochlorite reagent 5. Measure in colorimeter

Methods of analysis and synopsis of procedure—cont'd

Test	Method	Synopsis of procedure
Urea nitrogen	Karr	1. Make filtrate 2. Add buffer solution to control pH 3. Add enzyme urease and incubate to decompose urea and form ammonium carbonate 4. Add gum ghatti as protective colloid 5. Add Nessler's solution to convert ammonium carbonate to yellow dimercuric ammonium iodide 6. Measure in colorimeter
	Van Slyke-Cullen	1. Add buffer solution to oxalated blood to control pH 2. Add enzyme urease to decompose urea and form ammonium carbonate 3. Add potassium carbonate to liberate ammonia 4. Collect ammonia in boric acid solution 5. Titrate with standard acid solution and find urea nitrogen by calculation
	Gentzkow	1. Dilute oxalated blood 2. Add enzyme urease to decompose urea and form ammonium carbonate 3. Precipitate proteins 4. Add Nessler's solution to convert ammonium carbonate to yellow dimercuric ammonium iodide 5. Measure in colorimeter
	Folin-Svedberg	1. Make filtrate 2. Add buffer solution to control pH 3. Add enzyme urease to decompose urea and form ammonium carbonate 4. Incubate to enhance reaction 5. Add sodium borate to liberate ammonia 6. Collect ammonia in dilute hydrochloric acid 7. Add Nessler's solution to convert ammonium salt to yellow dimercuric ammonium iodide 8. Measure in colorimeter
	Berthelot color reaction	1. Add buffered urease to serum or plasma to decompose urea and form ammonia 2. Incubate to enhance reaction 3. Add phenol color reagent and alkali-hypochlorite reagent to develop color 4. Incubate to enhance reaction 5. Add water 6. Measure in colorimeter
	Urograph	1. Place serum or plasma in tube 2. Add Urograph paper strip 3. Incubate 4. Measure height of color developed

REFERENCES

1. Folin, O., and Doisy, E. A.: Impure picric acid as a source of error in creatine and creatinine determinations, J. Biol. Chem. **28**:349, 1917.
2. Folin, O., and Wu, H.: A system of blood analysis, J. Biol. Chem. **38**:81, 1919.
3. Folin, O.: On the determination of creatinine and creatine in urine, J. Biol. Chem. **17**:469, 1914.
4. Archibald, R. M.: Colorimetric measurement of uric acid, Clin. Chem. **3**:102, 1957.
5. Jorgensen, S., and Nielsen, A. T.: Uric acid in human blood corpuscles and plasma, Scandinav. J. Clin. & Lab. Invest. **8**:108, 1956.
6. Henry, R. J.: Clinical chemistry; principles and technics, New York, 1964, Paul B. Hoeber, Inc., Medical Book Department of Harper & Row, Publishers.
7. Henry, R. J., Sobel, C., and Kim, J.: A modified carbonate-phosphotungstate method for

the determination of uric acid and comparison with the spectrophotometric uricase method, Am. J. Clin. Path. **28:**152, 645, 1957.

8. Koch, F. C., and McMeekin, T. L.: A new direct nesslerization micro-Kjeldahl method and a modification of the Nessler-Folin reagent for ammonia, J. Am. Chem. Soc. **46:**2066, 1924.

9. Gentzkow, C. J.: Accurate method for determination of blood urea nitrogen by direct nesslerization, J. Biol. Chem. **143:**531, 1942.

10. Chaney, A. L., and Marbach, E. P.: Modified reagents for determination of urea and ammonia, Clin. Chem. **8:**131, 1962.

11. Erickson, M. M., Verdun, R. M., and White, W. L.: An evaluation of the Urograph method for determining blood urea nitrogen, Am. J. Med. Tech. **31:**127, Sept.-Oct., 1965.

Chapter 10

Proteins

As was previously mentioned, substances containing nitrogen are divided into nonprotein nitrogens and proteins. The former have already been discussed. This chapter considers the proteins. These substances are of chief interest in nephrosis, a disease of the kidneys.

Since the proteins are usually determined as a unit, they will be discussed as a unit. The discussion covers the following:

Calibration curve for total protein and albumin
Total protein in spinal fluid
Total protein of urine
Macroglobulinemia
Cryoglobulinemia
Electrophoresis

Information significant to the student

The blood proteins are made up partially of antibodies, enzymes, and hormones. These substances have varied functions. As a group, one of their major functions is to maintain the water balance between the blood and tissues.

Under normal conditions, the water balance is at equilibrium. However, if blood proteins are lost, the density of the blood decreases, and water flows toward the tissues. Swelling, or edema, results. This is found in nephrosis, a disease of the kidneys characterized by appearance of albumin in the urine.

The proteins of significance to the medical technologist are albumin, globulin, and total protein. These substances are the most abundant solid material in blood, and their values are given in grams per 100 ml. of serum. The normal values are given below:

Albumin   3.5 to 5.5 gm./100 ml. of serum
Globulin   1.3 to 3.3 gm./100 ml. of serum
Total protein   6.0 to 8.0 gm./100 ml. of serum

The relationship between albumin and globulin is commonly referred to as the A/G ratio. Under normal conditions, this is roughly 2 to 1 or, more exactly,

Table 25. Conditions accompanied by abnormal protein values

Disease	Albumin	Globulin	Total protein
Nephrosis	Decreased	Normal	Decreased
Multiple myeloma	Normal	Increased	Increased
Infectious hepatitis	Decreased	Increased	Decreased
Cirrhosis of liver	Decreased	Normal	Decreased

is between 1.5 to 1 and 2.5 to 1. For example, if a patient's albumin value is 4 gm. and his globulin value is 2 gm., his A/G ratio is 4/2. This is usually written 2/1 or 2:1.

Since albumin is lost in nephrosis, the A/G ratio is disturbed. In severe nephrosis an inverted ratio, such as 1:2, may be found.

Some significant diseases in which abnormal protein values may be expected are given in Table 25.

The more commonly used methods for the determination of proteins are listed below. A brief discussion of each follows.

> Greenberg method
> Kingsley biuret reaction
> Micro-Kjeldahl method
> Looney-Walsh method
> Kingsley serum protein biuret method, modified by Weichselbaum

Greenberg method

1. The albumin is determined as follows. A sodium sulfate solution is added to a portion of serum. This precipitates globulin, which is removed by filtering or by centrifuging. (If done by centrifuge, ether is added to aid in the separation.) To the filtrate—containing the albumin—is added the phenol reagent of Folin and Ciocalteu. A blue color is produced, which is measured in a colorimeter and compared with a standard tyrosine solution.

2. The total protein is determined as follows. Another portion of serum is diluted with sodium chloride solution. The same phenol reagent of Folin and Ciocalteu is added. A blue color is produced. The depth of color is measured in a colorimeter and compared with a standard tyrosine solution.

3. The globulin is found as follows: Globulin = Total protein − Albumin.

Kingsley biuret reaction

1. The albumin is determined as follows. A sodium sulfate solution is added to a portion of serum. This precipitates the globulin, which is removed by filtering or by centrifuging. (If the centrifuge is used, ether is added to aid in the separation.) To the filtrate—containing the albumin—is added a biuret reagent that forms a reddish purple complex (the biuret reaction). The depth of color is measured in a colorimeter and compared with a standard.

2. The total protein is determined as follows. Another portion of serum is diluted with sodium chloride solution. The same biuret reagent is added. This forms a reddish purple complex. The depth of color is measured in a colorimeter and compared with a standard.

3. The globulin is determined as follows: Globulin = Total protein − Albumin.

Micro-Kjeldahl method

1. The total protein is found as follows. (The test calls for two separate determinations and a calculation.)

In the first determination, the total nitrogen is determined on serum by a micro-Kjeldahl method. This entails adding a digestion mixture, heating with a flame to decompose nitrogenous substances, adding Nessler's solution to bring out the yellow color, and then measuring the depth of color in a colorimeter.

In the second determination, the nonprotein nitrogen is determined on serum by the Kjeldahl method. This again calls for digestion and nesslerizing.

In the calculation, the total protein is found from the formula: Total protein = (Total nitrogen − Nonprotein nitrogen) × 6.25, where the 6.25 is a factor converting nitrogen to protein.

Example: Total nitrogen value is found to be 1000 mg./100 ml., and nonprotein nitrogen is found to be 30 mg./100 ml. Therefore, total protein = (1000 − 30) × 6.25 = 6062.50 mg./100 ml., or 6.1 gm./100 ml.

2. The albumin is determined as follows. The globulin is removed from the serum by precipitating with sodium sulfate and filtering. The filtrate contains the albumin. This is digested and nesslerized to determine the total nitrogen. The albumin is found from the formula: Albumin = (Total nitrogen − Nonprotein nitrogen) × 6.25, where 6.25 is a factor converting nitrogen to protein. The nonprotein nitrogen value used above is derived from the total protein determination.

Example: Total nitrogen value is found to be 700 mg./100 ml., and nonprotein nitrogen is 30 mg./100 ml. Therefore: Albumin = (700 − 30) × 6.25 = 4187.50 mg./100 ml., or 4.2 gm./100 ml.

3. The globulin is found as follows: Globulin = Total protein − Albumin.

Example: Using the above figures for total protein and albumin, Globulin = 6.1 − 4.2 = 1.9 gm./100 ml.

Looney-Walsh method

1. The globulin is determined as follows. Serum is diluted with saline solution. To this is added gum ghatti and saturated ammonium sulfate, their function being to precipitate the globulin in the form of a colloidal suspension. The turbidity of the solution is then compared in a colorimeter with a standard that has been similarly treated.

2. The total protein is determined as follows. Serum is diluted with saline solution. To this is added gum ghatti and sulfosalicylic acid, their purpose being to precipitate the proteins in the form of a colloidal suspension. The turbidity of the solution is then compared in a colorimeter with a standard that has been similarly treated.

3. The albumin is found as follows: Albumin = Total protein − Globulin.

Procedures for the serum proteins

The following general considerations pertain to the procedures for albumin, globulin, and total protein.

1. Preparation of patient: fasting not necessary.
2. Preparation of blood: serum.
3. Preservation of serum: may be stored overnight in a refrigerator.
4. Precautions: follow directions *exactly* as given in procedure.

Kingsley serum protein biuret method, modified by Weichselbaum

The biuret method is a fast, simple, and accurate procedure for protein determination. However, lack of sensitivity of the method makes it not too satisfactory for cerebrospinal fluid and urine protein analysis.

Protein produces a violet color in the presence of cupric ions in an alkaline solution, reaching its maximum color within 15 minutes. The color is then stable for several hours.

Weichselbaum added sodium potassium tartrate as a complexing agent and potassium iodide to prevent autoreduction.[1,2]

Reagents needed

Biuret Reagent	(C-33)
Physiological Saline, 0.9%	(C-34)
Sodium Sulfate, 24.5%	(C-35)
Anhydrous Ether	

Procedure for albumin

1. Pipet 0.5 ml. of serum into a test tube approximately 16 × 125 mm.
2. Add 7.5 ml. of 24.5% sodium sulfate, using a 10 ml. serological pipet. Stopper and shake vigorously. (Note: Sodium sulfate at this concentration has a tendency to crystallize when the room temperature falls below 25° C. If the room temperature is below 25° C. place the rack of tubes and a flask of 24.5% sodium sulfate in a large pan of water and adjust the temperature to 25° to 30° C. by adding warm water, or use a water bath if available.)
3. Allow the tubes to stand for 15 minutes and then add approximately 3 or 4 ml. of ether by pouring directly from the ether can into the tube. *Do not pipet ether! Do not smoke or have an open flame near this area.* Ether vapors travel along the tabletops of work area.
4. Shake the tubes vigorously. Use finger cots on the thumbs. At the beginning of shaking the tubes, carefully release the thumbs to relieve the pressure built up in the tube. This will prevent any ether and solution splattering around the laboratory.
5. Centrifuge the tubes 3 to 4 minutes at about 3000 RPM. The precipitated globulin will be packed in a firm layer between the top ether layer and the bottom solution layer containing the albumin.
6. This next step requires a careful technique. Using a 5.0 ml. volumetric pipet, place the forefinger over the mouthpiece opening of the pipet to keep any ether or globulin from entering the tip. Tilt the tube to a slanting position to dislodge the globulin layer. If it still adheres to the tube, gently tap the tube over the globulin area with the pipet. Carefully lower the pipet under the globulin layer and down into the albumin layer. Slowly pipet 5.0 ml. of the albumin layer into a test tube (large) or a Coleman cuvette.
7. Add 5.0 ml. of saline.
8. Add 10.0 ml. of biuret reagent and mix.
9. Prepare a reference blank as follows:
   a. Pipet 5.0 ml. of 24.5% sodium sulfate into a large test tube or a Coleman cuvette.
   b. Add 5.0 ml. of saline.
   c. Add 10.0 ml. of biuret reagent and mix well.

10. Place all tubes into a water bath at 30° to 32° C. for 30 minutes.
11. Read O.D. at 555 mμ, or read % T and convert to O.D.
12. Refer to the calibration curve to convert O.D. readings to grams of albumin/100 ml.

Procedure for total protein

1. Pipet 0.5 ml. of serum into a large test tube (18 × 150 mm.).
2. Add 20 ml. of saline. (Use buret.) *Mix well.*
3. Transfer 5.0 ml. of diluted serum to another tube (e.g., a 19 × 150 mm. Coleman cuvette).
4. Add 5.0 ml. of biuret reagent and mix well.
5. Prepare a reference blank by mixing 5.0 ml. of saline with 5.0 ml. of biuret.
6. Place the tubes in a water bath set at 30° to 32° C. for 30 minutes.
7. Read O.D. at 555 mμ.
8. Refer to the calibration curve to convert O.D. reading to grams of protein/100 ml.

Procedure for globulin

The amount of globulin is obtained by subtracting the amount of albumin found from the amount of total protein found.

Example:

Total protein	7.0 gm./100 ml. or gm.%
Albumin	4.0 gm./100 ml.
Globulin	3.0 gm./100 ml.

Note: The presence of lipids may cause a turbidity in the solutions. This may be solved by the following method. Freeze the serum; this splits the protein-lipid bond. Leave the specimen in the freezer overnight. Then allow the frozen specimen to come to room temperature. Add an equal volume of ether to the tube and shake vigorously. Centrifuge for about 3 minutes. Suction off the top ether layer. If the specimen is not clear, extract with ether a second time. Proceed with the routine protein analysis.

CALIBRATION CURVE FOR TOTAL PROTEIN AND ALBUMIN

For each new bottle of biuret reagent, a new calibration curve must be made. This is accomplished by using the new biuret solution with a *standard* protein solution, taking readings on the spectrophotometer, and plotting these readings against the concentration of protein on linear graph paper.

Standard protein solution preparation

A 2.8 mg./ml. solution of protein may be prepared from a serum of known protein value.

Example: The commercial serum chosen has a known protein value of 7.0 gm. %, and 7.0 gm. % = 70 mg./ml. Let x represent the amount of standard to be used. Then:

$$\frac{2.8}{x} = \frac{70}{100}$$

$$70 x = 280$$

$$x = \frac{280}{70}$$

$$x = 4.0 \text{ ml. of control serum needed}$$

With a 4.0 ml. volumetric pipet, pipet 4.0 ml. of commercial serum into a 100 ml. volumetric flask. Dilute to 100 ml. with physiological saline. Mix well. This solution now contains 2.8 mg./ml., of protein.

Procedure

1. Set up the following tubes in duplicate, using volumetric pipets.

Tube	Protein standard	Saline (physiological)	Biuret
1	1.0 ml.	4.0 ml.	5.0 ml.
2	2.0 ml.	3.0 ml.	5.0 ml.
3	3.0 ml.	2.0 ml.	5.0 ml.
4	4.0 ml.	1.0 ml.	5.0 ml.

2. Mix well and place in 30° to 32° C. water bath for 30 minutes. Obtain O.D. readings at a 555 mμ wavelength. Plot the O.D. readings against the protein concentration on linear graph paper. The above readings will be plotted on one sheet of graph paper for both the total protein and the albumin. The protein concentration chart, calculated and ready for the graph paper, is as follows:

Tube	Total protein (gm.%)	Albumin (gm.%)
1	2.3	1.79
2	4.6	3.58
3	6.9	5.38
4	9.2	7.17

Method of obtaining protein concentrations

1. *Total protein*   Adding 0.5 ml. of serum to 20.0 of saline gives a volume of 20.5 ml. as the total volume of diluted serum. Therefore:

$$\frac{0.5 \text{ ml. of serum used}}{20.5 \text{ ml. or total volume of diluted serum}} = 0.0244 \text{ ml. of serum/ml. of diluted serum}$$

Now 5.0 ml. of this diluted serum are used. Therefore $0.0244 \times 5 = 0.122$ ml. of serum actually used. This must be corrected to 100 ml. so that the result may be expressed in gm./100 ml.:

$$\frac{100}{0.122} = 819.6 \text{ or } 820, \text{ which is the dilution factor}$$

To determine what the readings of the four standards should be plotted against, in grams percent, multiply the known amount of protein (2.8 mg. = 0.0028 gm.) by the dilution factor of 820. Therefore:

Total protein (gm.%)

$$0.0028 \text{ gm. (1 ml.)} \times 820 = 2.3$$
$$0.0056 \text{ gm. (2 ml.)} \times 820 = 4.6$$
$$0.0084 \text{ gm. (3 ml.)} \times 820 = 6.9$$
$$0.0112 \text{ gm. (4 ml.)} \times 820 = 9.2$$

2. *Albumin*   By calculation we find:

$$\frac{0.5 \text{ ml. of serum used}}{8.0 \text{ ml. or total volume of diluted serum}} = 0.0625 \text{ ml. of serum/ml. of diluted serum}$$

Now 5.0 ml. of this diluted serum (filtrate) are used. Therefore $0.0625 \times 5 = 0.3125$ ml. of serum actually used. This must be corrected to 100 ml. so that the result may be expressed in gm./100 ml.:

$$\frac{100}{0.3125} = 320$$

This 320 must be multiplied by 2 because the total volume of the final albumin dilution is 20 (it is 10 for the total protein). Therefore, $320 \times 2 = 640$, the dilution factor for albumin.

To determine what the readings of the four standards should be plotted against, in grams percent, multiply the known amounts of protein by the dilution factor of 640:

$$\begin{array}{l}
\text{Albumin} \\
\text{(gm.\%)}
\end{array}$$

$$0.0028 \text{ gm. (1 ml.)} \times 640 = 1.79$$
$$0.0056 \text{ gm. (2 ml.)} \times 640 = 3.58$$
$$0.0084 \text{ gm. (3 ml.)} \times 640 = 5.38$$
$$0.0112 \text{ gm. (4 ml.)} \times 640 = 7.17$$

TOTAL PROTEIN IN SPINAL FLUID[3]

If red cells are present in a sample of cerebrospinal fluid, the fluid must be centrifuged and decanted before an analysis is done. Cells will greatly elevate the values. Elevated proteins are found in most types of meningeal inflammation, latent syphilis, brain tumor, subarachnoid hemorrhage, and sometimes in contamination of blood as mentioned above. The blood contamination results from a trauma during the withdrawal of the fluid.

Meulemans method

Principle

Trichloroacetic acid is added to the spinal fluid and the protein is precipitated as a fine suspension. The turbidity of the suspension is measured in a colorimeter and compared with a standard.

Reagents needed

Trichloroacetic Acid, 3%   (C-36)
Working Standard:

Prepare fresh daily. Transfer 0.5 ml. of serum with a known protein concentration to a 100 ml. volumetric flask. Dilute to volume with physiological saline, stopper, and mix thoroughly.

To determine the protein concentration of this solution in milligrams percent, multiply the serum protein concentration in grams percent by 5. The 5 is obtained by the following computation:

$$\frac{0.5 \times 1000}{100}$$

For example, control values of the serum standard $\times 5 = $ mg.% solution value:

$$6.6 \text{ gm.\%} \times 5 = 33 \text{ mg.\%}$$
$$6.8 \text{ gm.\%} \times 5 = 34 \text{ mg.\%}$$
$$7.0 \text{ gm.\%} \times 5 = 35 \text{ mg.\%}$$
$$7.2 \text{ gm.\%} \times 5 = 36 \text{ mg.\%}$$

Procedure

1. Set up the following tubes:
   Blank
      5.0 ml. of 3% trichloroacetic acid
   Standard
      1.0 ml. of working standard
      4.0 ml. of 3% trichloroacetic acid
   Unknown
      1.0 ml. of spinal fluid
      4.0 ml. of 3% trichloroacetic acid

2. Mix and let stand for 10 minutes.
3. Remix and read O.D. at 450 mμ (or read % T and convert to O.D.)

Calculations

$$\frac{\text{O.D. of unknown}}{\text{O.D. of standard}} \times \text{Concentration of standard} = \text{Mg. protein/100 ml.}$$

Normal range
15 to 45 mg./100 ml.

TOTAL PROTEIN OF URINE

Shevky-Stafford[4] rapid approximate sedimentation method

The following procedure deviates in a few details from the original description. The first variation is in the dilution of the urine. Nephritic urines are usually diluted tenfold. However, urines yielding very small amounts of protein should be diluted much less or not at all for accurate results. Occasionally a urine will be found with more than 2.8% protein. If a 1:10 dilution is not adequate, use a 1:20 dilution.

Reagents needed

Tsuchiya's Reagent   (C-37)

Procedure

1. Pipet 4.0 ml. of diluted urine into a special graduated centrifuge tube.[*]
   Since the 4 ml. mark on the tube may serve as a measurement, the serological pipet is used for convenience, to avoid spilling the urine and to allow better control for the proper measurement to the 4 ml. mark.
2. Add Tsuchiya's reagent until the tube is filled to the 6.5 ml. mark.
3. Stopper and invert slowly three times to mix.
4. Let stand for 10 minutes.
5. Centrifuge for 10 minutes (use timer) at 1800 RPM.
6. Read the volume of precipitate on the scale.

Calculation

Milliliters of precipitate read $\times$ 7.2 $\times$ Urine dilution = Grams of protein/liter of urine

MACROGLOBULINEMIA

Macroglobulins consist of proteins with a molecular weight exceeding 1,000,000, and a sedimentation constant of 20 or more. Under normal conditions these account for 3 to 5% of the total serum proteins. Under abnormal conditions, as in Waldenström's macroglobulinemia, these proteins comprise over 20% of the total proteins.[6] Ultracentrifugation is required for the definite diagnosis of this disease. A simple qualitative test may be done, due to the solubility of macroglobulins in electrolyte solutions and their precipitation by dilution. High serum viscosity and a rapid erythrocyte sedimentation rate may also suggest macroglobulinemia.

---

[*]Special equipment needed: The graduated centrifuge tube is a special calibrated tube that may be obtained from the following distributors: Phipps & Bird, Richmond, Va.; Coffman & Ladimer, Columbus, Ohio; Palo Laboratories, New York, N. Y.; Howe & French, Boston, Mass.; George T. Walker, Minneapolis, Minn.

Sia test (water-dilution test)

Reagents needed

Physiological Saline, 0.9%   (C-34)

Procedure

1. Fill a small test tube with distilled water.
2. *Drop* 1 drop of serum into the distilled water. Use either pipet or dropper.
3. Negative results: the serum either disperses or forms a slight haziness.
4. Positive results: a heavy precipitate forms, dropping to the bottom of the tube when macroglobulins are present.
5. If positive, centrifuge and pour off supernatant.
6. Redissolve the precipitate in a small amount of 0.85% sodium chloride (saline) solution.
7. Reprecipitate by adding distilled water to the small volume of saline. This suggests the presence of macroglobulins.

False positive reactions may occur with the Sia test. The test usually shows negative results when small or even moderate numbers of macroglobulins are present. Consistent positive results are not always found with large quantities of macroglobulin.

CRYOGLOBULINEMIA[5]

Cryoglobulins are a group of proteins that precipitate from cooled serum and redissolve upon warming or returning to room temperature. Cryoglobulinemia is usually found in patients having multiple myeloma, although it may be found associated with other conditions or by itself. The cryoglobulins may be detected by a variety of methods based upon the effects of temperature and their solubility. Two simple methods are given below. The specimen *must not* be refrigerated before the test.

Refrigeration of serum

Procedure

1. Place fresh serum in the refrigerator for a minimum of 4 hours or overnight.
2. If there is a gelatinous precipitate at the end of the chilling period, proceed with step 3.
3. Bring to room temperature by putting tube into a beaker of water at room temperature.
4. Cryoglobulins will redissolve upon warming.

Erythrocyte sedimentation rate—at 37.5° and at 10° C.

1. In the cold at 10° C., the red cells do not settle out, due to the precipitation and gel formation of cryoglobulins.
2. For serum warmed to 37.5° C., the sedimentation rate is usually abnormally rapid.

ELECTROPHORESIS

The following proteins are found in plasma: albumin, alpha globulin, beta globulin, gamma globulin, and fibrinogen. The normal values for these proteins are given in Table 26. In disease, these figures may vary. Recently they have become of considerable interest in diagnosis.

The serum or plasma proteins may be separated and analyzed by the process

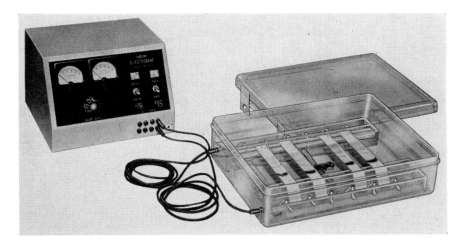

Fig. 45. Electrophoresis apparatus. (Courtesy Labline, Inc., Chicago, Ill.)

Table 26. Normal percentages of plasma proteins

Protein	Percentage
Albumin	55
Alpha globulin	14
Beta globulin	13
Gamma globulin	11
Fibrinogen	7
Total protein	100

of electrophoresis. In electrophoresis, advantage is taken of the fact that the serum or plasma proteins have different molecular weights and also different electric charges. Consequently, when they are placed in an electric field, they migrate at different rates of speed. In so doing, they form patterns. These patterns serve as pictures of their respective concentrations.

An electrophoresis apparatus is illustrated in Fig. 45. It operates as follows. A sample of serum is placed on a strip of paper that has been saturated with a buffer solution. The strip of paper is then laid on a migration chamber in such a manner that both ends dip into a buffer solution. An electric current is turned on. The protein particles then migrate along the strip of paper at speeds governed by their molecular weight and electric charge.

After a definite period of time, the strip of paper is removed and is dried by heat. This fixes the position of the protein particles. The paper is then stained. Finally, it is evaluated either by comparison with standard patterns, by a colorimetric procedure, or by a densitometer.

STUDENTS' SUMMARY FOR THE PROTEINS

The significant information consists of the following:
Methods of analysis and synopsis of procedures
Normal and abnormal values
Conversion of total protein in gm./100 ml. to meq./liter

Methods of analysis and synopsis of procedures

Test	Method	Synopsis of procedure
Albumin	Greenberg	1. Obtain serum 2. Add sodium sulfate to precipitate globulin 3. Centrifuge to remove globulin 4. Add phenol reagent to form blue color complex 5. Measure in colorimeter and compare with standard tyrosine solution
Total protein	Greenberg	1. Obtain serum 2. Dilute with sodium chloride 3. Add phenol reagent to form blue color complex 4. Measure in colorimeter and compare with standard tyrosine solution
Globulin	Greenberg	1. Globulin = total protein − albumin
Albumin	Kingsley biuret reaction	1. Obtain serum 2. Add sodium sulfate to precipitate globulin 3. Add biuret reagent to form reddish purple complex 4. Measure in colorimeter
Total protein	Kingsley biuret reaction	1. Obtain serum 2. Dilute with sodium chloride 3. Add biuret reagent to form reddish purple complex 4. Measure in colorimeter
Globulin	Kingsley biuret reaction	1. Globulin = total protein − albumin
Total protein	Micro-Kjeldahl	1. Obtain serum 2. Digest and nesslerize to determine nonprotein nitrogen and total nitrogen 3. Subtract nonprotein nitrogen from total nitrogen to find protein nitrogen 4. Multiply protein nitrogen by factor 6.25 to find protein
Albumin	Micro-Kjeldahl	1. Obtain serum 2. Add sodium sulfate to precipitate globulin 3. Filter to remove globulin 4. Digest and nesslerize filtrate to determine total nitrogen 5. Subtract nonprotein nitrogen from total nitrogen to find albumin nitrogen 6. Multiply albumin nitrogen by factor 6.25 to find albumin
Globulin	Micro-Kjeldahl	1. Globulin = total protein − albumin
Globulin	Looney-Walsh	1. Obtain serum 2. Dilute with saline 3. Add gum ghatti and ammonium sulfate to form colloidal suspension of globulin 4. Compare turbidity with standard in colorimeter
Total protein	Looney-Walsh	1. Obtain serum 2. Dilute with saline 3. Add gum ghatti and sulfosalicylic acid to form colloidal suspension of protein 4. Compare turbidity with standard in colorimeter
Albumin	Looney-Walsh	1. Albumin = total protein − globulin
Albumin	Weichselbaum biuret reaction	1. Obtain serum 2. Add sodium sulfate to precipitate globulin 3. Extract globulin with ether 4. Centrifuge and pipet aliquot of albumin solution 5. Add biuret reagent to form reddish purple complex 6. Measure in colorimeter

Methods of analysis and synopsis of procedures—cont'd

Test	Method	Synopsis of procedure
Total protein	Weichselbaum biuret reaction	1. Obtain serum 2. Dilute with sodium chloride 3. Add biuret reagent to form reddish purple complex 4. Measure in colorimeter
Globulin	Weichselbaum biuret reaction	1. Globulin = total protein − albumin
Total protein, cerebrospinal fluid	Muelemans	1. Obtain cerebrospinal fluid 2. Add 3% trichloroacetic acid 3. Measure in colorimeter against a standard
Total protein, urine	Shevky-Stafford	1. Obtain urine and measure volume 2. Add Tsuchiya's reagent and mix 3. Centrifuge 4. Read concentration from calibrated centrifuge tube
Sia test		1. Obtain serum 2. Drop serum into distilled water 3. Observe precipitate and report as positive or negative
Cryoglobulin test		1. Obtain serum or EDTA blood 2. Chill serum and then return it to room temperature 3. Observe precipitate and record as positive or negative 4. With EDTA blood, run sedimentation rates at temperatures of 10° and 37.5° C.; record results
Electrophoresis paper		1. Obtain serum, cerebrospinal fluid, or urine 2. Dialyze cerebrospinal fluid and urine 3. Place on buffered paper strip 4. Maintain constant voltage for definite period of time for migration of proteins according to molecular weights 5. Dry strips, stain, and then read by comparing with standard patterns or by colorimetric methods

Normal and abnormal values

Test	Normal values (gm./100 ml.)	When increased	When decreased
Albumin	3.5–5.5		Nephrosis Infectious hepatitis Cirrhosis of liver
Globulin	1.3–3.3	Multiple myeloma Infectious hepatitis	
Total protein	6.0–8.0	Multiple myeloma	Nephrosis Infectious hepatitis Cirrhosis of liver

Conversion of total protein in gm./100 ml. to meq./liter

To convert total protein in gm./100 ml. to meq./liter, use this formula:

$$\text{Meq./liter} = \text{Gm./100 ml.} \times 2.43$$

Example: Convert 5.0 gm./100 ml. of total protein to meq./liter, using the formula:

$$
\begin{aligned}
\text{Meq./liter} &= \text{Gm./100 ml.} \times 2.43 \\
&= \quad 5.0 \quad\quad \times 2.43 \\
&= \quad 12.15
\end{aligned}
$$

REFERENCES

1. Weichselbaum, T. E.: An accurate and rapid method for the determination of proteins in small amounts of blood serum and plasma, Am. J. Clin. Path. **16** (Tech. Sec. **10**):40, 1946.
2. Henry, R. J.: Clinical chemistry; principles and technics, New York, 1964, Paul B. Hoeber, Inc., Medical Book Department of Harper & Row, Publishers.
3. Meulemans, O.: Determination of total protein in spinal fluid with sulphosalicylic acid and trichloroacetic acid, Clin. Chim. Acta **5**:757, 1960.
4. Peters, John P., and Van Slyke, Donald D.: Quantitative clinical chemistry, vol. 2, Baltimore, 1956, The Williams & Wilkins Co.
5. Page, L. B., and Culver, P. J.: A syllabus of laboratory examinations in clinical diagnosis, rev. ed., Cambridge, Mass., 1961, Harvard University Press.
6. Waldenström, J.: Abnormal proteins in myeloma, Adv. Int. Med. **5**:298, 1952.

Chapter 11

Liver function tests

The liver is the largest organ in the body, weighing about 3 pounds in the average adult. It has two major functions: (1) to manufacture and distribute food supplies and (2) to remove poisons.

One of the more common manifestations of disorders of the liver is known as jaundice. Jaundice is characterized by the presence of excessive bile pigment, which produces a yellow coloration of the skin. The disease may be divided into three groups: (1) obstructive jaundice, which is caused by a blockage of the flow of bile, (2) hemolytic jaundice, which is caused by excessive hemolysis of red cells, and (3) hepatic jaundice, which is caused by a toxic condition of the liver.

Because the liver has many functions, it has been possible to devise numerous liver function tests. None, however, give a clear-cut picture, and the physician often supplements liver function tests with additional blood chemistry tests such as blood sugar, urea nitrogen, and total protein.

This chapter considers the more commonly used liver function tests. They are listed below:

Icterus index	Thymol turbidity
Bilirubin	Thymol flocculation test
Bromsulphalein (BSP)	Cephalin-cholesterol flocculation

Liver function tests that are performed on urine are given in the chapters on urine analysis.

A students' summary of significant information is given at the end of this chapter.

ICTERUS INDEX

Discussion here covers information significant to the student and a procedure for the test.

Information significant to the student

Bilirubin is a bile pigment that gives serum a yellow color. In general, the more bilirubin present, the deeper the yellow color is. The depth of color may be measured by a test known as the icterus index.

The normal values for the icterus index are 4 to 6 units. Decreased values may be found in hypochromic microcytic anemia. Increased values are found in the following diseases:

> Obstructive jaundice
> Hemolytic jaundice
> Hepatic jaundice
> Infectious hepatitis
> Pernicious anemia

The icterus index may rise to 15 units before the eyes or skin shows the yellow pigmentation of jaundice. The zone between 6 and 15 units is therefore called the zone of latent jaundice.

The eating of carrots gives serum a yellow color that may be mistaken for a high icterus index. Consequently, the diet should be free of carrots for at least 2 days prior to the test.

Due to lack of specificity, the icterus index is losing its effectiveness as a diagnostic tool.

The more commonly used methods for the icterus index are listed below. A brief discussion follows.

> Meulengracht method
> Newberger method

Meulengracht method

Serum is obtained. This is diluted with either saline or a buffer solution. The depth of yellow color is compared with a standard potassium dichromate solution or measured in a photoelectric colorimeter.

Newberger method

Serum is obtained. Acetone is added to remove interfering substances such as fat. After centrifuging, the depth of yellow color is compared with a standard potassium dichromate solution or measured in a photoelectric colorimeter.

Procedure for icterus index

The following general considerations pertain to the procedure for the icterus index.

1. Preparation of patient: must be fasting.
2. Preparation of blood: serum.
3. Preservation of serum: may be stored overnight in a refrigerator.
4. Precautions:
   a. Avoid excessive hemolysis of red cells, which may be caused (1) by failure to remove needle from syringe when transferring blood to test tube and (2) by allowing blood to stand for several hours in a warm area.
   b. Follow directions *exactly* as given in the procedure.

Determination of icterus index[1,2]

The intensity of the yellow pigmentation of serum is compared with a standard potassium dichromate solution. The yellow pigmentation is chiefly due to the presence of hemobilirubin or cholebilirubin. The color depth is not directly proportional to the amount of bilirubin present. With equal amounts of hemobilirubin and cholebilirubin, the cholebilirubin gives a deeper color. The icterus index test does not always agree with the van den Bergh test.

Reagents needed

Sodium Citrate, 5%	(C-38)
Physiological Saline, 0.9%	(C-34)
Potassium Dichromate, Stock Standard, 1%	(C-39)
Working Standard, 0.1%	

Using a volumetric pipet, pipet 10.0 ml. of stock standard into a 100 ml. volumetric flask and dilute to mark with distilled water.

Procedure (Meulengracht method[1])

Note: The serum may be diluted with either saline or sodium citrate solution.

1. Prepare two standards and the unknown as follows:

    Standard 1
    - a. Pipet into a test tube 9 ml. of saline and 1 ml. of working standard.
    - b. Stopper and mix.

    Standard 2
    - a. Pipet into a test tube 8 ml. of saline and 2 ml. of working standard.
    - b. Stopper and mix.

    Unknown
    - a. Pipet into a test tube 9 ml. of saline and 1 ml. of clear serum.
    - b. Stopper and mix.

2. Read all tubes against a water blank at 420 mμ.

Calculations

Use the standard that reads nearest the unknown. If the color is darker than standard 2, dilute the unknown and multiply the answer by the dilution.

Standard 1:
$$\frac{\text{O.D. of unknown}}{\text{O.D. of standard}} \times 10 = \text{Icterus index units}$$

Standard 2:
$$\frac{\text{O.D. of unknown}}{\text{O.D. of standard}} \times 20 = \text{Icterus index units}$$

A standard curve may be made if desired. A curve should be made, however, when any repair work has been done on the colorimeter or old lamps have been replaced.

Standardization or calibration curve for the icterus index procedure

Set up the following tubes and read O.D. or % T at 420 mμ against a water blank.

Icterus index (units)	Saline (ml.)	Working standard (ml.)	Readings
1	9.9	0.1	
3	9.7	0.3	
5	9.5	0.5	
8	9.2	0.8	
10	9.0	1.0	
15	8.5	1.5	
20	8.0	2.0	
30	7.0	3.0	
50	5.0	5.0	

Plot % T readings for each tube on semilogarithmic graph paper.

BILIRUBIN

The discussion covers information significant to the student, procedure for the test, and recommended standardization.

Information significant to the student

Bilirubin is a bile pigment which is normally present in blood. The normal values are 0.2 to 0.8 mg./100 ml. of serum. Increased values are found in the following diseases:

> Obstructive jaundice
> Hemolytic jaundice
> Hepatic jaundice
> Infectious hepatitis
> Pernicious anemia

Bilirubin is usually determined now by the method of Malloy and Evelyn. This method is essentially the same as the outdated procedure of van den Bergh.

In the van den Bergh method, both a qualitative test and a quantitative test for bilirubin were made. These tests were based on a color reaction. The absence of color development was normal for the qualitative test. If color did develop, however, it was then measured quantitatively.

It was formerly thought that the time interval of color development had a definite correlation with the origin of the bilirubin present. If the reaction took place immediately, the bilirubin came from bile (obstructive jaundice). If the reaction was delayed, the bilirubin came from hemolyzed red cells (hemolytic jaundice). Recent investigations, however, have ruled out this theory.

The qualitative test of van den Bergh was known as the direct reaction, whereas the quantitative test was referred to as the indirect reaction.

Like the van den Bergh, the method of Malloy and Evelyn also calls for a direct and an indirect reaction.

In the direct reaction, serum that is free from hemolysis is obtained. To this is added Ehrlich's diazo reagent, which reacts with the bilirubin to form a pink to reddish purple color. The depth of color is measured in a colorimeter.

In the indirect reaction, the tube containing the serum and the diazo reagent is used. To this is added alcohol, which extracts the coloring matter. The depth of color is then measured in a colorimeter.

Procedure for bilirubin

The following general considerations pertain to the procedure for bilirubin.

1. Preparation of patient: must be fasting.
2. Preparation of blood: serum.
3. Preservation of serum: may be stored overnight in a refrigerator.
4. Precautions:
   a. Avoid excessive hemolysis of red cells, which may be caused (1) by failure to remove needle from syringe when transferring blood to test tube and (2) by allowing blood to stand for several hours in a warm area.
   b. Follow directions *exactly* as given in the procedure.

Malloy-Evelyn modification for determination of direct and total bilirubin by diazo reaction[3,4]

In 1883, Erhlich described the diazotizing reaction of bilirubin with a mixture of sulfanilic acid, hydrochloric acid, and sodium nitrite, resulting in the final violet compound called "azobilirubin."

Thirty years later, 1913, van den Bergh and Snapper quantitated this reaction. This bilirubin determination is known as the van den Bergh procedure using Ehrlich's diazo reagent.[5]

Malloy and Evelyn in 1937 published their adaptation of the above procedure to the photoelectric cell colorimeter.[3]

The serum is treated with Ehrlich's reagent, and the bilirubin in the serum reacts with the reagent, forming a red-violet (or purple) compound known as "azobilirubin." The intensity of the color is proportional to the bilirubin present in the serum and is measured photometrically against a standard.

Reagents needed

Methanol, Absolute, A.R. Grade	
Diazo Blank Solution	(C-40)
Solution A (Sulfanilic Acid, 0.1%)	(C-41)
Solution B, Stock (Sodium Nitrite, 5%)	(C-42)
Solution B, Working (Sodium Nitrite, 0.5%)	(C-43)
Working Diazo Reagent *(prepared just before using)*	

    Mix 0.3 ml. of working solution B with 10.0 ml. of solution A.

Precautions

1. Dilute the serum sample with water just before analysis. This is done to minimize the effect of the proteins slowly precipitating from the serum. Since "salt" interferes with the diazo reaction, do not use saline as a diluent.
2. The reagents must be added with exact measurements and in the sequence given in the method, or a precipitate will form, invalidating the test.
3. Bilirubin is sensitive to light (artificial and sunlight). If the serum is allowed to stand in a well-lighted area, there may be as much as a 50% drop in bilirubin concentration within 1 hour. Keep the serum in *total darkness* until analysis. Bilirubin in serum is considered stable under the following conditions[4]:
   a. In total darkness at room temperature, 2 days
   b. In refrigerator, 4 to 7 days
   c. If frozen, up to 3 months

Normal range

Direct levels	Less than 0.4 mg./100 ml. or mg.%
Total levels	Less than 0.8 mg./100 ml. or mg.%

Procedure

1. Set up two colorimeter tubes for each test. Label one *blank* and the other *unknown*. Pipet into *each* tube:
   a. 0.4 ml. of serum
   b. 3.6. ml. of distilled water
2. To the *blanks*, add 1.0 ml. of diazo blank solution. Mix.
3. To the *unknowns*, add 1.0 ml. of diazo reagent. Mix.
4. *Exactly* 1 minute later (use timer), read the *unknown* (tube 2) against its *blank* (tube 1) at 540 mμ wavelength. If only the total bilirubin is requested, omit this reading and proceed to the next step.

5. Pipet 5 ml. of fresh methanol to each tube and mix by inverting gently. Avoid bubbles. Old methanol has a tendency to cause decreased results.[6]
6. Let the tubes stand at room temperature for 15 minutes and read the unknowns against their blanks. This is the total bilirubin.
7. Caution: If the solutions are transferred to small cuvettes, bubbles may cling to the sides of the cuvettes. Clear or dislodge the bubbles by tapping the cuvette gently.

Note: This method may be converted to the micromethod by scaling down ten or twenty times. Since the final volume is 1/10 or 1/20 the volume in the macroprocedure, it is necessary to use an instrument adapted for microcuvettes.

Calculation

Example: The bilirubin standard has a value of 5 mg./100 ml. Since 0.4 ml. of the serum standard is used in the analysis, there is 0.02 mg. of bilirubin in the 0.4 ml. of serum.

A_1 = Absorbance of sample at 1 minute
A_s = Absorbance of standard at 15 minutes
A_t = Absorbance of sample at 15 minutes

$$\frac{A_1}{2A_s} \times 0.02 \times \frac{100}{0.4} =$$

$$\frac{A_1}{A_s} \times 2.5 = \text{Mg. of bilirubin/100 ml. at 1 minute or } \textit{direct bilirubin}$$

$$\frac{A_t}{A_s} \times 0.02 \times \frac{100}{0.4} =$$

$$\frac{A_t}{A_s} \times 5 = \text{Mg. of } \textit{total bilirubin}\text{/100 ml.}$$

Total bilirubin − Direct bilirubin = Indirect bilirubin

Recommended standardization[7,8]

The need for a reliable bilirubin standard has become most evident in recent years. There is a more knowledgeable understanding of the severe jaundice caused by Rh and ABO incompatibility between a mother and her infant. Exchange transfusions are used to keep the bilirubin below 20 mg./100 ml. in full-term infants and below 18 mg./100 ml. in premature babies. Determining the need for the exchange is very dependent upon the bilirubin result.

There has been great variation from one laboratory to another. In order to standardize the method and obtain a uniform bilirubin standard, a subcommittee of the American Academy of Pediatrics[*] has made a study of various types of standards in use. The standard recommended was a crystalline bilirubin, defined in terms of its solubility and color intensity in chloroform. The color intensity must be read under strictly controlled conditions of temperature, light, weight, volume, wavelength, optical density, and light path.

Obviously, most laboratories do not have all the ideal conditions along with the proper spectrophotometer for measuring the color intensity (molar absorptivity). Various manufacturers[†] have bilirubin standards in serum that meet

---

[*]The Joint Bilirubin Committee is composed of members from the American Academy of Pediatrics, the College of American Pathologists, the American Association of Clinical Chemists, and the National Institutes of Health.
[†]Dade Reagents, Miami, Fla.; Hyland Laboratories, Los Angeles, Calif.; and Warner-Chilcott, Morris Plains, N. J.

the requirements suggested by the committee. These are more stable, uniform, and accurate than the standards most hospital laboratories are able to prepare. The controls are made under rigid quality control conditions, are assayed, and are then lyophilized. Lyophilizing is the process of quickly freezing the serum under unusually low temperatures and then using a high vacuum to dehydrate the frozen mass quickly. The product is stable under refrigeration. When reconstituted, the serum should be kept in the dark and used within 2 hours.

A calibration curve may be made with the lyophilized serum, or standards may be included with each group of bilirubin determinations.

BROMSULPHALEIN (BSP)

The discussion covers information significant to the student and procedure for the test.

Information significant to the student

When Bromsulphalein, an organic dye, is injected into the bloodstream, it is removed by the liver and is excreted into the bile. A healthy liver removes the dye at a faster rate than a diseased liver. Consequently, the rate of removal can be used as a test of liver function.

A commonly used method for the Bromsulphalein test is the procedure of Rosenthal and White, introduced in 1925. In this method, the patient is given 2 mg. of dye/kg. of body weight. The sterile solution of dye is injected into the patient's vein by the physician, special care being taken to see that a tourniquet is *not* used while the injection is being made.

Two samples of blood are taken, one 5 minutes after the injection and the other 30 minutes after the injection. Serum is obtained. Sodium hydroxide is added to bring out the color of the dye. The concentration of dye is then found either from a colorimeter reading or from a comparison with standards representing known quantities of Bromsulphalein.

With a healthy liver, the 5-minute sample of serum contains 20 to 50% of the dye and the 30-minute sample contains no dye. With a diseased liver, the 30-minute sample contains from 5 to 100% of the dye.

In 1939, MacDonald increased the amount to 5 mg. of dye/kg. of body weight. This measure is used almost exclusively because it increases the sensitivity of the test in detecting liver impairment. With the larger amount of dye injected, usually only one blood specimen is taken, 45 minutes later. Normally, less than 5% of the dye is retained 45 minutes after the injection.

In 1957, Seligson and co-workers introduced the use of an alkaline buffer to develop the color and an acid buffer for the blank. This was found to minimize errors caused by icterus, hemolysis, and lipemia. They also showed that free BSP has a different absorptivity and absorption peak than when it is bound to albumin as in serum. This was corrected by adding large amounts of the anion, *p*-toluene-sulfonate, to the alkaline buffer.

Procedure for Bromsulphalein (BSP)

The general considerations on the following page pertain to the procedure for Bromsulphalein.

1. Preparation of patient: must be fasting.
2. Preparation of blood: serum.
3. Preservation of serum: may be stored overnight in a refrigerator.
4. Precautions:
   a. If the patient has obstructive jaundice, this test should not be run, because the obstruction prevents the removal of dye and thus renders the test inaccurate.
   b. In some patients, the injected dye may cause chills, faintness, or headache. On rare occasions there may be a severe reaction. For this reason, the dye should be injected into the patient only by a physician.
   c. Follow directions *exactly* as given in the procedure.
5. Even though the technician should not inject BSP dye, he should be able to calculate the amount needed. Weigh the patient and calculate the amount of dye to be injected (5 mg./kg.) by the following formula:

$$\frac{\text{Weight in pounds}}{22} = \text{Ml. of dye needed}$$

6. Table 27 shows the amount of dye needed according to the patient's weight in pounds.
7. Exactly 45 minutes after the injection of the dye, obtain a blood specimen from the arm not injected. Allow blood to clot, centrifuge, and remove the serum.

Table 27. BSP dye dosages

Patient weight in lb.	BSP dye in ml.,* at 5 mg./kg.
60	2.7
70	3.2
80	3.6
90	4.1
100	4.5
110	5.0
120	5.5
130	5.9
140	6.4
150	6.8
160	7.3
170	7.7
180	8.2
190	8.6
200	9.1
210	9.5
220	10.0

*The amount of dye is given to the nearest 0.1 ml.

Seligson, Marino, and Dodson method for sulfobromophthalein (BSP)[9]

Serum is diluted with an alkaline buffer and the absorbance is measured at 580 mμ. Acid buffer is then added and the absorbance measured. The difference of absorbance represents the BSP present.*

---

*Available from Hynson, Westcott, & Dunning, Baltimore, Md.; or from Dade Reagents, Miami, Fla.

Reagents needed

|---|---|
Alkaline Buffer, pH 10.6 to 10.7	(C-44)
Acid Reagent, 2 M NaH_2PO_4	(C-45)
BSP Standard, 5 mg./100 ml.°	(C-46)

Procedure

1. Prepare the following tubes:
   Standard (50% retention standard)
   a. Pipet 1.0 ml. of standard into a colorimeter or test tube.
   b. Add 7.0 ml. of alkaline buffer.
   c. Mix.
   Unknown (serum)
   a. Pipet 1.0 ml. of serum into a colorimeter or test tube.
   b. Add 7.0 ml. of alkaline buffer.
   c. Mix.
2. Read the absorbance of both tubes against a water blank at a wavelength of 580 mμ or a filter of similar wavelength.
3. To the *unknown* tube:
   a. Pipet 0.2 ml. of acid reagent.
   b. Mix.
   c. Read the absorbance against a water blank at 580 mμ.

Calculation

$$\frac{\text{Absorbance of alkaline buffer} - \text{Absorbance of acid buffer}}{\text{Absorbance of standard}} \times 50 = \% \text{BSP}$$

Make the following corrections for body weight[10]:

110 to 149 lb. Add 1% retention
150 to 169 lb. No correction
170 to 189 lb. Subtract 1% retention
190 to 279 lb. Subtract 3% retention

The color of the Seligson method is stable for at least 24 hours and obeys Beer's law up to 100% retention.

Normal values

For dosage of 5 mg./kg. of BSP:

Time	Retention
30 minutes	Less than 10%
45 minutes	Less than 6%
60 minutes	Less than 3%

BSP is eliminated faster in infants and children than in adults.

THYMOL TURBIDITY

The discussion covers information significant to the student, procedure for the test, and directions for calibrating a colorimeter.

Information significant to the student

When the serum of a normal person is added to a buffered thymol solution, no appreciable precipitation occurs. However, when the serum of a patient with liver disease is added to a buffered thymol solution, a definite precipitation is produced. Consequently, the procedure can be used as a test of liver function.

°Diluted standard is stable for 1 week.

The precipitation (turbidity) reaction is not completely understood. It is activated with an increase in the gamma (∂) globulin and is inhibited with a quantitative or qualitative decrease or change in the albumin.

The method of Maclagan, modified by Shank and Hoagland, is commonly used. In this method, serum is obtained. To this is added a thymol solution which has been buffered to a pH of 7.55. After 30 minutes, any turbidity produced is measured in a colorimeter or compared with a standard.

The normal values for the thymol turbidity test are 0 to 5 S.H. units. These values are exceeded in the following diseases:

Infectious hepatitis
Cirrhosis of the liver
Cancer of the liver
Diabetes
Nephrosis
Weil's disease
Parenchymatous liver disease

Procedure for thymol turbidity test

The following general considerations pertain to the procedure for the thymol turbidity test.

1. Preparation of patient: must be fasting.
2. Preparation of blood: serum.
3. Preservation of serum: may be stored overnight in a refrigerator.
4. Precautions:
    a. Follow the directions *exactly* as given in procedure.
    b. Avoid using lipemic serum.

Shank-Hoagland modification of Maclagan method[11,12]

To obtain a visual comparison of turbidity, the original Maclagan method used Kingsbury's gelatin standards. These permanent standards were also used for protein determinations in urine with sulfosalicylic acid.[13]

Shank and Hoagland adapted the method for a photometer or spectrophotometer by using $BaSO_4$ suspensions for standardization and reading the turbidities.

If the pH of the thymol-barbital buffer used is changed from a pH 7.80 to a pH 7.55, the sensitivity of the test is greater for detecting hepatocellular dysfunction, without an introduction of false positives.

Temperature control is important because the turbidity of the test decreases with an increase in the temperature. The pH of the thymol buffer also decreases with a temperature increase, affecting the sensitivity of the test. A maximum error of 10% may be found if the temperature deviates beyond $\pm$ 3° C.; therefore the safe range is between 22° and 28° C. If necessary, use a controlled temperature water bath at 25° C.[12]

Reagents needed

Thymol-Barbital Buffer, pH 7.55	(C-47)

Normal values

Shank-Hoagland units (buffer pH 7.55)	Range 0 to 5 units
Shank-Hoagland units (buffer pH 7.80)	Range 0 to 4 units

Procedure

1. Pipet 6.0 ml. of thymol-barbital buffer into two 19 x 150 mm. cuvettes.
2. Pipet 0.1 ml. of water into the "blank" cuvette containing the thymol buffer. Mix.
3. Pipet 0.1 ml. of serum into the "unknown" cuvette containing the thymol buffer. Mix.
4. Let the tubes stand for 30 minutes at a temperature of $25° \pm 3°$ C. Use a controlled temperature water bath if necessary.
5. Set the blank at 100% T and read the unknown in percent transmission at 650 mμ.

Calculation

The calculations may be done by reading from a calibration curve or by using a constant (K), which is averaged from three independent batches of barium chloride reagent.

Note: Since this method uses a 0.0962 *normal* solution of barium chloride, the results are recorded in Shank-Hoagland units. If the method used a 0.0962 *molar* solution of barium chloride, the results would be recorded in Maclagan units. Two Shank-Hoagland units equal one Maclagan unit.

The technician may wonder why emphasis on the molarity and normality of the barium chloride solution is made.

In 1946, Shank and Hoagland[12] published the method of mixing barium chloride with dilute sulfuric acid for the barium sulfate suspensions. A misprint using the symbol N (normality) instead of M (molarity) occurred, resulting in the values for the unknowns being twice the results of the original method and the standards being only half the value expected. Although the authors corrected the error in reprints that were requested, many established this now-popular method in their laboratories, using the 0.0962 normality value. The Commission on Liver Disease of the Armed Forces Epidemiological Board has recommended that Shank-Hoagland units be adopted.

Calibration curve

Make the following reagents:

1. Barium chloride standard, 0.0962 normal
   a. Weigh 1.173 gm. of barium chloride ($BaCl_2 \cdot 2H_2O$) and place into a 100 ml. volumetric flask.
   b. Dissolve and dilute to mark with water (distilled).
2. Sulfuric acid, 0.2 N
   a. In a volumetric flask, dilute 6 ml. of concentrated sulfuric acid to 1 liter with distilled water. *Caution:* add the acid to the water and then dilute to 1 liter.
   b. Standardize to 0.2 N.

Table 28. Chart for thymol turbidity calibration

Units	$BaSO_4$ (ml.)	H_2SO_4 (ml.)	% T (average of three readings)
0	0	10.00	
5	1.35	8.65	
10	2.70	7.30	
15	4.05	5.95	
20	5.40	4.60	
25	6.75	3.25	
30	8.10	1.90	
35	9.45	0.55	

3. Stock barium sulfate
   a. Pipet 5.0 ml. of the barium chloride standard into a 100 ml. volumetric flask. Chill to 10° C.
   b. Dilute to mark with cold (10° C.) 0. 2 N sulfuric acid.
   c. Mix well.

Set up the tubes as indicated in Table 28 and read each tube three times against the zero standard at a wavelength of 660 mμ. Average each set of readings and draw the curve. Use semilog paper when plotting % T, or linear paper for O.D.

Obtain the constant (K) by converting the % T readings to O.D. (see Table 19):

$$K = \frac{Units}{O.D.}$$

Obtain an average K value from the readings and use this to calculate the thymol turbidity units of serum specimens:

O.D. × K = Thymol turbidity units

THYMOL FLOCCULATION TEST[14]

The physiological significance of this test is essentially the same as that of the test referred to as the "c.c.floc."

Sometimes the physician requests a thymol flocculation test. It is done by extending the reading of the thymol turbidity test done quantitatively. After the thymol turbidity has been done, let the tubes sit for 24 hours. If any flocculation occurs, it is recorded as 1+, 2+, 3+, or 4+. Normally there is no flocculation.

CEPHALIN-CHOLESTEROL FLOCCULATION[15-17]

The discussion covers information significant to the student and the procedure for the test.

Information significant to the student

In health, there is a balance between the albumin and gamma globulin of the serum. In liver disease, however, this balance is disturbed. This disturbed balance produces a precipitation in a solution of cephalin and cholesterol.

For the test, the procedure of Hanger is commonly used. Two test tubes are prepared. One tube contains the patient's serum plus physiological saline solution and the emulsion of cephalin and cholesterol. The other tube contains only physiological saline solution and the emulsion of cephalin and cholesterol. This tube serves as a control. Both tubes are put aside and inspected for flocculation at the end of 24 and 48 hours.

A normal value is zero to 1 plus. In liver disease, there are varying degrees of flocculation. These flocculations are reported as 1+, 2+, 3+, and 4+.

Procedure for cephalin-cholesterol flocculation

The following general considerations pertain to the procedure for the cephalin-cholesterol flocculation test:

1. Preparation of patient: does not have to be fasting.
2. Preparation of blood: serum.
3. Preservation of serum: fresh serum should be used, if possible; however, serum may be refrigerated overnight; frozen serum may be used if it is thawed quickly at 45° C. to avoid alteration of the proteins.

4. Precautions:
    a. Unclean glassware may produce a false flocculation.
    b. Follow the *exact* directions given in the procedure.

Hanger method

Reagents needed

Ether
Physiological Saline, 0.9%   (C-34)

Procedure

1. Prepare a *stock* ether solution of cepahlin-cholesterol as follows. Vials containing the dried cephalin and cholesterol may be purchased from the Wilson Laboratories or the Difco Laboratories. If the vial containing the dried cephalin and cholesterol is from the Wilson Laboratories, add 8 ml. of ether and mix. If the vial containing the dried cephalin and cholesterol is from the Difco Laboratories, add 5 ml. of ether and mix. This stock solution is stable if kept in a refrigerator.

2. Prepare the *emulsion* of cephalin and cholesterol as follows. Place 30 ml. of distilled water in a 50 ml. beaker. Note the height of the water in the beaker and mark the spot with a marking pencil. Add 5 more ml. of distilled water. Heat to 65° to 70° C. While stirring the distilled water, slowly add 1 ml. of the stock ether solution of cephalin and cholesterol. Heat slowly to boiling. Let simmer until the final volume is 30 ml. as noted by the mark on the beaker. Allow to cool to room temperature. Examine the emulsion in a strong light. If there is a precipitate, centrifuge the emulsion at high speed for 20 to 25 minutes. If a button of lipid material has risen to the top, gently push it aside and remove the smooth, milky supernatant emulsion by aspiration. This emulsion, when stored in a refrigerator, is stable for 1 week.

3. Pipet 0.2 ml. of serum into a 12 ml. conical-tipped centrifuge tube. Add 4.0 ml. of saline. Each series of tests should include an emulsion control (4.0 ml. of saline) and a negative and positive control serum when possible. Add 1.0 ml. of cephalin-cholesterol emulsion to each tube, including the emulsion control. Mix and stopper. Place the tubes in a dark cabinet at 25° ± 3° C. and read the reaction at the end of 24 hours (and at 48 hours, if requested). The degree of flocculation usually increases slightly in the second 24-hour period; i.e., a 1+ may become a 2+, etc. Normal sera also show this shift. Since there is no concrete evidence that a 48-hour reading increases the accuracy of the test and since this would produce a 1-day delay in reporting results, a single reading at 24 hours is believed to be sufficient.[4,18]

    The following alternate procedure may be used: place the tubes in the dark at 37° C. for 3 hours, then centrifuge at about 3000 R.P.M. for 5 minutes, and read flocculation. Results obtained after 3 hours at 37° C. agree very closely with the results obtained after 24 hours at 25° C.[4,16]

4. Read the reaction as follows:
        Negative. No flocculation or precipitation
        1+ Trace of flocculation or precipitation
        2+ Definite flocculation or precipitation
        3+ Heavy flocculation or precipitation, but with the supernatant remaining turbid
        4+ Precipitation complete and supernatant fluid clear
The emulsion control should be negative.

Normal range

0 to 1+

STUDENTS' SUMMARY FOR LIVER FUNCTION TESTS

The significant information consists of the following:
Methods of analysis and synopsis of procedures
Normal and abnormal values

Methods of analysis and synopsis of procedures

Test	Method	Synopsis of procedure
Icterus index	Meulengracht	1. Obtain serum 2. Dilute with saline or buffer solution 3. Measure yellow color in colorimeter or compare with standard potassium dichromate solution
	Newberger	1. Obtain serum 2. Add acetone to remove interfering substances 3. Centrifuge 4. Measure yellow color in colorimeter or compare with standard potassium dichromate solution
Bilirubin	Malloy-Evelyn	*Direct reaction:* 1. Obtain serum 2. Add Ehrlich's diazo reagent which reacts with bilirubin to form red-violet (or purple) color 3. Measure in colorimeter *Indirect reaction:* 1. Add alcohol to above tube to extract coloring matter 2. Measure in colorimeter
Bromsulphalein	Seligson, Marino, and Dodson	1. The physician injects the proper dosage of dye into patient's vein 2. Remove samples of blood 45 minutes after injection 3. Obtain serum 4. Dilute serum with alkaline buffer and measure absorbance 5. Add acid buffer and measure absorbance 6. Calculate
Thymol turbidity	Maclagan (modified by Shank and Hoagland)	1. Obtain serum 2. Add buffered (pH 7.55) thymol solution 3. Let stand 30 minutes 4. Measure turbidity in colorimeter or compare with standard
Cephalin-cholesterol flocculation	Hanger	1. Obtain serum 2. Add saline 3. Add emulsion of cephalin and cholesterol 4. Prepare control of saline and emulsion of cephalin and cholesterol 5. Read degree of flocculation at 24 and 48 hours

Normal and abnormal values

Test	Normal values	When increased	When decreased
Icterus index	4 to 6 units	Obstructive jaundice Hemolytic jaundice Hepatic jaundice Infectious hepatitis Pernicious anemia	
Bilirubin	0.2 to 0.8 mg./100 ml. of serum	Same as above	
Bromsulphalein	30-minute sample contains no dye	30-minute sample contains 5 to 100% of dye in liver disease	
Thymol turbidity	0.4 to 4.0 units	Infectious hepatitis Cirrhosis of liver Cancer of liver	
Cephalin-cholesterol flocculation	0 to 1+	Liver disease	

REFERENCES

1. Frankel, S., and Reitman, S., editors: Gradwohl's clinical laboratory methods and diagnosis, ed. 6, St. Louis, 1963, The C. V. Mosby Co.
2. Hawk, P. B., Oser, B. L., and Summerson, W. H.: Practical physiological chemistry, ed. 13, New York, 1954, The Blakiston Co., Inc.
3. Malloy, H. T., and Evelyn, K. A.: The determination of bilirubin with the photoelectric colorimeter, J. Biol. Chem. **119**:481, 1937.
4. Henry, R. J.: Clinical chemistry; principles and technics, New York, 1964, Hoeber Medical Division, Harper & Row, Publishers.
5. Page, L. B., and Culver, P. J., editors: A syllabus of laboratory examinations in clinical diagnosis, rev. ed., Cambridge, Mass., 1961, Harvard University Press.
6. Michaelsson, M.: Bilirubin determination in serum and urine, Scandinav. J. Clin. Lab. Invest. **13** (supp. 56): 1, 1961.
7. Gambino, S. R.: Bilirubin measurement in the newborn: need for a common reference standard in serum, Hosp. Topics, Feb., 1964.
8. Committee report: Recommendation on a uniform bilirubin standard, Clin. Chem. **8**:405, 1962.
9. Seligson, D., Marino, J., and Dodson, E.: The determination of sulfobromophthalein in serum, Clin. Chem. **3**:638, 1957.
10. Zieve, L., and Hill, E.: An evaluation of factors influencing the discriminative effectiveness of a group of liver function tests, Gastroenterology **28**:766, 1955.
11. Maclagan, N. F.: The thymol turbidity test as an indicator of liver dysfunction, Brit. J. Exper. Path. **25**:234, 1944.
12. Shank, R. E., and Hoagland, C. L.: A modified method for the quantitative determination of the thymol turbidity reaction of serum, J. Biol. Chem. **162**:133, 1946.
13. Kingsbury, F. B., Clark, C. P., Williams, G., and Post, A. L.: The rapid determination of albumin in urine, J. Lab. & Clin. Med. **2**:981, 1926.
14. Annino, J. S.: Clinical chemistry; principles and procedures, ed. 3, Boston, 1964, Little, Brown & Co.
15. Hanger, F. M.: The flocculation of cephalin-cholesterol emulsions by pathological sera, Tr. A. Am. Phys. **53**:148, 1938.

16. Bunch, L. D.: A rapid cephalin-cholesterol flocculation test, Am. J. Clin. Path. **28:**111, 1957.
17. Knowlton, M.: Cephalin-cholesterol flocculation test. In Seligson, D., editor: Standard methods of clinical chemistry, vol. 2, New York, 1958, Academic Press, Inc.
18. Reinhold, J. G.: Flocculation tests and their application to the study of liver disease. In Sobotka, H., and Stewart, C. P., editors: Advances in clinical chemistry, vol. 3, New York, 1960, Academic Press, Inc.

Chapter 12

Lipids

Lipids[1-3] may be defined as substances or compounds having the following characteristics: (1) insoluble in water; (2) soluble in one or more organic solvents such as benzene, chloroform, ether, and acetone; and (3) related to fatty acids by being either an actual or a potential ester.

In the chemistry laboratory, the technician's main interest is with the serum, plasma, and feces. Serum or plasma (blood) lipids consist of the following: cholesterol, cholesterol esters, phospholipids, triglycerides, fatty acids, and neutral fat. The methods for complete lipid studies are tedious and time-consuming. This chapter will consist of the following:

> Total lipids in serum
> Total cholesterol and cholesterol esters
> Fecal lipids

The method chosen for the total serum lipids can easily be done in a routine laboratory. At the present time there is really no completely satisfactory method for serum lipids. Most of the methods now employed in laboratories use part of or all of the following steps: extraction, evaporation, filtration, weighing, colorimetry, and purification.

Around 1918, Bang developed a procedure for oxidizing the lipids; he then titrated the excess dichromate with sodium thiosulfate. Bloor, taking this method, first quantitated the oxidation and later modified the method to a colorimetric procedure. The method has been further modified. Bloor's method or one of the many modifications is now in use in many of the laboratories. The gravimetric method of analysis was developed by Sperry and Brand. This employs weighing and purifying in the absence of auto-oxidation.

TOTAL LIPIDS IN SERUM[4,5]

Elevated results may occur when patients are on a fatty diet or in patients with hyperlipemia due to nephrosis, diabetes, arthritis, or hypothyroidism. The patient should be fasting when the blood is drawn.

It is not known whether the fat extraction is complete or whether the released lipid material is completely free of nonlipid contaminants. The reagent gives reproducible results and recoveries. According to Brandstein and Castellano, the method, for clinical purposes, conforms to Bragdon's colorimetric method and to the method of Sperry and Brand. The Schain method was compared against these two methods.

Schain test method

A quick and simple method that may be utilized in the routine diagnostic laboratory is the method based on the Schain test for butterfat, employing detergents in the form of a single reagent that releases the lipids from the serum. The complete test is done in the Babcock skim milk bottle and the result is read directly from the calibrated neck of the bottle. Table 29 can be used to convert the readings to mg.%.

The total time for the test, run in duplicate, is 30 minutes, of which 3 to 5 minutes is actual working time. This method is reproducible and is accurate

Table 29. Total lipid conversion table*

Scale readings	Mg. %	Scale readings	Mg. %
1	35	26	910
2	70	27	945
3	105	28	980
4	140	29	1015
5	175	30	1050
6	210	31	1085
7	245	32	1120
8	280	33	1155
9	315	34	1190
10	350	35	1225
11	385	36	1260
12	420	37	1295
13	455	38	1330
14	490	39	1365
15	525	40	1400
16	560	41	1435
17	595	42	1470
18	630	43	1505
19	665	44	1540
20	700	45	1575
21	735	46	1610
22	770	47	1645
23	805	48	1680
24	840	49	1715
25	875	50	1750

*Scale readings are multiplied by 35, giving the mg.% for the total lipid. Instead of rounding off the scale reading to the next number, three fractions are used in calculating the mg.%. Add the mg.% of the fraction to the mg.% of the whole number. The fractions are not marked but are ¼, ½, and ¾ of the way to the next number. The mg.% values for these three fractions are, respectively, 8.8, 17.5, and 26.3. In the example given here, therefore, a scale reading of 25 and ½, the reading in mg.% would be 875 + 17.5 = 892.5 or 893 mg.% total lipid.

within $\pm$ 50 mg./100 ml. of blood. This is based on recoveries within the total lipid range of 600 to 1750 mg./100 ml. of blood.

Normal range

600 to 800 mg.% (mg./100 ml. blood)

Special apparatus needed

Babcock skim milk test bottle (Kimble No. 530)

Reagents needed

Schain Test Reagent*

This reagent consists of a saline solution of a nonionic detergent (alkylphenylpolyethylene glycol ether) in a delicate balance with an anionic detergent (dioctyl sodium phosphate). Added to this reagent is an oil red O that colors the released lipids for easier reading. The functions of the two detergents are as follows: (1) the nonionic detergent releases the lipids quantitatively from the serum and (2) the anionic detergent removes the interfering substances.

Physiological Saline, 0.9% (C-34)

Physiological Saline with 10% Methanol (C-48)

Precautions

1. The serum must be at room temperature and be mixed just before using, since lipid materials tend to separate upon standing for a period of time.
2. Great care and accuracy must be maintained in pipetting the serum into the Babcock bottle.
3. Use caution in underlaying the serum with the Schain test reagent so the serum layer will float. If the 20 ml. are introduced too fast or the bottle is jostled, the serum layer will disperse into the reagent, resulting in poor separation of the lipid from the serum and giving low results.
4. Heat for 10 minutes *exactly* in a boiling water bath.
   a. Heating over 10 minutes will give falsely high results, because the detergent has a fat-miscible component that will add (or attach) to the fat layer of the serum.
   b. Heating under 10 minutes or at a low temperature will result in low readings, since the temperature or time is then not sufficient for the lipid to separate from the protein.
5. The structure of the Babcock bottle is such that small fat globules may be trapped behind the angle of the delivery tube; so the bottle must be held at a 45-degree angle and tapped gently with the rubber end of a pencil to release the particles.

Procedure

1. Thoroughly mix the serum to obtain an even dispersion of lipids.
2. Pipet (volumetric pipet) 2.0 ml. of serum into the Babcock bottle, which is held at a 45-degree angle. *Do each test in duplicate.*
3. Pipet (volumetric pipet) 2.0 ml. of physiological saline into the bottle, carefully washing down the side arm of the bottle to remove any remaining serum.
4. Gently but thoroughly mix the serum and saline.
5. Pipet (volumetric pipet or buret) 20 ml. of Schain's reagent, dropwise, until the mixture is above the opening of the delivery tube. If this is done correctly, the serum layer will float on the surface of the reagent. After the mixture is above the opening of the delivery tube the reagent may be added slowly instead of dropwise.

---

*May be obtained from Merck & Co., Inc., Rahway, N. J. (Lipitest), or from most laboratory supply companies.

6. Let the test stand at room temperature for 10 to 15 minutes to allow the serum to disperse through the reagent.
7. Place the bottle in a boiling water bath for exactly 10 minutes. Be sure that the water level is above the reagent level and that enough water is boiling so there will be continuous boiling despite the immersion of the bottles.
8. At the end of 10 minutes, immediately transfer the bottles to a room temperature water bath for 2 minutes.
9. Place the saline-alcohol mixture in a small beaker and at the end of the 2 minutes add in three steps (having about a 10-second delay between additions) enough saline-alcohol to raise the dark red lipid material into the calibrated neck of the bottle.
10. Tilt the bottle to a 45-degree angle and tap it gently to release any lipid particles clinging to the angle of the delivery tube.
11. Hand whirl the bottle in a centrifugal motion twenty-five times.
12. Allow the test to stand for 5 minutes.
13. Read the graduated column to the nearest one fourth of a division. The duplicate tests must read within two scale divisions.

Calculation

1. Multiply the scale reading by 35 to obtain mg.% total lipids. Refer to Table 29.
Note: The Babcock bottles were calibrated in the following way. Weighed increments of Lipomul were added to a sample of human serum and total lipids were determined. The value derived for each scale unit was 35 mg.% of vegetable lipid. Further tests were done to validate the 35 mg.% per scale unit.
2. Elevated samples over 50 units (1750 mg.%) may be diluted with normal serum of a known lipid value and calculated in the same manner as the following example:
    The normal serum has a value of 750 mg.% total lipid.
    The abnormal serum has an unknown value above 1750 mg.% total lipid.
Pipet into the Babcock bottle 1.5 ml. of the normal serum and 0.5 ml. of the abnormal serum. Continue the test according to the directions. The final reading of the diluted serum is 1505 mg.% total lipid. Calculate as follows:

$$\frac{\text{Mg.\%} \times \text{Volume of mixture} - \text{Mg.\%} \times \text{Volume of known}}{\text{Volume of unknown serum}}$$
$$= \text{Mg.\% of unknown (abnormal) serum}$$
$$\frac{(1505 \times 2) - (750 \times 1.5)}{0.5} = \frac{1885}{0.5}$$
$$= 3770 \text{ mg.\% total lipid content of abnormal serum}$$

TOTAL CHOLESTEROL AND CHOLESTEROL ESTERS[6,7]

The discussion covers information significant to the student, procedures for the test, and directions for calculating results.

Information significant to the student

Cholesterol is a fatlike substance that is found in blood, bile, and brain tissue. It serves as a precursor of bile acids and various steroid hormones.

Although the metabolism of cholesterol is not clearly understood, the technician should be acquainted with the known factors. We will not get involved too deeply.

Cholesterol is a very important member of a group of substances called

Table 30. Conditions accompanied by abnormal total cholesterol values

When increased		When decreased
Obstructive jaundice	Lipemia	Pernicious anemia
Nephrosis	Celiac disease	Hyperthyroidism
Diabetes	Leukemia	Severe infections
Hypothyroidism	Multiple sclerosis	Epilepsy
Xanthomatosis	Pregnancy	Gaucher's disease
Eclampsia	Aplastic anemia	Inanition
		Intestinal obstruction

sterols. Sterols are complex hydroaromatic alcohols distributed throughout all living matter. After extensive research, some evidence has shown that the animal sterol (cholesterol) is a mixture of two or more sterols that differ in respect to their biological and physiochemical properties.

The animal sterols are probably absorbed from the intestinal tract along with neutral fats and other lipids. They form esters with the fatty acids and thus act as a vehicle for their carriage into the bloodstream. Some cholesterol is formed in the disintegration of red blood cells, and some is synthesized by the body but just "where" it is synthesized is unknown.

The cholesterol is more or less evenly divided between the plasma and the erythrocytes. In the blood cells and the tissue cells the cholesterol is almost all free, while in the serum about 60 to 70% is present as cholesterol esters of fatty acids. The serum and plasma studies have more clinical value than those of whole blood.

Normally, the serum cholesterol is relatively constant. However, disorders such as pernicious anemia may lower the cholesterol level to 50 mg./100 ml. Hemolytic jaundice produces a low cholesterol level, while obstructive jaundice maintains an elevated level of cholesterol.

Total cholesterol consists of free cholesterol and cholesterol esters. In discussions, when the word "cholesterol" is used by itself, it implies total cholesterol.

The normal values for total cholesterol are 140 to 250 mg./100 ml. of serum. Increased or decreased values may be found in those conditions listed in Table 30. Abnormal values are of primary interest in the disorders given in italics.

The normal value for cholesterol esters is 60 to 70% of the total cholesterol. Decreased values are found in diseases of the liver.

In clinical work it is sometimes necessary to determine free cholesterol and cholesterol esters separately instead of total cholesterol only. This is made possible by the fact that free cholesterol unites with digitonin to form cholesterol digitonide. This is insoluble in acetone ether, in which the cholesterol esters are freely soluble. The following three methods are discussed:

> Bloor method
> Schoenheimer-Sperry method
> Saifer-Kammerer method

Bloor method

A commonly used method for the determination of total cholesterol and cholesterol esters is the method of Bloor. A brief discussion follows.

To determine the total cholesterol, serum is obtained. An alcohol-ether mixture is added to extract the cholesterol. The alcohol-ether is driven off by evaporating just to dryness on a hot plate. The cholesterol is then taken up with chloroform. Acetic anhydride and sulfuric acid are added. This produces a green color (the Liebermann-Burchardt reaction). The depth of color is measured in a colorimeter.

To determine cholesterol esters, serum is obtained. An alcohol-ether mixture is added to extract both the free cholesterol and the cholesterol esters. This is then filtered. To the filtrate is added an alcohol solution of digitonin. This precipitates the free cholesterol as cholesterol digitonin. The alcohol-ether is driven off by evaporating just to dryness on a hot plate.

The cholesterol esters in the residue are taken up with petroleum ether, the cholesterol digitonin being insoluble in petroleum ether. The ether is driven off on a hot plate. The cholesterol esters are then taken up with chloroform. To this is added acetic anhydride and sulfuric acid. A green color (the Liebermann-Burchardt reaction) is produced. The depth of color is measured in a colorimeter.

Schoenheimer-Sperry method

The cholesterol and proteins are extracted by boiling solvents. The esters are then saponified or split into the free form by incubation with potassium hydroxide. The excess KOH is then neutralized with acetic acid. Digitonin, a complex polysaccharide that combines with free cholesterol to form an insoluble compound (cholesterol digitonide), is added to the filtrate that precipitates only free cholesterol. It is also added to the saponified filtrate that precipitates the total cholesterol. The two are left standing overnight to allow complete precipitation of cholesterol digitonide. Any impurities are washed out by acetone-ether, which also takes the precipitate from an aqueous medium to a completely dry state. Since the cholesterol digitonide is sparingly soluble, the precipitates are preheated in order to facilitate its solution in acetic acid. Acetic anhydride-sulfuric acid reagent is added to develop the color. After 30 minutes in the dark, the depth of color is read in a spectrophotometer and compared with standards.

Saifer-Kammerer method

The cholesterol and proteins are extracted by heated acetic anhydride-dioxane. Sulfuric acid is added to an aliquot of the extract, producing a green color, the Leibermann-Burchardt reaction. The color is developed in 18 minutes, and the concentration is read against a standard with a colorimeter.

Procedures for total cholesterol and cholesterol esters

The following general considerations pertain to the procedures for total cholesterol and cholesterol esters:

1. Preparation of patient: must be fasting.
2. Preparation of blood: serum.
3. Preservation of serum: may be stored for a few hours in a refrigerator.
4. Precautions:
   a. Before use, all pipets and other glassware must be dry because moisture interferes with the color development.
   b. During evaporation of the alcohol-ether, scorching of the residue

must not occur. It is better to remove the tube while the residue
is slightly moist than to allow scorching to take place.

   c. Follow the *exact* directions given in the procedure.

Schoenheimer-Sperry method for cholesterol and esters[8]

The total cholesterol method has approximately ± 5% accuracy, while an
approximate ± 2% accuracy may be obtained with the percentage of esters.
This accuracy is, of course, dependent upon the technician's willingness to use
good technique and to resist taking shortcuts. Although this is a very accurate
method, it is also very exacting.

Reagents needed

Acetone-Alcohol Mixture	(C-49)
Digitonin Solution	(C-50)
Acetic Acid, 10% (v/v)	(C-51)
Acetone-Ether Mixture	(C-52)
Potassium Hydroxide Solution	(C-53)
Phenolphthalein, 1%	(C-54)

Acetic Acid, Glacial
    Use only the highest purity.
Acetic Anhydride-Sulfuric Acid Reagent
    Make just before using. Do *not* use reagent if over 1 hour old. Place
    20 ml. of acetic anhydride in a glass-stoppered cylinder and chill in
    an ice water bath. When thoroughly chilled, cautiously add 1.0 ml. of
    concentrated sulfuric acid, mix gently, and cool. After cooling, stopper
    the cylinder, shake vigorously, and return to the ice bath. Keep in
    the ice bath during use. Larger quantities may be made if needed,
    using the same proportions.

Procedure

1. Into a 25 ml. Pyrex graduated mixing cylinder, pipet 1.0 ml. of serum.
2. Blow into the tube 10 ml. of acetone-alcohol solution.
3. Place tubes into boiling water bath and bring contents to boil; remove
   from bath.
4. Use glass stirring rods to break up protein clumps.
5. Cool to room temperature in a water bath at room temperature.
6. Dilute to 25 ml. with acetone-alcohol.
7. Filter into 125 ml. Erlenmeyer flask and stopper to eliminate evaporation.

Total cholesterol

1. Into a 12 ml. heavy-duty centrifuge tube, pipet 4.0 ml. of the above
   filtrate.
2. To each tube add 3 drops of 50% KOH. Stir with glass stirring rods
   until thoroughly mixed. (Note: The rods are bent on one end so they
   can hang onto the side of the tube while the test is incubating.)
3. Incubate the tubes at 37° C. for 45 minutes. Mix the solutions once or
   twice during the incubation.
4. After the incubation, add 2 ml. of acetone-alcohol solution and 1 drop
   of phenolphthalein to each tube.
5. Add 10% (v/v) acetic acid dropwise with mixing until the pink color
   completely disappears.
6. Add 1 drop of acetic acid in excess.

Free cholesterol

1. Into a 15 ml. centrifuge tube, pipet 8.0 ml. of filtrate.
2. Add 1 drop of 10% (v/v) acetic acid. Mix with glass stirring rods.

Total and free cholesterol

Both tests may now be continued together.

1. Pipet 3.0 ml. of digitonin into the total cholesterol tubes and 4.0 ml. of digitonin into the free cholesterol tubes. (This is 0.5 ml. of digitonin for every 1.0 ml. of acetone-alcohol.)
2. Mix well with stirring rods.
3. Cover tubes to eliminate light, and let stand overnight to allow complete precipitation of the cholesterol digitonide. (The digitonin forms a 1:1 complex of cholesterol digitonide with the cholesterol.)
4. The next day, remove the stirring rods and hang them on a numbered rod, with the number corresponding to the tube number. This equipment can be made by taping numbers onto a glass or metal rod attached to a ring stand or similar supporting object.
5. Centrifuge tubes for 15 minutes, at 3000 RPM.
6. Pour off (decant) the supernatant from the packed precipitate.
7. Pipet 4.0 ml. of acetone-ether into each tube, replace stirring rods, and mix thoroughly. Remove stirring rods.
8. Centrifuge tubes for 15 minutes, at 3000 RPM.
9. Decant the supernatant.
10. Wash the total cholesterols once more with the acetone-ether, and the free cholesterols twice more. Total washings for the total cholesterols—three, and total washings for the free cholesterols—four.
11. To remove the last traces of the acetone-ether left after the final decanting of the supernatant, place the tubes in warm water for a few minutes.
12. Replace the rods and place the tubes in a preheated sand bath at 110° C. for 30 minutes. (The sand bath may contain about 3 cm. of sand.)
13. Remove the tubes one at a time from the sand bath and add, immediately, 2.0 ml. of glacial acetic acid, mixing well with the stirring rod.
14. Prepare working standards as follows (19 × 105 mm. cuvette):
    a. Pipet 1.0 ml. of working standard and 1.0 ml. of glacial acetic acid into a cuvette (125 mg./100 ml.).
    b. Pipet 2.0 ml. of working standard into a cuvette (250 mg./100 ml.).
15. Prepare the *blank* by pipetting 2.0 ml. of glacial acetic acid into another cuvette.
16. Prepare enough of the acetic anhydride-sulfuric acid reagent to allow 4.0 ml. for each tube, including the blank and standards.
17. Set a timer for 30 minutes but do not start timing.
18. Add 4.0 ml. of the anhydride-sulfuric reagent to the blank tube, mix well with a stirring rod, and start timer. Pour the mixed solution into the cuvette for reading. Continue with each tube at 30-second intervals. Timing must be exact.
19. Place the rack of cuvettes in a dark place (cabinet or drawer) where the temperature is constant.
20. *Exactly* 30 minutes after the timer was started, set the blank at zero and read at 625 mμ. The readings are made at 30-second intervals, so that each density is read exactly 30 minutes after the reagent was added to the tube.

Calculations

Total cholesterol

$$\text{O.D. of unknown} \times \frac{\text{Concentration of standard}^*}{\text{O.D. of standard}} = \text{Mg./100 ml. total cholesterol}$$

---

*Since the two standards are run, covering two ranges, factors should be calculated for each, and the average of both used in the calculations.

Free cholesterol

The factor for the total cholesterol calculation is based on the volume of filtrate used, 4.0 ml. Since the free cholesterol uses 8.0 ml. of filtrate, the formula is multiplied by $\frac{4}{8}$ or 0.5:

$$\text{O.D. of unknown} \times \frac{\text{Concentration of standard}^*}{\text{O.D. of standard}} \times 0.5 = \text{Mg./100 ml. free cholesterol}$$

Cholesterol esters

Subtract the free cholesterol from the total cholesterol to obtain the concentration of the cholesterol ester. To report the esters in terms of percent of the total cholesterol, calculate as follows:

$$\frac{\text{Mg./100 ml. esters}}{\text{Mg./100 ml. total}} \times 100 = \% \text{ Esters}$$

Complete results should be reported as follows:

Total cholesterol, in mg./100 ml.
Free cholesterol, in mg./100 ml.
Cholesterol esters, in mg./100 ml.
Cholesterol esters, in % of total

Normal range of various age groups

Age (years)	Mean (mg./100 ml.)	Range (mg./100 ml.)
20	174	99 - 248
30	195	101 - 289
40	219	127 - 312
50	248	142 - 354
60	253	173 - 333

The data shown here applies to about 98% of the population. It is noted that in the older age groups, the level of cholesterol is significantly higher.[9,10]

Saifer-Kammerer modified method for total cholesterol

Serum or plasma mixed with acetic anhydride-dioxane is heated in a boiling water bath for 30 minutes, where extraction of cholesterol and cholesterol esters, precipitation of proteins, and conversion of water present into acetic acid occur simultaneously.

The color development of the test is the Leibermann-Burchardt reaction, producing a green color after the addition of sulfuric acid. Twelve to eighteen tests may be run in one group. It is better to develop the color in groups of twelve. This depends upon the technique and the speed a technician can manage accurately within 10 to 15 minutes.

Reagents needed

Acetic Anhydride-Dioxane (known as A-D Solution)   (C-55)
Concentrated Sulfuric Acid
Standard Cholesterol Solution (0.2 mg./ml.)   (C-56)

Procedure

1. Set up the following 15 ml. graduated centrifuge tubes. (These should have been washed in chromic acid and thoroughly dried. Water affects

---

*Since the two standards are run, covering two ranges, factors should be calculated for each, and the average of both used in the calculations.

the test by drastically lowering the values. Due to toxic and unpleasant fumes, do the test under a fume hood.)

Blank

a. Pipet 0.45 ml. of distilled water into the labelled tube.

Standards (three tubes)

a. Pipet 0.45 ml. of distilled water into each tube.

b. Pipet 5.00 ml. of cholesterol standard into each tube.

Unknown

a. Pipet 0.50 ml. of serum or plasma into the tube.

2. From a buret (attached to a reservoir jar) add the A-D solution at a fast rate up to the 10 ml. mark on each tube.

3. Mix thoroughly with glass stirring rods, scraping the clinging precipitate from the sides of the tubes.

4. Stopper with small air condensers (corks with small glass tubes drawn to a fine tip) and place in a boiling water bath for 30 minutes.

5. Remove the tubes from the boiling water bath and let cool to room temperature. Let stand or use a room temperature water bath.

6. Check the solution volume of each tube and, if necessary, add A-D solution to the 10.0 ml. mark.

7. Stopper the tubes and mix thoroughly by inverting.

8. Remove the stoppers and centrifuge for 10 minutes at 3000 RPM.

9. With volumetric pipets, transfer 5.0 ml. of the supernatant to a 19 mm. cuvette.

10. Set timer for 18 minutes. Upon the addition of the sulfuric acid to the blank tube, start the timer.

11. Add to all tubes, 0.25 ml. of concentrated sulfuric acid.

12. Mix *thoroughly*.

13. By the timer, let the tubes be at room temperature for 5 minutes. This includes the time used in pipetting the acid.

14. For the remaining 13 minutes, place the tubes in a water bath at 30° to 32° C. Read % T (and convert to O.D.) at a wavelength of 625 mμ.

Calculation

$$\frac{\text{O.D. reading of unknown}}{\text{O.D. reading of standard}} \times 0.5 \times \frac{100}{0.25} = \text{Mg.\% total cholesterol}$$

or

$$\frac{\text{O.D. reading of unknown}}{\text{O.D. reading of standard}} \times 200 = \text{Mg.\% total cholesterol}$$

Dilutions

1. Pipet 0.25 ml. of serum or plasma and 0.225 ml. of distilled water into a 15 ml. graduated centrifuge tube. Bring volume to 10 ml. with A-D solution. Multiply the result by 2.

2. Pipet 0.125 ml. of serum or plasma and 0.338 ml. of distilled water into a 15 ml. graduated centrifuge tube. Bring volume to 10 ml. with A-D solution. Multiply the result by 4.

FECAL LIPIDS[6,11]

Normally, the lipids of the feces have little to do with the lipids of the diet. They resemble the lipids of the blood and are undoubtedly secreted by the small intestine. Abnormal increase in the lipid is due to the food lipids, not those secreted by the liver or intestinal mucosa. Such increases may be due to blockage of the bile ducts or pancreatic ducts, failure of the pancreas to secrete pancreatic juice, or malabsorption. Malabsorption results when there is increased motility of the upper intestine and the food rushes through too rapidly. When the feces contain large amounts of fat, fatty acids, and soaps, the condition is called steatorrhea.

The term "malabsorption syndrome" is commonly used to describe a condition wherein absorption of the main nutrients is defective. This usually results in the passage of bulky, pale, fluid or semifluid, offensive, fatty stools. There are five main groups of disorders in which a malabsorption syndrome may develop. One group results from surgical operations on the gastrointestinal tract; a second is associated with constitutional diseases, such as diabetes; a third is due to granulomatous or neoplastic disease of the intestines; a fourth group is attributable to faulty preparation of food for absorption in the intestinal lumen; and a fifth group, which may be termed the "sprue group," includes such clinical conditions as celiac disease, idiopathic steatorrhea (nontropical sprue), and tropical sprue.

The estimation of fecal fat output is an important aid in diagnosing a malabsorption syndrome.

Determination of fat in feces
van de Kamer modified method[12,13]

An aliquot of a 72-hour collection of feces is saponified with concentrated potassium hydroxide in ethyl alcohol. This solution contains the soaps that were originally present in the stool plus those derived from the neutral fats and fatty acids. Hydrochloric acid is added to the solution to liberate the fatty acids. They are then extracted with petroleum ether. Ethyl alcohol is added to an aliquot of the petroleum ether layer, and the fatty acids are titrated with a standard solution of potassium hydroxide. Thymol blue is used as an indicator.

Preparation of patient and collection of feces

1. The patient should be on a known fat intake of at least 50 gm. of fat/day. If lower quantities are consumed, the fat in the feces originating from bacteria, intestinal cells, or bile (a total of 1 to 2 gm. are excreted every 24 hours) will influence the results.
2. The patient is given a carmine red dye capsule at the beginning of a 72-hour period and another at the end of 72 hours.
3. The collection of the stool should begin when the first red dye marker appears. All stool is then collected in the preweighed jar (2 or 4 qt.) until the second red dye marker appears. This may take more or less than 72 hours depending on intestinal motility.
4. The jar should be kept refrigerated during the collection.

Reagents needed

Ethyl Alcohol, 95%, containing 0.4% capryl alcohol	(C-57)
Ethyl Alcohol, 95%, neutral to thymol blue	
Potassium Hydroxide, KOH, 33%	(C-58)
Hydrochloric Acid, HCl, 25% (sp. gr. 1.13)	(C-59)
Petroleum Ether, boiling point 90° to 100° C.	
Sodium Hydroxide, NaOH, 1.000 Normal	(C-60)
Thymol Blue, 0.2% in 50% Ethyl Alcohol	(C-61)

Special equipment

1. Large mixer* to homogenize the entire 72-hour stool collection.
2. Infrared lamp heater.

---

*May be obtained from Ivan Sorvall, Inc., Norwalk, Conn. This mixer has an adapter to fit Mason-type collection jars. The total specimen may be homogenized in its collection jar.

3. Round-bottom centrifuge bottles, 250 ml. capacity.
4. Centrifuge carrier to hold the 250 ml. bottles.
5. Mason-type glass jars, 2 and 4 quart capacity.
6. Microburet, 1.0 ml. capacity.

Procedure

1. Weigh the jar containing the stool collection and record the weight.

   Weight of stool = Total weight − Weight of empty jar

2. If the stool is formed (not watery), add enough water to equal about ⅔ the weight of the stool. Weigh the jar and record:

   Weight of blended stool = Total weight − Weight of empty jar

3. Attach the jar to the mixer and blend until the stool and water are thoroughly homogenized.
4. Weigh two 250 ml. round-bottom centrifuge bottles. Do the test in duplicate.
5. Using a rubber bulb and a large-bore pipet (cut the tip off a 25 ml. or 50 ml. volumetric pipet), pipet about 10 gm. of the homogenized feces into each 250 ml. centrifuge bottle. Weigh the bottles:

   Weight of blended sample = Total weight − Weight of empty bottle

6. To each bottle:
   a. Pipet 10 ml. of 33% KOH.
   b. Add 40 ml. of 95% ethyl alcohol containing 0.4% capryl alcohol.
   c. Add 10 to 12 glass beads.
7. Attach an air condenser to each bottle and set the bottles over an infrared lamp until the contents have boiled for 30 minutes. (A 25 ml. volumetric pipet with the mouthpiece inserted through a cork serves well as a condenser.)
8. Cool in a room temperature water bath.
9. Add 17 ml. of 25% HCl and cool again in the water bath.
10. Add 50 ml. of petroleum ether (boiling point, 90° to 100° C.).
11. Stopper the bottles and shake vigorously for 1 minute.
12. Centrifuge at moderate speed for 5 minutes or allow the bottles to stand until the layers separate. (The concentration of the ethanol is such that, after the mixture has been shaken, the petroleum ether and the acid ethanol layers separate rapidly.)
13. Transfer (use volumetric pipet) 25 ml. of the petroleum ether layer to a 50 ml. beaker or Erlenmeyer flask.
14. Add 3 or 4 glass beads (or small piece of filter paper) and evaporate the petroleum ether. Do not evaporate to dryness or char the residue. When the ether layer is gone, the odor will no longer be evident.
15. Add 10 ml. of neutral 95% ethyl alcohol.
16. Titrate the fatty acids with 1.00 N NaOH from a microburet, using thymol blue as an indicator (4 drops).

Calculation

The calculations are based upon the assumption of an average molecular weight of 265 for fatty acids in stool:

$$A = \text{Milliliters of 1.00 N NaOH used in titration}$$
$$B = \text{Total weight (in grams) of blended stool}$$
$$S = \text{Grams of blended feces taken for analysis}$$

$$\frac{A \times 265 \times 1.04 \times 2 \times B}{1000 \times S} =$$

$$\frac{A \times 0.551 \times B}{S} = \text{Grams of fat in 72-hour stool}$$

The correction factor 1.04 must be used, since the petroleum ether layer increases 1% in volume when shaken with alcoholic hydrochloric acid and 3% of the amount of fatty acids remains in solution in the acid alcohol layer.

Precautions

1. Use either glass beads or a small piece of filter paper to prevent bumping (irregular boiling). Do not use pumice, which absorbs fatty acids.
2. It is not necessary to evaporate the petroleum ether quantitatively, since small amounts do not affect the titration.
3. The extraction is complete after 1 minute. Excessive shaking, beyond a 1-minute period, does not extract more fat.
4. The molecular weight of the fatty acids depends on the kind of fat consumed. For general purposes (both in cases of normal fat excretion and in steatorrhea) 265 was chosen, with palmitic acid being the main component.
5. Weigh and label the jars before sending any to the patient.
6. Weighings must be accurate. If accurate technique is used, the method has an accuracy of $\pm$ 2%.

Normal values

Normal values are expressed as percent of fat retained or "% retention." For normal, healthy adults, a fat retention of 95 to 98% is found. For example, if a patient has injested 150 gm. of fat during the 3-day stool collection period, then a total stool fat of 3 to 7.5 gm. would be considered normal.

STUDENTS' SUMMARY FOR LIPID TESTS

The significant information consists of the following:
Normal and abnormal values
Methods of analysis and synopsis of procedures

Normal and abnormal values

Test	Normal values	When increased	When decreased
Total lipid	600 to 800 mg.%	Nephrosis Diabetes Arthritis Hypothyroidism	
Total cholesterol	140 to 250 mg.%	Obstructive jaundice Diabetes mellitus Hypothyroidism Nephrosis Celiac disease Chronic glomerulonephritis	Pernicious anemia Hyperthyroidism Severe infections Epilepsy Gaucher's disease Intestinal obstruction
Cholesterol esters	60 to 70% of total cholesterol	Lipoid nephrosis Amyloid nephrosis Chronic glomerulonephritis	Degenerative liver disease
Fecal lipids	95 to 98% retention		Tropical sprue Idiopathic steatorrhea Celiac disease Blockage of bile ducts Failure of pancreas to secrete pancreatic juice

Methods of analysis and synopsis of procedures

Test	Method	Synopsis of procedures
Total lipid	Schain	1. Obtain serum 2. Dilute with saline 3. Add Schain test reagent to separate lipid from serum 4. Heat to activate the above action 5. Read scale of Babcock bottle 6. Calculate to mg.%
Total cholesterol	Bloor	1. Obtain serum 2. Add alcohol-ether mixture to extract total cholesterol (both free cholesterol and cholesterol esters) 3. Heat to drive off alcohol-ether 4. Add chloroform to dissolve cholesterol 5. Add acetic anhydride and sulfuric acid to form blue-green color 6. Measure in colorimeter
Cholesterol esters	Bloor	1. Obtain serum 2. Add alcohol-ether mixture to extract total cholesterol 3. Add digitonin to precipitate free cholesterol and leave cholesterol esters 4. Heat to drive off alcohol-ether 5. Add petroleum ether to residue to take up cholesterol esters 6. Heat to drive off ether 7. Add chloroform to take up cholesterol esters 8. Add acetic anhydride and sulfuric acid to form blue-green color 9. Measure in colorimeter
Total cholesterol	Schoenheimer-Sperry	1. Obtain serum 2. Add acetone-ether to extract total cholesterol (both free cholesterol and cholesterol esters) 3. Add KOH to convert esters to free cholesterol 4. Add digitonin to precipitate free cholesterol 5. Wash precipitate with acetone-ether 6. Heat to drive off acetone-ether 7. Add glacial acetic acid to dissolve cholesterol digitonide 8. Add acetic anhydride-sulfuric acid reagent to develop color 9. Measure colorimetrically
Cholesterol esters	Schoenheimer-Sperry	1. Obtain serum 2. Add acetone-alcohol to extract total cholesterol 3. Add digitonin to precipitate free cholesterol and leave cholesterol esters 4. Wash precipitate with acetone ether 5. Heat to drive off acetone-ether 6. Add glacial acetic acid to dissolve cholesterol digitonide 7. Add acetic anhydride-sulfuric acid reagent to develop color 8. Measure colorimetrically
Total cholesterol	Saifer-Kammerer	1. Obtain serum 2. Add acetic anhydride-dioxane to extract total cholesterol 3. Develop color by adding concentrated sulfuric acid 4. Read colorimetrically
Fecal lipid	van de Kamer—modified	1. Collect 72-hour stool specimen 2. Saponify the stool with KOH in ethyl alcohol 3. Liberate the fatty acids with HCl 4. Extract the fatty acids with petroleum ether 5. Titrate with standard solution of KOH 6. Calculate

REFERENCES

1. Bang, L.: Die Mikrobestimmung der Blutlipoide, Biochem. Ztschr. **91**:235, 1918.
2. Bloor, W.: The determination of small amounts of lipid in blood plasma, J. Biol. Chem. **77**:53, 1928.
3. Bloor, W.: A colorimetric procedure for the determination of small amounts of fatty acids, J. Biol. Chem. **190**:513, 1951.
4. Schain, P.: The use of detergents for quantitative fat determination. I. Determination of fat in milk, Science **110**:121, 1949.
5. Brandstein, M., and Castellano, A.: A simple method for determination of total lipids in serum, J. Lab. & Clin. Med. **57**:300, 1961.
6. Kleiner, I. S., and Orten, J. M.: Biochemistry, ed. 6, St. Louis, 1962, The C. V. Mosby Co.
7. Cantarow, A. C., and Trumper, M.: Clinical biochemistry, ed. 3, Philadelphia, 1945, W. B. Saunders Co.
8. Sperry, W. M.: A micromethod for the determination of total and free cholesterol, J. Biol. Chem. **150**:315, 1943.
9. Annino, J. S.: Clinical chemistry: principles and procedures, ed. 2, Boston, 1960, Little, Brown & Co.
10. Keys, A., Mickelsen, O., Miller, E. v. O., Hayes, E. R., and Todd, R. L.: The concentration of cholesterol in the blood serum of normal man and its relation to age, J. Clin. Invest. **29**:1347, 1950.
11. Frazer, A. C.: The malabsorption syndrome, with special reference to the effects of wheat gluten. In Sobotka, H., and Stewart, C. P., editors: Advances in clinical chemistry, vol. 5, New York, 1962, Academic Press, Inc.
12. van de Kamer, J. H., ten Bokkel Huinink, H., and Weijers, H. A.: Rapid method for the determination of fat in feces, J. Biol. Chem. **177**:347, 1949.
13. van de Kamer, J. H.: Total fatty acids in stool. In Seligson, D., editor: Standard methods in clinical chemistry, vol. 2, New York, 1958, Academic Press, Inc.

Chapter 13

Electrolytes

This chapter considers the following tests for electrolytes:

> Sodium
> Potassium
> Chloride
> Carbon dioxide combining power
> CO_2 content
> Blood pH
> Blood pCO_2
> Calcium
> Ionized (diffusible) calcium
> Phosphorus

A students' summary is given at the end of the chapter.

In good health, the body maintains a balance of electrical neutrality. This means there is a balance or equality between the cation and anion groups. Sodium, potassium, calcium, and magnesium ions make up the cation group, sometimes called the total base. The anion group (from inorganic and organic acids) make up the electrolytes consisting of chloride, bicarbonate, protein, phosphate, sulfate, bromide, and iodide ions. These two groups in balance are shown in Table 31.

Although the technician does not have the responsibility of evaluating results or recommending therapeutic measures, he should be aware of the relationship between the electrolytes in order to recognize any inaccuracy of results before they are reported.

Since the complete set of the cation and anion groups are seldom run, the technician may check the electrolyte balance as suggested in the following paragraphs. Referring again to Table 31, you will note that the sodium ion has the highest concentration of the cation group while the bicarbonate and chloride ions have the largest concentration of the anion group. Total the bicarbonate and chloride ions and subtract that total from the sodium ions. Normally, this difference averages 10 meq./L. with variation either way of 1 or 2 meq. However, in

Table 31. Electrolyte composition of human plasma (approximate)

Cation	meq./L.	Anion	meq./L.
Na (sodium)	143.0	Cl (chloride)	104
K (potassium)	4.5	HCO₃ (bicarbonate)	29
Ca (calcium)	5.0	Protein	16
Mg (magnesium)	2.5	HPO₄ (phosphate)	2
		SO₄ (sulfate)	1
		Organic acids	3
Total	155.0	Total	155

a serious illness (pathological condition) the difference may be appreciably greater than 10 or may be less than 5.

If there is a difference greater than 15 meq./L., look at the other anions for an elevated value. Here are three of the most common causes of a great difference[1]:

1. Kidney damage or uremia resulting in an elevated BUN or NPN. In addition there is a retention of endogenous acids that are either organic (amino or keto acids) or inorganic (phosphate or sulfate).

2. Diabetic acidosis with a retention of keto acids in the blood. There will be an elevation in the blood sugar, blood acetone, and a positive acetone result with the urine.

3. Various poisonings in which there are unmeasured acids in the bloodstream. An example would be poisoning from methanol where it is converted to formic acid.

A difference of less than 5 meq./L. is not as prevalent as the greater variation. Decreased albumin may be the cause of a close difference. The smaller amount of protein requires less sodium for electrical neutrality; therefore there will often be a low sodium accompanying a low albumin. However, look at the electrolyte results and repeat the test showing the most suspicious result first.

The total of the bicarbonate and chloride should *always be less* than the sodium. A quality control (QC) is most beneficial in eliminating doubts of a technical error. The electrolytes should always be added and compared with previous work on the patient. Other tests such as urea nitrogen, sugar, and protein are taken into consideration when totaling the electrolyte balance. Records of each abnormal test, with the patient's name and test results, are invaluable tools for the technician.

There are times when results will not "check out" even after repetition of all tests and checking of the instruments. A new specimen should be requested because of two main problems that may arise before the blood reaches the laboratory:

1. A wet or contaminated syringe may have been used.

2. Blood may have been drawn during an intravenous infusion. Infusion may cause a great dilution factor or, if the infusion contains electrolytes, the sample will be contaminated.

Since urinary electrolytes are not excreted in a uniform concentration throughout the day, a 24-hour specimen should be collected. Electrolytes in the urine are dependent upon the following factors: (1) acid-base balance of the

Table 32. Approximate normal values for urine electrolytes

Electrolytes	Range
Sodium	75 to 200 meq./24 hours
Potassium	40 to 80 meq./24 hours
Chloride	75 to 200 meq./24 hours
CO_2	None
Calcium	5 to 15 meq./24 hours
Phosphorus	0.3 to 1.0 gm./24 hours

body, (2) intake of water and various ions, (3) state of body water: whether the patient is dehydrated or has an excess of fluids (edema), and (4) functioning ability of the kidneys.

Refer to Table 32 for approximate normal values obtained from normal individuals under an average diet and exercise program.

SODIUM

The discussion covers information significant to the student, procedures for the test, and calculations.

Information significant to the student

Sodium is absorbed into the bloodstream from the small intestine. It plays a major role in controlling the water balance between blood and body cells. The normal concentration of sodium is 135 to 155 meq./L. or 310 to 356 mg./100 ml. of serum.[8] A decreased value is of primary concern in Addison's disease—functional failure of the adrenal glands characterized by anemia, digestive disturbances, and bronzelike pigmentation of the skin. Conditions in which increased or decreased sodium values may be expected are given in Table 33.

Procedure for sodium

The following general considerations pertain to the procedure for sodium:

1. Preparation of patient: must be fasting.
2. Preparation of blood: serum or heparinized plasma.
3. Preservation of serum: may be stored overnight in a refrigerator.
4. Precautions: follow the directions exactly as given in the procedure.

The following pages contain a colorimetric procedure. For methods employing the flame photometer, refer to the manufacturer's manual. The Coleman method is included.

Table 33. Conditions accompanied by abnormal sodium values

When increased	When decreased
Nephritis	Addison's disease
Pyloric obstruction	Alkali deficit
Hypercorticoadrenalism	Dehydration
	Myxedema
	Sprue

Coleman Flame Photometer, model 21

Since the Coleman Flame Photometer is widely used, the method for this instrument is presented. The location of the instrument is important for the effectiveness of its performance. The following steps should be followed:

1. Place the instrument on a vibration-free table.
2. Keep the instrument from bright overhead lights or light coming through a window. Stray light will cause a fluctuation of readings.
3. Avoid direct drafts.
4. Keep area above the flame clear to avoid any dirt particles that might fall into the flame and result in erroneous values. Overhead obstacles would also be affected by the constant heat.
5. Ventilation requirements are the same as for a Bunsen burner.
6. Since the instrument is not water-cooled, there is no problem of water supply.

Oxygen

Installation of the oxygen tank should be within 6 feet of the instrument so that the technician will have easy access to the adjustments. A large tank with a two-stage regulator is preferable. The regulator should read in 1-pound intervals in the range between 10 and 15 pounds per square inch. The oxygen requirement is about 10 to 12 cubic feet per hour. A safety surge valve is connected to the output hose nipple of the oxygen regulator. This is a most important part of the instrument. The valve will instantly cut off the flow of oxygen to the flame photometer, and remain closed until the differential pressure across it drops below 2 pounds per square inch if any of the following conditions occur: (1) improper lighting of the flame, (2) accident, or (3) oxygen line rupture or detachment.

Gas

The burner of the model 21 will work with either natural gas or any manufactured gas having a BTU (British Thermal Units) of 800 or over. If the gas pressure of the natural gas is low or irregular, a booster pump may be used. If no natural gas is available, use either propane or butane if the city fire laws permit. The propane requirement is 3 cubic feet per hour, and the butane is 2 cubic feet per hour. (Caution: the tanks must stand upright to prevent the liquid from entering the regulator.) The regulator should have an output pressure gauge calibrated to allow a setting at 5 pounds per square inch.

Gas and oxygen adjustment

The technician has often hesitated to adjust a faulty flame, thus not obtaining full efficiency of the instrument. The procedure is as follows.

Natural or city gas. During his first experience of adjusting the flame the technician may be a bit apprehensive, but the method of adjustment is simple. Refer to Fig. 46, which shows the three valves involved in the adjustment. Use a large screwdriver (not the pocket-size variety) for the valve adjusting. Better control is maintained for minute adjustments needed. During the adjustment, the machine will be noisy with a husky roar. This is a natural sound when too much gas and oxygen are coming through the mixing valve. If the flame "pops out" during the adjustment, the safety valve on the oxygen tank automatically cuts off the oxygen supply. Just turn the shutoff valve to the left. This cuts off both

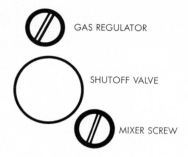

Fig. 46. Coleman flame adjustment valves.

the gas and the oxygen supply to the burner. Close the oxygen regulator and start over again by lighting the flame.

Procedure

1. Remove the two panel caps (chrome buttons) beside the shutoff valve. The top cap is the gas regulator and the cap in the five o'clock position is the mixer regulator for the gas and oxygen.
2. Remove the chimney for a better view of the flame.
3. Be sure the oxygen regulator valve on the oxygen tank is shut off.
4. With a screwdriver, close the mixer valve by turning the screw to the right. Just turn the valve until it stops—do *not* use force! When it stops, the valve is closed.
5. Open the shutoff valve by turning the large knob to the right.
6. Light the gas by holding the match flame inside the top edge of the screen.
7. If the height of the gas column is more than 8 to 10 inches, adjust it by turning the regulator valve to the right until the flame is decreased to the proper height.
8. Now adjust the oxygen regulator on the tank until the gauge reads 3 to 5 pounds per square inch. The flame should be centered in the cylindrical (large) screen.
9. However, if the flame sounds rough or husky and starts to lift off the burner, slowly turn the mixer valve to the left until the sound is a steady hiss.
10. If a yellow color appears around the base of the flame or if dull yellow streaks appear at the bottom of the inner cone, slowly turn the mixer valve to the right until the yellow disappears. Sometimes just half a turn will correct this.
11. If the base of the flame turns yellow and then to a brilliant yellow-white flare with a blue column to the tip, too much oxygen is in the mixture. Reduce the oxygen by means of the regulator at the tank until the flame lifts from the atomizer tip; then adjust with the mixer valve again.
12. Increase the oxygen regulator until the pressure is 10 pounds per square inch. *If the flame rumbles or lifts from the burner,* lessen the pressure and adjust the mixer valve by turning to the *right* slowly. *If the flame shrinks* to half its original height, adjust the gas flow by turning the regulator valve to the right until the correct height, of about 3½ inches, is obtained.
13. Increase the oxygen to 13 pounds per square inch. Adjust with either the gas regulator valve or the mixer valve if necessary.
14. The fine adjustment is now made by slowly turning the mixer valve to the left until a yellow color just appears; then very carefully close

the valve to the right until the yellow color disappears. You should
have the following:
- a. Slightly fuzzy blue inner cone, of about ¼ to ⅜ inch, burning
  steadily.
- b. Steady hissing sound, with no great change in sound when atomizing water.
15. If you have the following, instead, adjust as indicated:
    - a. Unsteady flame—turn the mixer valve to the right until the flame
      is settled.
    - b. Cone that is high and yellow-tipped—too much gas is supplied;
      turn gas regulator to the left.
    - c. Husky roar when atomizing a sample—mixer valve is closed too
      far; turn the valve back to the left until a steady flame is obtained.
16. Replace the chrome caps into the panels and place the chimney back
    on the instrument.

When the instrument is operating normally, the burner body will remain
around body temperature. However, the cylindrical and conical screens will
be hot but not glowing. The unit is not water-cooled because of the "floating
flame," resulting in a low burner temperature.

Propane or butane. The adjustment is the same as for natural or city gas,
with the exception of using a built-in regulator for the gas tank. Then the valve
of the regulator is adjusted for flame height. When operating on propane or
butane the shutoff valve on the instrument panel must be left open *at all times*
to prevent pressure building up in the gas hose should the tank regulator
leak.

Procedure
1. Close the needle valve on the tank regulator by turning the valve to
   the right.
2. Turn the gas regulator handle to the left until the regulator is closed
   off and the handle turns freely.
3. Open the shutoff valve on top of the gas tank. Turn about one full turn.
4. Turn the gas regulator handle to the right until 5 pounds per square
   inch shows on the gauge.
5. Light a match and hold by the cylindrical screen to light the burner.
6. Turn the needle valve until the flame height is 8 to 10 inches.
7. Adjust the oxygen and the mixer as given in the preceding directions.

•   •   •

Turning flame on
1. First, light the match. *Then* turn the gas on. You may either approach
   the burner through the door of the instrument or lift off the chimney.
2. As soon as the fluffy gas flame appears, turn the oxygen up to 13
   pounds per square inch slowly while you observe the flame for any
   abnormalities.
3. Once the flame is adjusted there is usually no problem. Watch to be
   sure there is plenty of oxygen and gas (if using tanks) before you start.

Turning flame off
1. Turn off the oxygen.
2. Then *immediately* turn off the gas. If using a tank, turn off the gas
   with the tank regulator or the tank shutoff valve. *Leave the needle
   valve alone.* If the machine is to be idle for any length of time, shut
   off both the tank shutoff valve and the regulator.

Cleaning the atomizer

For a trouble-free operation of the flame photometer, the burner system must be clean. During continued use of the instrument, the following units of the burner system may become ineffective due to accumulation of dirt and salts of various specimens. The problem may be solved as follows:

1. If during operation of the instrument the flame suddenly sits at a crooked angle or the atomizer does not take up the solution at a constant rate, close down the instrument. Allow a minute or so for cooling, then remove the atomizer and run a 0.012-inch cleaning wire through the *bottom end* of the capillary. A collection of salt may have accumulated at the atomizer orifice. Clean this by carefully scraping the crust off with your fingernail or a small brush. However, you should *never* let the atomizer get in this condition.
2. If the wire fails to help the situation and the flame is still crooked, the oxygen line is clogged. With the cleaning tool carefully thread the tubular shaft over the atomizer capillary. With a careful but firm motion, push straight up against the sliding plug of the atomizer. Do not bend the capillary. The machine may be running while you do this. By pressure against the sliding plug the capillary will be raised, ejecting anything in the oxygen passage. This will cut off the oxygen supply temporarily and the large fluffy gas flame will appear. When you release the pressure, the oxygen will again flow into the burner and the flame will revert to the original mixture.

Cylindrical and conical flame screens

Another common problem that should never happen is the use of dirty flame screens. At the end of every day, the screens and atomizer should be cleaned. If this does not always take place, you may obtain reading drifts while atomizing a sample or you will observe that the flame persists in showing a luminous light when distilled water is aspirated.

1. Turn the instrument off and allow the screens to cool.
2. With a brush wash the screens, in a solvent if needed; rinse well with tap water and then with distilled water.
3. Dry by shaking or by patting carefully with a towel. Reinstall on the burner.

Precautions

1. All glassware and distilled water must be cation-free. Wash the glassware in either Sterox SE or equivalent. All glassware used for calciums must be acid-washed.
2. It is best to check the new distilled water supply against the old. The water used for making the reagents should be used to dilute the specimens. The mixing of distilled water is one of the largest sources of error in flame photometry. To check the water, prepare a new reagent No. 1 and read against the old, using a sodium filter. The method is as follows:
   a. The pure reagent No. 1 (old) is poured into a sample cup or beaker.
   b. The sodium filter is inserted and the machine set at zero without aspirating a sample.
   c. While atomizing the old reagent No. 1, set the galvanometer on zero (the black scale).
   d. Pour the new reagent No. 1 into a beaker. If the reading lies within 0.2 division of zero, the water is satisfactory.

Sodium and potassium by flame photometry, using model 21 Coleman Flame Photometer

This procedure is done from a single dilution of plasma or serum. The volumes of specimen may be as small as 0.02 ml. For making the reagents, you are referred to the manual of the instrument. This manual should be thoroughly studied and all parts of the instrument learned. The direct reading scale panel is recommended to eliminate calibrating the instrument, as well as to keep down a source of error in the final calculations.

Reagents needed

Reagent No. 5, Sterox SE, 0.02%   Refer to the manual
Reagent No. 15:   Refer to the manual
    Sodium, 1.5 meq./L.
    Potassium, 0.05 meq./L.
    Sterox SE, 0.02%

Procedure

1. Obtain heparinized blood and centrifuge. Do not allow the specimen to stand longer than necessary.
2. Pipet 0.5 ml. of plasma into a 50 ml. volumetric flask. Use an Ostwald-Folin pipet. If using a smaller volume of plasma, dilute as follows:
   a. With 0.10 ml. plasma, use a 10.0 ml. volumetric flask
   b. With 0.05 ml. plasma, use a 5.0 ml. volumetric flask
   c. With 0.02 ml. plasma, use a 2.0 ml. volumetric flask
3. Dilute to mark with working reagent No. 5.
4. Stopper and mix thoroughly.
5. If diluted sample is *over 5.0 ml.*, use the regular 10 ml. beaker or plastic cup and fill no more than 4/5 full.
   If the diluted sample is *5.0 ml. or under*, use the Coleman Micro Sample Container and fill to the top.
6. Turn the galvanometer coarse control to the left completely and the galvanometer fine adjustment halfway to the left. This will allow for adjustments needed during running of tests.
7. Light the flame.
8. Place the filter (sodium) into the slot but do not press down until ready to use.
9. Attach the connecting cable in the back of the galvanometer. This connects the galvanometer to the flame photometer.
10. Now press the filter down to release the cutout switch. This switch protects the photometric system by disconnecting the circuit unless the filter is inserted completely into the filter slot.
11. On the flame photometer panel, you will find the BLK Coarse and the BLK Fine controls. Without aspirating any sample, and with the door closed, set the galvanometer index to zero on the left side of the scale.
12. Place a beaker 4/5 full of reagent No. 15 into the beaker holder attached to the door of the instrument. Close the door.
13. Turn the door latch to the right to raise the beaker to the atomizer.
14. Using the GALV Coarse Adjustment and the GALV Fine Adjustment, set the No. 15 working standard at 150 meq./L. on the direct reading scale.
15. Clean the atomizer with reagent No. 5. Check the zero and reset if necessary.
16. Repeat the adjustment with the standard reagent No. 15. It may take two or three adjustments to stabilize the instrument. If it needs these adjustments, make them. Take no shortcuts. This is another area in which gross errors are made.

17. After the machine is properly adjusted, read the plasma dilution.
18. Read the standard before *every* unknown and if necessary adjust the zero again.

Potassium

19. Aspirate distilled water and reagent No. 5 to cleanse the atomizer.
20. Replace the sodium filter with the potassium filter.
21. Again, zero the machine, with the door closed and nothing aspirating.
22. Set reagent No. 15 on 5.0 meq./L. on the direct reading scale.
23. Clean the atomizer with reagent No. 5.
24. Adjust the zero and standard until the machine is stable.
25. Read the plasma potassium, rinsing the machine after every reading *and* checking the standard before every unknown.

Sodium by chemical analysis[2]

Although flame photometry is established in most laboratories there may be instrument problems, or no flame photometer available. Therefore the method of Albanese and Lein for a chemical determination is given. This method gives a reasonable correlation with a flame photometer method.

With this method, the sodium is precipitated as sodium uranyl acetate. It is then dissolved in water and determined photometrically by the intensity of its yellow color.

Reagents needed

Uranyl Zinc Acetate Reagent	(C-62)
Ethanol, 95% *(Do not use absolute ethyl alcohol)*	
Trichloroacetic Acid, 10%	(C-63)
Sodium Standard, 0.64 mg. Na/ml.	(C-64)

Procedure

Do all tests (unknowns) in duplicate and average results. This will give a closer limit ($\pm$ 3.6%) in agreement with the flame photometer.

1. Pipet 0.50 ml. of serum into a 15 $\times$ 125 mm. test tube.
2. Pipet 2.0 ml. of 10% trichloroacetic acid in the tube and mix.
3. Let stand for 5 minutes.
4. Set up the following tubes in duplicate:
   Blank
       Pipet 0.50 ml. of distilled water.
   Standard
       Pipet 0.50 ml. of standard (0.32 mg. of Na) into *three* test tubes.
   Unknown
       Pipet 0.50 ml. of supernatant into the test tubes.
5. Add 1.0 ml. of uranyl zinc acetate reagent to all tubes and mix.
6. Refrigerate for 1 hour; then centrifuge.
7. Carefully pour off and discard supernatant. Drain tubes thoroughly.
8. Wash down the sides of the tube with 2 ml. of 95% ethyl alcohol and resuspend the precipitate (Fig. 54) in the wash fluid. This method of mixing is sometimes called "spanking the tube."
9. Centrifuge the tubes and drain the supernatant as before.
10. Pipet 5.0 ml. of distilled water into each tube and dissolve by spanking the tube. If turbid, centrifuge.
11. Transfer to spectrophotometer tubes and read against the reagent blank at 430 mμ.

Calculation

$$\frac{\text{O.D. (unknown)}}{\text{O.D. (standard)}} \times 0.32 \times \frac{100}{0.1} =$$

$$\frac{\text{O.D. (unknown)}}{\text{O.D. (standard)}} \times 320 = \text{Mg. sodium/100 ml.}$$

or

$$\frac{\text{O.D. (unknown)}}{\text{O.D. (standard)}} \times 139 = \text{meq. sodium/liter}$$

POTASSIUM

The discussion covers information significant to the student, procedure for the test, and calculations.

Information significant to the student

Potassium is absorbed into the bloodstream from the small intestine. A large portion enters the tissues of the body. Here it plays a major role in regulating the distribution of water between the tissues and blood.

The concentration of potassium is normally 3.6 to 5.5 meq./L. or 14 to 21.5 mg./100 ml. of serum.[8] Conditions in which increased or decreased potassium values may be expected are given in Table 34.

Table 34. Conditions accompanied by abnormal potassium values

When increased		When decreased
Addison's disease	Hyperinsulinism	Hypercorticoadrenalism
Acute infections	Diabetes	Malignant growths
Pneumonia	Hereditary periodic paralysis	Chronic nephritis
Uremia	Overdosage of testosterone	Severe diarrhea
Acute bronchial asthma	Overdosage of desoxycorticosterone	Sprue

Procedure for potassium

The following general considerations pertain to the procedures for potassium:

1. Preparation of patient: must be fasting.
2. Preparation of blood: serum or heparinized plasma. The serum or plasma must be obtained 20 minutes after blood is withdrawn from patient.
3. Preservation of serum: may be stored overnight in a refrigerator.
4. Precautions: follow directions *exactly* as given in procedure.

Potassium by chemical analysis[3]

Flame photometry is the preferred method for potassium determinations because of the accuracy and the speed of the instrument. However, if the flame photometer is not available, the method of Lochhead and Purcell can be used for the chemical determination. In the determination of potassium, regardless of the method used, there must be *no* hemolyzed cells in the serum. The specimen must be allowed to clot, be centrifuged as soon as possible, and the serum be removed from the clot. The use of heparinized plasma minimizes hemolysis and eliminates the waiting time for the clot to retract before centrifuging.

With the chemical method of analysis given, potassium is precipitated directly from the serum or plasma as potassium sodium cobaltinitrite. The cobalt in the precipitate is determined photometrically. The alkaline solutions of cobalt, in the presence of a trace of an amino acid such as glycine, reduce the Folin-Ciocalteu phenol reagent to a blue color. The intensity of the color is then measured against a standard.

Reagents needed

Sodium Cobaltinitrite Reagent	(C-65)
Sodium Acetate, Half-Saturated	(C-66)
Wash Solution, Saturated with Potassium Sodium Cobaltinitrite	(C-67)
Glycine, 7.5%	(C-68)
Sodium Carbonate, 25%	(C-69)
Phenol Reagent of Folin-Ciocalteu, Stock	(C-70)
Potassium Standard, 0.2 mg. K/ml.	(C-71)

Working Phenol Reagent
> Prepare fresh. Mix 1 volume of the stock phenol reagent with 2 volumes of distilled water.

Procedure

Before starting the procedure, refilter the volume of sodium colbaltinitrite needed for the test and make certain that a centrifuge is available for the immediate centrifugation needed throughout the test.

1. Using 12 ml. or 15 ml. conical-tipped graduated centrifuge tubes, set up the following in duplicate (the *blank* is set up later).
   Standard
   > Pipet 0.20 ml. of standard into the tubes. This is a 0.04 mg. concentration.
   Unknown
   > Pipet 0.20 ml. of serum or plasma into the conical tubes.
2. Pipet 0.20 ml. of half-saturated sodium acetate. Mix.
3. While constantly shaking the tubes, slowly add 0.5 ml. of sodium colbaltinitrite.
4. Let the tubes stand at room temperature for 45 minutes. Use timer for exact timing.
5. Add 1.0 ml. of distilled water. Mix.
6. Centrifuge *immediately* for *exactly* 15 minutes at 3000 RPM.
7. Carefully pour off supernatant and drain the tubes for about 15 minutes.
8. Add 1.0 ml. of wash solution without disturbing the precipitate.
9. *Immediately* centrifuge for 15 minutes.
10. Pour off supernatant and drain the tubes for 5 or 10 minutes.
11. Pipet 1.0 ml. of 70% ethanol and mix thoroughly with a glass stirring rod. Add 3.0 ml. of 70% ethanol, completely rinsing the precipitate off the stirring rod.
12. *Immediately* centrifuge for 5 minutes.
13. Pour off supernatant and drain the tubes for at least 5 minutes.

Note: The test may be stopped at this point and continued the next day. If it is to be held overnight, add 1 drop of distilled water to each tube to replace any lost by evaporation and stopper the tubes firmly.

14. Label a *blank* tube and add 2.0 ml. of distilled water to the blank and all tubes.
15. Place the tubes in a boiling water bath for 15 to 20 minutes, until the precipitate dissolves. If a minute amount of precipitate remains, this will not affect the analysis.

16. While the tubes are still hot, add 1.0 ml. of glycine solution.
17. Add 1.0 ml. of sodium carbonate solution. Mix.
18. Add 1.0 ml. of working phenol reagent. Mix.
19. Place the tubes in a 37.5° C. water bath for 15 minutes.
20. Cool to room temperature.
21. Add distilled water to the 6.0 ml. mark. Stopper and mix.
22. Read against a water blank at 660 mμ. Convert the percent transmission to optical density.

Calculation

$$\frac{\text{O.D. of unknown} - \text{O.D. of blank}}{\text{O.D. of standard} - \text{O.D. of blank}} \times 0.04 \times \frac{100}{0.2} = \text{Mg. K/100 ml.}$$

$$\frac{\text{O.D. of unknown} - \text{O.D. of blank}}{\text{O.D. of standard} - \text{O.D. of blank}} \times 5.1 = \text{meq. K/100 ml.}$$

CHLORIDE

The majority of methods used for the determination of chloride are based on the principle of precipitating the chloride as an insoluble salt. The analysis is done on either the precipitate or the excess precipitant. However, one of the most common methods of determining chloride concentration is the method of Schales and Schales, who in 1941 adapted the mercurimetric method for use in chloride determination. The chloride ion, in a tungstic acid filtrate of plasma or serum, is titrated with a standard solution of mercuric ions, with the formation of the soluble compound mercuric chloride ($HgCl_2$), which does not dissociate to form mercuric ions. The organic indicator 5-diphenylcarbazone yields a purple color when the excess mercury combines with the indicator. The color is stable although rather difficult to determine with urine, pleural fluids, and serum with elevated bilirubin.

Since the titration end point is dependent upon the technician's experience and eyesight, potentiometric methods have gained popularity by being simple, fast, accurate, and versatile. Icteric sera or turbid specimens pose no problem with these methods. In general, potentiometric methods utilize two electrodes, a voltmeter, and a galvanometer. The electrodes are immersed in a dilute nitric acid solution containing the specimen to be analyzed. By the means of adding silver ions with a microburet the chloride is precipitated as silver chloride. When the chloride has been precipitated, free silver ions change the potential, resulting in a shift in the reading on the galvanometer.

A recently manufactured instrument has eliminated the need for adding the silver ions with a microburet. The Buchler-Cotlove Chloridometer (Fig. 47) has a spool of silver wire that is immersed with the electrodes in a dilute nitric acid solution. The small stirrer, also attached to the electrode assembly, thoroughly mixes the specimen as it is being analyzed. With this instrument, the silver ions are released into the solution at a constant rate and when the chloride in the solution has been used completely, the machine automatically shuts off. Since the silver ions are being added at a constant rate, the amount of chloride in the sample is proportional to the length of time in seconds necessary to complete the titration. A reagent blank and chloride standard are run and the reaction time of the unknown is calculated against the standard. A direct reader may be obtained with the instrument, which eliminates calculations. This potentiometric method is very satisfactory because it has greater sensitivity than the titration or colorimetric methods. The operation is simple, rapid, and auto-

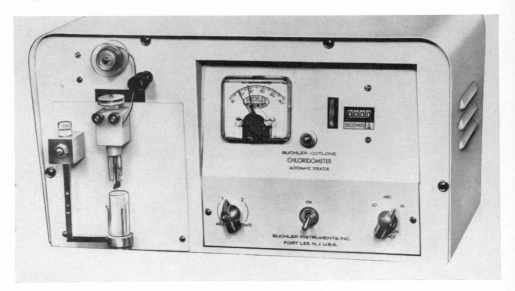

Fig. 47. Buchler-Cotlove Chloridometer. (Courtesy Buchler Instruments, Inc., Fort Lee, N. J.)

matic, eliminating technical errors and time-consuming precipitation of serum, tissue, urine, spinal fluid, or other biological fluids.

Large quantities of bromide given to a patient will result in a falsely elevated chloride. This may be corrected by converting the bromide mg.% to bromide meq./liter. The bromide value is then subtracted from the chloride value. If the bromide is calculated as sodium bromide, convert to bromide. Refer to Chapter 15. The calculation of an example is as follows:

$$\text{Cl meq./L.} - \frac{\text{Bromide (mg. \% } \times 10)}{80} = \text{True chloride value}$$

$$112 \quad - \frac{120 \times 10}{80} =$$

$$112 \quad - \quad 15 \quad = 97 \text{ meq. chloride/L. (true chloride value)}$$

The following discussion covers information significant to the student and procedures for the test.

Information significant to the student

Chloride is absorbed into the bloodstream from the small intestine.

Note that whole blood has lower values than serum or plasma. Red cells, which make up almost half of whole blood, contain much less chloride than serum or plasma.

The normal concentration of chlorides is 98 to 109 meq./L., or 348 to 387 mg./100 ml., of serum or plasma and 122 to 132 meq./L., or 433 to 458 mg./100 ml., of spinal fluid.[8]

An increase in the chloride value is of primary concern in nephritis, prostatic obstruction, and eclampsia (convulsions). Conditions in which an increased or a decreased chloride level may be expected are given in Table 35.

Table 35. Conditions accompanied by abnormal chloride values

When increased	*When decreased*	
Nephritis	Addison's disease	Ether anesthesia
Prostatic obstruction	Burns	Typhus fever
Eclampsia	Diabetes	Anaphylactic shock
Anemia	Fevers	Uremia
Cardiac conditions	Intestinal obstruction	Vomiting
Hyperventilation	Metallic poisoning	Polycythemia
Hypoproteinemia	Pneumonia	Profuse sweating
Serum sickness	Heat cramps	Fasting
Urinary obstruction	Diarrhea	Hypercorticoadrenalism

For the determination of chloride, the methods listed below are commonly used. A brief discussion of each follows.

Whitehorn method
Schales-Schales method
Sendroy method

Whitehorn method

A protein-free filtrate is made. Nitric acid and a *measured excess* of standard silver nitrate solution are added to precipitate the chloride as silver chloride. An indicator is added and the excess silver nitrate is titrated with a standard thiocyanate solution. The amount used is an index of the chloride content. This is found by calculation.

Schales-Schales method

A protein-free filtrate is made. An indicator is added. The filtrate is then titrated with a standard mercuric nitrate solution. This reacts with the chloride to form undissociated mercuric chloride. When all the chloride had been removed, the addition of more mercuric nitrate gives a color reaction with the indicator. The amount of standard mercuric nitrate used in the titration is an index of the chloride content. This is then found by calculation.

Sendroy method

Serum or plasma is obtained. A phosphoric-tungstic acid solution is added to precipitate the proteins. Excess silver iodate is added to precipitate the chloride as silver chloride. This leaves free iodate which is proportional to the amount of silver chloride precipitated. The mixture is filtered. The free iodate is converted to free iodine by the addition of phosphoric acid and potassium iodide. The free iodine produces a color, the depth of which is measured in a colorimeter.

Procedures for chloride

The following general considerations pertain to the procedures for chloride:

1. Preparation of patient: need not be fasting.
2. Preparation of blood: serum or plasma. Do not use a tourniquet when withdrawing blood. If it is necessary to use a tourniquet to locate the vein, release it before withdrawing the blood. Note: the serum or plasma should be obtained 30 minutes after the blood is withdrawn.

3. Preservation of serum or plasma: may be stored overnight in a refrigerator.
4. Precautions: follow the directions *exactly* as given in the procedure.

The following procedures are given below:

Whitehorn titration method

Schales-Schales titration method

Whitehorn titration method*

The standard thiocyanate solution which is listed below may be made of sodium, potassium, or ammonium thiocyanate. Thiocyanate is often called sulfocyanate, and the ferric ammonium sulfate is often referred to as ferric alum.

Reagents needed

Concentrated Nitric Acid	
Ferric Ammonium Sulfate	
Standard Silver Nitrate Solution	(C-72)
Standard Thiocyanate Solution	(C-73)

Procedure

1. Get materials for a venipuncture and an oxalated tube. Make a venipuncture and withdraw about 6 ml. of blood. Gently expel the blood into the oxalated tube and invert several times to dissolve the oxalate.
2. Make a protein-free filtrate.
3. Pipet 10 ml. of the filtrate into a porcelain dish. Add exactly 10 ml. of the standard silver nitrate solution and *stir thoroughly* with a glass rod. Add 5 ml. of the concentrated nitric acid and stir. Let stand 5 minutes to allow precipitation of the chloride as silver chloride.
4. Using a spatula, add about 0.3 gm. of the indicator, ferric ammonium sulfate.
5. Titrate with the standard thiocyanate solution until the salmon-red color of ferric thiocyanate persists for 15 seconds.

Calculation

1 ml. of the standard thiocyanate solution is equivalent to 1 ml. of standard silver nitrate which, in turn, is equivalent to 1 mg. of sodium chloride. To find the number of milligrams of sodium chloride per 100 ml. of blood, proceed as follows. Subtract the milliliters of standard thiocyanate required from the milliliters of standard silver nitrate used (10 ml.). Now multiply by 100.

Example: Suppose 5.5 ml. of the standard thiocyanate solution were required in the titration.

$$\begin{array}{c}\text{Standard silver} \\ \text{nitrate used}\end{array} - \begin{array}{c}\text{Standard thiocya-} \\ \text{nate required}\end{array} \times 100 = \begin{array}{c}\text{Mg. of NaCl/100 ml. of} \\ \text{blood}\end{array}$$

$$(10) \quad - \quad (5.5) \quad \times 100 = \begin{array}{c}\text{450 mg. of NaCl/100 ml.} \\ \text{of blood}\end{array}$$

The figure 100 appears in the calculation because the 10 ml. of filtrate used represents only 1 ml. of blood. This 1 ml. of blood must be multiplied by 100 to give the report in the usual milligrams per 100 ml.

This titration is what is known as a back-titration. We know that we have added exactly 10 ml. of the standard silver nitrate and we are titrating back to find out how much was not used to precipitate the chloride. In

---

*Adapted from Whitehorn, J. C.: System of blood analysis, J. Biol. Chem. **45**:449, 1921.

the above example, 5.5 ml. of the silver nitrate were *not* used. Therefore, 4.5 ml. were used (10.0 − 5.5 = 4.5), and each milliliter of this 4.5 represents 1 mg. of chloride expressed as sodium chloride.

Schales-Schales titration method*

Reagents needed

Diphenylcarbazone Indicator	(C-74)
Standard Sodium Chloride, 10 meq./L. or 58.5 mg.%	(C-75)
Standard Mercuric Nitrate Solution	(C-76)

Procedure

1. Get materials for a venipuncture and an oxalated tube. Make a venipuncture and withdraw about 6 ml. of blood. Gently expel the blood into the oxalated tube and invert several times to dissolve the oxalate.
2. Make a tungstic acid filtrate.
3. Pipet 2 ml. of the filtate into a small flask.
4. Add 4 drops of the indicator diphenylcarbazone. Using a microburet graduated in hundredths, titrate with the standard mercuric nitrate solution. The end point is reached when the solution turns a pale violet or light purple color.

Calculation

Where E equals the number of milliliters of mercuric nitrate solution required for 2 ml. of standard sodium chloride solution:

$$\frac{\text{Ml. of standard mercuric}}{\text{nitrate used}} \times 5.85 \times \frac{100}{E} = \frac{\text{Mg. of sodium chloride/100}}{\text{ml. of blood}}$$

CARBON DIOXIDE COMBINING POWER

The discussion covers information significant to the student and procedures for the test.

Information significant to the student

Carbon dioxide (CO_2) is a gas which is present in the blood largely as bicarbonate salts. The gas is a waste product of cellular activity, and the blood acts as middleman in its transfer to the lungs.

The plasma has the ability to combine with CO_2 forming bicarbonate depending upon the amount of available alkali present. When the technician does a test of CO_2 combining power or CO_2 capacity of plasma, he is measuring the alkali reserve of the body.

There are two ways to measure the CO_2: the volumetric method that measures the gas volume at a constant pressure, and the manometric method measuring the pressure of the gas at a constant volume. The latter is used more widely because of better control over the techniques used and because the accuracy is more consistent.

With the manometric method the oxalated plasma is saturated with CO_2 at the tension of that gas in alveolar air. (This is exhaled air, which is approximately 5% CO_2.) Using a tank of 5% CO_2 is a more convenient way to saturate the plasma.

About 3 ml. of the plasma are placed in a separatory funnel, and while it is

---

*Adapted from Schales, O., and Schales, S. S.: Simple and accurate method for determination of chloride in biological fluids, J. Biol. Chem. **140:**879, 1941.

being exposed to the 5% CO_2 or alveolar air, the funnel is rotated continually so that a thin layer of plasma is in contact with the CO_2. A measured amount is then placed into the Van Slyke apparatus where the total CO_2 concentration is determined. Therefore, the more alkaline material present in the plasma, the higher is the CO_2 combining power.

An abnormal CO_2 may be an indication of either acidosis or alkalosis.

Acidosis is a term applied to a condition that results from a formation or absorption of acids at a rate exceeding the rate of their neutralization or elimination. Acids are absorbed into the blood in both pathological and normal conditions, neutralizing some of the alkali. The kidneys normally excrete these acids. Therefore the urine is usually acid, from pH 5 to 7, while the blood remains slightly alkaline at pH 7.4. However, with abnormal retention of acids, the alkali reserve and the bicarbonate level may be lowered below the normal range, and then the blood pH shifts toward the acid side of normal. This condition is known as metabolic acidosis.

If the respiratory apparatus is affected to the extent that excess CO_2 cannot be eliminated, then the blood CO_2 content will be elevated and the blood pH may again shift toward the acid side. This condition is known as respiratory acidosis.

Alkalosis occurs when an excessive amount of acid is lost without a comparable loss of alkali or when alkali is formed at a greater rate than the body is able either to neutralize or to eliminate it.

If a person hyperventilates for a long enough period of time, the blood CO_2 will be considerably lowered and the blood pH may shift toward the more alkaline side of normal. This condition is known as respiratory alkalosis.

If there is a great loss of chloride ions, with an accompanying loss of hydrogen ions, through excessive vomiting, the blood pH may shift toward the alkaline side and the blood CO_2 will be elevated. This condition is known as metabolic alkalosis.

Conditions accompanied by acidosis and alkalosis are given in Table 36. Those conditions given in italics are of primary concern; the others are of somewhat lesser interest.

Normal blood has a CO_2 combining power of 55 to 75 ml./100 ml. or 24 to 33 meq./L. of plasma. When the value is given in milliliters of gas per 100 ml. of plasma, it is usually reported as volumes percent.

For the determination of the carbon dioxide combining power, the method of Van Slyke is commonly used. In this method, plasma is obtained. If the test

Table 36. Conditions showing an abnormal CO_2 combining power

Decreased CO_2 combining power (acidosis)	*Increased CO_2 combining power (alkalosis)*
Diabetes	*Excessive alkali therapy*
Nephritis	Intestinal obstruction
Toxic conditions	Hypercorticoadrenalism
Diarrhea	Respiratory diseases
Eclampsia	Tetany
Hemorrhage	Typhus fever
Renal rickets	Oxygen therapy
Anesthesia	Acute vomiting
	Emphysema

is not performed immediately, the plasma is kept under oil to prevent the loss of carbon dioxide. The plasma is placed in a 30 ml. separatory funnel and saturated with CO_2 by blowing into the funnel. Beads in a connecting bottle collect moisture from the breath.

A sample of the saturated plasma is then transferred to a Van Slyke gas apparatus. Alcohol is added to prevent foaming. Lactic acid is added to help liberate the carbon dioxide. A partial vacuum is created in the container to complete the liberation of the carbon dioxide.

The carbon dioxide is then placed under atmospheric pressure by adjusting a mercury levelling bulb. The volume of milliliters that the gas occupies is read from a scale and the report is given in volumes percent.

Procedures for the carbon dioxide combining power

The following general considerations pertain to the procedures for the carbon dioxide combining power:

1. Preparation of patient: must be fasting. Instruct patient to avoid vigorous exercise for at least 1 hour before blood is withdrawn.
2. Preparation of blood: plasma. Note: Do not use a tourniquet when withdrawing the blood. If it is necessary to use a tourniquet to locate the vein, release it before withdrawing the blood.
3. Centrifuge the specimen immediately and perform the test as soon as possible.
4. Precautions: follow the directions *exactly* as given in the procedures.

This section contains the following procedures:

Procedure with the volumetric Van Slyke apparatus
Procedure with the manometric Van Slyke apparatus

Procedure with the volumetric Van Slyke apparatus

The Van Slyke volumetric procedure is somewhat complicated, and the student should perform several trial runs on normal blood before attempting to test a patient's blood. The procedure will be broken down into the following steps:

Collection of blood and preparation of plasma
Saturation of plasma with carbon dioxide
Determination of carbon dioxide

Reagents and apparatus needed

Caprylic Alcohol
Lactic Acid, 10%   (C-77)
Mercury
Van Slyke Apparatus

Collection of blood and preparation of plasma

1. Get materials for a venipuncture and an oxalated tube. Make a venipuncture without the use of a tourniquet. If it is necessary to use a tourniquet to locate the vein, release it before withdrawing the blood. Withdraw about 8 ml. of blood. Gently expel the blood into the oxalated tube and dissolve the oxalate with as little shaking as possible, for increased agitation may cause loss of carbon dioxide.
2. Centrifuge at high speed for 10 minutes and pipet off the plasma. Perform the test as soon as possible after centrifuging.

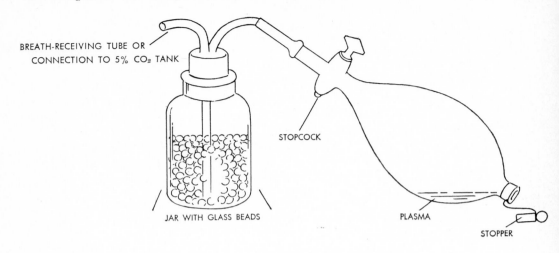

BREATH-RECEIVING TUBE OR
CONNECTION TO 5% CO₂ TANK

STOPCOCK

JAR WITH GLASS BEADS

PLASMA

STOPPER

Fig. 48. Separatory funnel used to saturate plasma with CO_2.

Saturation of plasma with carbon dioxide

1. Get a separatory funnel similar to that illustrated in Fig. 48.
2. Place about 3 ml. of plasma in the separatory funnel.
3. Open the stopcock and stopper. Blow your breath (containing the carbon dioxide) through the breath-receiving tube several times in order to flush out the air in the funnel. (The function of the beads is to remove moisture.) Close the stopper. Again blow your breath into the breath-receiving tube. Toward the end of the expiration, close the stopcock to trap the carbon dioxide over the plasma.
4. Detach the jar of glass beads. Complete the saturation of plasma by rotating the flask for 3 minutes in such a manner that the plasma is spread evenly over the sides of the funnel.

Determination of carbon dioxide

1. Before attempting the operation of the Van Slyke apparatus, the operator should familiarize himself with the various parts as illustrated in Fig. 49. In the following discussion, stopcock *e* will be referred to as the upper stopcock, and stopcock *f* will be referred to as the lower stopcock. Position 1 of the mercury levelling bulb will be referred to as the upper position, position 2 as the middle position, and position 3 as the lower position.
2. Force air out of the extraction chamber of the Van Slyke apparatus (Fig. 49) and test for leaks by doing the following. Open the upper stopcock by turning it to position X. Open the lower stopcock by turning it to position Y. Take the levelling bulb containing the mercury and raise it to the upper position. Allow the mercury to flow through the apparatus until it is slightly above the upper stopcock. Now close the upper stopcock so that there is some mercury trapped above it. Now lower the levelling bulb to the lower position so that the mercury falls just below the lower stopcock. This, of course, creates a vacuum in the extraction chamber *(A)*. Now test for leaks by raising the levelling bulb back to the upper position. If there are no leaks, the mercury will hit the upper stopcock with a sharp metallic click. If there are no leaks, place the levelling bulb in the middle position. If there are leaks, however, the air will act as a cushion and no click will be heard. In this case, expel the air through outlet *a*. Next, lower the levelling

bulb to the lower position. Finally, check the stopcocks for leaks. Repeat the test until there is no air in the apparatus. When the apparatus has been freed from air, take a medicine dropper and remove any mercury that may be trapped above the upper stopcock.

3. Check to see that the levelling bulb is in the middle position and that the upper stopcock is closed. Add 1 ml. of distilled water to the receiving cup (*b*). Using a 1 ml. volumetric pipet, take 1 ml. of the plasma which has been saturated with carbon dioxide. Place the tip of the pipet *under* the water in the receiving cup. Gradually let the plasma *drain* from the pipet. Add 2 drops of caprylic alcohol to prevent foaming.

4. Put stopcock *f* in position Y. Gently open the upper stopcock and allow the plasma and about half the water to fall into the extraction chamber (*A*). Make sure to leave some water above the stopcock to indicate that the vacuum has been preserved.

5. Pipet about 2 ml. of the 10% lactic acid into the receiving cup (*b*). (The function of the lactic acid is to help liberate carbon dioxide.) Gently open the upper stopcock and allow the lactic acid to fall into

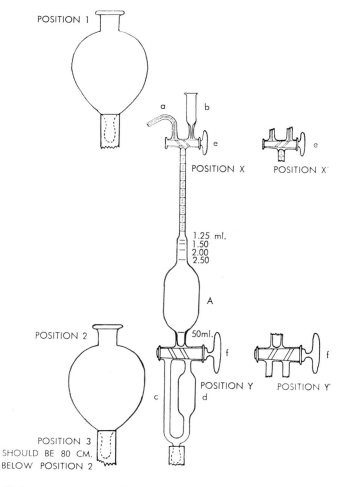

Fig. 49. Van Slyke apparatus. Volumetric. (From Levinson, S. A., and MacFate, R. P.: Clinical laboratory diagnosis, ed. 5, Philadelphia, 1956, Lea & Febiger.)

the extraction chamber *(A)* until the meniscus of the fluid reaches the 2.5 ml. mark on the stem. Close the upper stopcock. Place several drops of mercury in the receiving cup *(b)*. Gently turn the upper stopcock and allow a little mercury to enter the stem and thus seal it off. Any excess fluids remaining in the receiving cup may be removed with a medicine dropper.

6. *Carefully* lower the levelling bulb to the lower position so that the mercury falls to the 50 ml. mark. When the mercury level reaches the 50 ml. mark, close stopcock *f*. This allows the extraction chamber to contain the plasma and small amounts of water, lactic acid, and mercury.

7. Place the levelling bulb in the middle position. Remove the apparatus from the stand and invert about twelve times to aid in the liberation of carbon dioxide. Place the apparatus back in the stand.

8. The next step is to drain the greater portion of the fluid material contained in the extraction chamber *(A)* into the waste chamber *(d)* below. It requires precision. Care must be taken not to lose any gas; and it is better to leave a little fluid in the extraction chamber, as this can be compensated for in the calculation which follows. Hold the levelling bulb in your left hand at the middle position. With the right hand, gently open stopcock *f* to position Y. Gradually lower the levelling bulb and watch the liquid drop into the waste chamber *(d)* below. Just before all of it has fallen, quickly give the stopcock a half turn to position Y' so that the mercury may climb back into the extraction chamber. Then gradually raise the levelling bulb and allow the mercury to slowly enter the extraction chamber.

9. By manipulating the levelling bulb, make the level of the mercury in the levelling bulb come to *exactly* the same level as the mercury in the gas measuring tube (Fig. 50). Close the stopcock *f*. Now read off the number of milliliters of gas in the gas measuring tube.

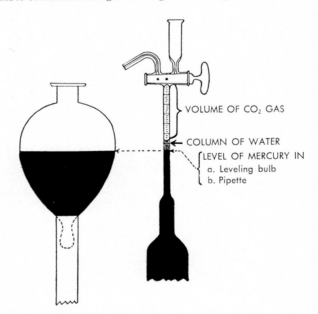

VOLUME OF CO₂ GAS

COLUMN OF WATER

⎰ LEVEL OF MERCURY IN
⎱ a. Leveling bulb
⎱ b. Pipette

Fig. 50. Final reading of Van Slyke apparatus. (From Levinson, S. A., and MacFate, R. P.: Clinical laboratory diagnosis, ed. 5, Philadelphia, 1956, Lea & Febiger.)

Calculation

Take the reading in milliliters and substract 0.12 (correction factor for uncombined carbon dioxide). This gives the number of milliliters of gas per milliliter of plasma. Since the report is given in percent, divide the corrected reading by 1 (milliliter of plasma used) and multiply by 100.

Example: Suppose the reading was 0.72 ml.

$$0.72 - 0.12 \text{ (correction factor)} = 0.60 \text{ ml. (corrected reading)}$$

$$\frac{0.6 \text{ (ml. of gas obtained)}}{1.0 \text{ (ml. of plasma used)}} \times 100 = 60\%$$

The report is usually given as volumes percent. Thus, the above value would be reported as 60 vol.%. For general clinical laboratory work it is not necessary to make corrections for barometric pressure and temperature. For research accuracy, of course, these corrections should be made.

Normal values
55 to 75 vol.% or 25 to 34 meq./L.

Cleaning the Van Slyke apparatus

Lower the levelling bulb to the lower position. Fill the extraction chamber *(A)* and waste chamber *(d)* with distilled water. Raise the levelling bulb to the upper position and expel the water through the outlet *a*. Repeat about three times. Fill with distilled water, place a small beaker over the receiving cup to keep out dust, and cover the apparatus. Many technicians find it good policy to frequently grease the stopcocks and apply new rubber bands to hold them in position.

Procedure with the manometric Van Slyke apparatus*

Reagents needed

Caprylic Alcohol
Lactic Acid, 0.1 N   (C-78)
Sodium Hydroxide, 5 N (carbonate-free)   (C-79)
Mercury

Procedure

1. Before beginning analysis for CO_2, remove metal jewelry such as rings and watches. Mercury forms amalgams with most metals, so do not dip coins or trinkets into the mercury. Although there is a temptation for the inexperienced technician to "play" with this element it must be stressed that continual carelessness may result in mercurial poisoning.
2. Expel water from the chamber by placing a vacuum hose into the cup and as the water is suctioned out of the cup, lift the mercury bulb carefully so the remaining water in the chamber and a few drops of mercury are expelled into the waste jar. Close stopcock No. 1 (Fig. 51). Place the levelling bulb in lower position.
3. Add 3 drops of caprylic alcohol to the cup and carefully turn the stopcock No. 1 until the stopcock channel is filled. Caprylic alcohol prevents foaming.
4. Add 3.0 ml. of 0.1 N lactic acid to the cup. The lactic acid liberates the carbon dioxide.
5. Using a Van Slyke pipet (or a 1 ml. graduated measuring pipet but not a blow-out pipet), add 0.5 ml. of serum that has been saturated with carbon dioxide to the cup. By placing the tip of the pipet into

---

*Arthur H. Thomas Co., Philadelphia, Pa.

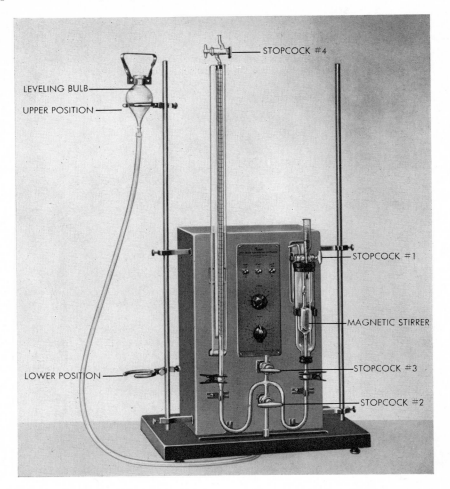

Fig. 51. Van Slyke manometric blood gas apparatus. (Courtesy Arthur H. Thomas Co., Philadelphia, Pa.)

the lactic acid near the bottom of the cup before releasing the serum, contact with air is avoided. For the *blank*, use 3.5 ml. of lactic acid instead of 0.5 ml. of serum and 3.0 ml. of lactic acid.

6. Slowly turn stopcock No. 1, releasing the serum and lactic acid into the chamber. Allow a drop of the caprylic alcohol to remain behind.

7. Seal the stopcock channel with mercury and lower the bulb to bring the mercury meniscus down to the 50 ml. mark. With the bulb in the lower position, agitate the contents in the extraction chamber for 2 minutes.

8. Carefully turn stopcock No. 2 and let the solution rise (without oscillation) to the 2 ml. mark.

9. Read the mercury manometer for P_1. The P_1 equals the millimoles of the initial gas pressure.

10. Add 0.3 ml. of 5 N NaOH to the cup.

11. Turn stopcock No. 1 carefully, admitting the alkali to the reaction chamber. No air must enter the chamber.

12. Seal the stopcock with mercury, and by raising and lowering the bulb

Table 37. Temperature factors for CO_2 determinations

Temperature (°C.)	Factor
18	0.2416
19	0.2404
20	0.2392
21	0.2380
22	0.2366
23	0.2354
24	0.2342
25	0.2330
26	0.2320
27	0.2308
28	0.2298
29	0.2286
30	0.2276
31	0.2266
32	0.2256
33	0.2246
34	0.2236

three times, raise and lower the contents of the chamber. This ensures complete absorption of carbon dioxide by the alkali.

Calculations

The *blank* value represents the amount of carbon dioxide in the reagents. The value usually runs between 1 and 4 mm. The P_1 value equals millimeters of the initial gas pressure. The P_2 value equals millimeters of pressure due to all gases except carbon dioxide:

$$P_1 - P_2 = \text{Mm. of carbon dioxide pressure}$$

The millimeter value of CO_2 pressure in the *blank* is subtracted from that of the serum, and the result is multiplied by the appropriate temperature factor (Table 37):

$$(P_1 - P_2) - \text{Blank} \times \text{Factor} = \text{meq./L.}$$

Refer to Table 38 for converting meq./L. to vol. %.

Care of the Van Slyke apparatus

Since the stopcocks are under pressure, they must be kept well greased. With the Arthur H. Thomas unit, whose method is described, the apparatus may be dismantled for cleaning. The ball-and-socket joint makes dismantling extremely easy. However, the unit may be cleaned without being dismantled. The following method may be used for the old and the new Van Slyke units.

1. Attach a vacuum line to the stopcock No. 4 at the top of the manometer column and suction out all the mercury.
2. With stopcock No. 1 open, and the vacuum line attached to the open stopcock No. 4, pour acetone into the cup until the complete system is filled.
3. Close stopcock No. 4 and allow the acetone to remain in the unit for 15 minutes to dissolve the grease particles.
4. Keeping stopcock No. 2 closed at all times, drain the system by vacuum through stopcock No. 3.

Table 38. Conversion of CO_2 combining power and bicarbonate values[*]

CO_2 combining power (vol. %)	Bicarbonate (meq./L.)	CO_2 combining power (vol. %)	Bicarbonate (meq./L.)	CO_2 combining power (vol. %)	Bicarbonate (meq./L.)
2.2	1.0	46.7	21.0	91.3	41.0
4.5	2.0	49.0	22.0	93.5	42.0
6.7	3.0	51.2	23.0	95.6	43.0
8.9	4.0	53.4	24.0	97.9	44.0
11.1	5.0	55.7	25.0	100.2	45.0
13.4	6.0	57.9	26.0	102.4	46.0
15.6	7.0	59.1	27.0	104.6	47.0
17.8	8.0	62.3	28.0	106.8	48.0
20.0	9.0	64.6	29.0	109.1	49.0
22.3	10.0	66.8	30.0	111.3	50.0
24.5	11.0	69.0	31.0	113.5	51.0
26.7	12.0	71.2	32.0	115.8	52.0
28.9	13.0	73.5	33.0	118.0	53.0
31.2	14.0	75.7	34.0	120.2	54.0
33.4	15.0	78.9	35.0	122.4	55.0
35.6	16.0	80.1	36.0	124.7	56.0
37.8	17.0	82.4	37.0	126.9	57.0
40.1	18.0	84.5	38.0	129.1	58.0
42.3	19.0	86.8	39.0	131.3	59.0
44.5	20.0	89.0	40.0	133.6	60.0

[*]CO_2 combining power in vol. % = 2.226 × bicarbonate in meq./L.

Bicarbonate in meq./L. $= \dfrac{\text{vol. } \% \ CO_2}{2.226}$

5. Repeat, filling the system with acetone, and let the acetone remain in the system for 15 minutes. After draining the acetone through stopcock No. 3, the system should be free of grease particles.
6. Fill the system with either chromic acid or 10% nitric acid. Let the cleaning solution remain in the system for at least 1 hour before draining.
7. Rinse the system at least three times with distilled water, then twice with acetone.
8. Leaving stopcocks No. 1 and No. 4 open, attach the vacuum to stopcock No. 3 to completely dry the system.
9. Carefully grease the stopcocks and fill the system with clean mercury.

Cleaning mercury

A simple way to clean mercury is to mix the mercury with sugar and then dissolve the sugar by washing with water. Place the dirty mercury in a large mortar. Pour the sugar into the mortar and grind the sugar and mercury with a pestle. The dirty sugar is then rinsed or dissolved off the mercury by running water. The water may be vacuumed off. The procedure is repeated until the sugar remains clean. All moisture is then vacuumed off the mercury, and it is ready to be filtered into the storage bottle. Place a small pinhole in the bottom of the filter paper. The mercury is then filtered to remove small traces of dirt not previously removed and to absorb any remaining moisture.

CO_2 CONTENT

When a CO_2 *content* is requested, it is necessary to draw, transport, and centrifuge the blood without exposure to air. This is accomplished by transferring the blood from a syringe to a tube of mineral oil with the tip of the syringe below the surface of the oil. After the tube of blood has been centrifuged, a pipet is inserted through the mineral oil layer and a measured sample is transferred directly to the Van Slyke apparatus without aerating. From this point, the procedure is the same as for CO_2 combining power.

BLOOD pH

The pH is a measure of the hydrogen ion concentration. The normal pH values for blood are 7.35 to 7.45. Increased pH values are found in uncompensated alkalosis. Decreased pH values are found in uncompensated acidosis.

Procedure

The determination of blood pH is done by means of a closed glass electrode whose voltage output at a given temperature and pH is read directly from the scale of a pH meter (Fig. 52).

The pH of venous blood is usually 0.02 to 0.04 pH units lower than that of arterial blood.

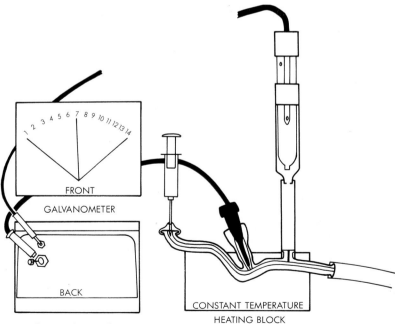

Fig. 52. Blood pH electrode unit.

In obtaining the blood, the syringe should be rinsed with a sterile solution of heparin before the sample is drawn. Do not use oxalates or fluorides as anticoagulants, because they will alter the pH of the blood.

Some techniques given below will help the technician do an accurate blood pH determination.

1. Draw the venous or arterial blood in the heparinized syringe. Avoid getting any air bubbles in the syringe. Place a cork on the end of the needle to prevent air from getting into the syringe or the blood from leaking out.
2. If unable to do the pH immeditely, place the syringe in ice to prevent glycolysis. The pH should be read within 10 minutes after the blood is drawn.
3. Most manufacturers of pH meters also have available an electrode system, specifically designed for blood pH, which allows the pH to be measured without exposing the blood to the air. This type of system is essential for an accurate blood pH.
4. Adjust the meter with a buffer, pH 7.0, and rinse the electrode with saline before introducing the blood.
5. Allow the blood to come to the temperature of the system before taking a reading.
6. Introduce more of the blood and take another reading. Repeat this procedure until readings are reproduceable. Usually the first reading is lower than the final one, due to dilution with saline.

BLOOD pCO$_2$

The pressure of carbon dioxide (pCO$_2$) in arterial blood may be determined by an indirect calculation of the pressure of CO$_2$ from a nomogram (Fig. 53) based on the Henderson-Hasselbalch equation. This equation is based on three unknowns: the blood pH, the plasma bicarbonate concentration, and the partial pressure of the CO$_2$ in the blood. If any two are known, the third may be calculated. The nomogram provides a means of obtaining a pCO$_2$ value without long calculations.

Great care must be used in doing a blood pH determination, for an error of 0.02 unit can mean an error of about 1.8 mm. Hg in the pCO$_2$ value.

Normal range (CO$_2$ tension, mm. Hg)

Arterial blood	About 33 to 48 mm. Hg
Venous blood	About 39 to 54 mm. Hg

An example in using the nomogram

A straight line drawn through the given points on any two scales crosses the other two scales at points indicating simultaneously occurring values. For example, Patient "x" has the following results: an arterial pH of 7.40 and a total CO$_2$ of 28 meq./L. (or millimoles/liter). The pCO$_2$ value is needed. Draw a line from the total CO$_2$ column reading 28 through the pH column, intersecting the 7.40 point. The line intersecting the mm. Hg column gives a value of 45. Therefore, the pCO$_2$ of patient "x" is 45 mm. Hg.

CALCIUM AND PHOSPHORUS

Calcium and phosphorus tend to maintain an equilibrium in the blood. They are usually considered together, since disturbances of one quite often result in a

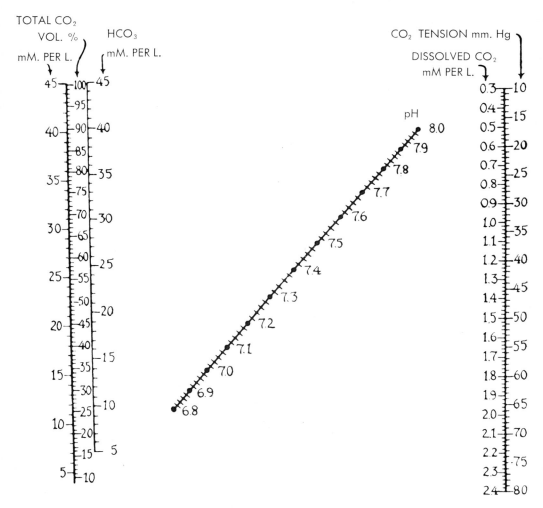

Fig. 53. Nomogram for calculating pCO_2. (From McLean, F. C.: Application of the law of chemical equilibrium (law of mass action) to biological problems, Physiol. Rev. **18**:495, 1938.)

disturbance of the other. A low calcium is often accompanied by a high phosphorus. This does not always hold true, however, since during bone formation high phosphorus and sometimes high calcium levels are noted. This is found when fractures are healing and also explains the higher phosphorus level in children. Rickets is another exception, in that calcium is usually normal while phosphorus may be down to 2 mg.%. In some cases, however, the results may be reversed, or both calcium and phosphorus levels may be low.

Patients with renal problems will have an elevated phosphorus level due to retention of phosphates, usually excreted in large quantities by normally functioning kidneys. An elevated BUN or NPN will generally accompany this situation.

The technician should not only be aware of the limitations of the methods used for calcium and phosphorus but also have a basic knowledge of the physiological utilization of calcium and phosphate ions. Additional reading should be done, that he may become acquainted with the various disorders and effects upon calcium and phosphorus content within the body.

Calcium exists in the body in an ionized form and in a protein-bound form, which is mainly attached to albumin. When a calcium determination is done, the *total* calcium is being determined, regardless of the proportion of the above two forms. The ionized fraction is normally about 5.9 to 6.5 mg.%, or about 50 to 60% of the total calcium, while the protein-bound calcium is 40 to 50% of the total.

CALCIUM

The discussion covers information significant to the student, procedures for the test, and calculations.

Information significant to the student

Calcium is absorbed into the bloodstream from the small intestine. It is used in the formation of bone and the clotting of blood. The normal calcium values are 9.0 to 11.5 mg./100 ml. of serum. In growing children, these values are slightly increased.

Decreased calcium values are of primary concern in tetany—a disease caused by faulty calcium metabolism and characterized by convulsions and muscular twitchings. Increased and decreased calcium values may be found in those conditions given in Table 39.

Table 39. Conditions accompanied by abnormal calcium values

When increased	When decreased	
Carcinoma	*Tetany*	Osteomalacia
Hyperparathyroidism	Celiac disease	Parathyroidectomy
Hypervitaminosis	Hypoparathyroidism	Pregnancy
Multiple myeloma	Nephritis	Rickets
Polycythemia vera	Nephrosis	Sprue
		Vitamin D deficiency

For the determination of calcium, the following methods are commonly used. A brief discussion of each is given.

Clark-Collip modification of Kramer-Tisdall method
Roe-Kahn method
Bachra, Dauer, and Sobel EDTA titration method

Clark-Collip modification of Kramer-Tisdall method

Serum is obtained. Ammonium oxalate is added to precipitate the calcium as calcium oxalate. This is centrifuged. The precipitate is washed with dilute ammonium hydroxide to remove impurities and excess oxalate. Dilute sulfuric acid is added to convert the calcium oxalate to oxalic acid. After being heated to about 70° to 90° C. (to enhance the following reaction) the oxalic acid is titrated with standard potassium permanganate. The titration is an oxidation-reduction reaction, the oxalic acid being oxidized and the permanganate being reduced. The calcium content is found by calculation and reported in milligrams/100 ml. of serum.

Roe-Kahn method

Serum is obtained. Trichloroacetic acid is added to precipitate the proteins. After filtering, sodium hydroxide and trisodium phosphate are added to precipitate the calcium as tricalcium phosphate. The mixture is centrifuged. The precipitate is washed with an alkaline alcohol solution to remove impurities and excess phosphate. Acid molybdate and aminonaphtholsulfonic acid reagent are added to form a color complex with the tricalcium phosphate. The depth of color is compared with a standard and measured in a colorimeter.

Bachra, Dauer, and Sobel EDTA titration method, using cal-red indicator.

Serum is obtained. Potassium hydroxide is added to make the serum alkaline. Cal-red indicator is added to the specimen, and titration with disodium ethylene-diaminetetra-acetate (EDTA) is done immediately. The calcium content is found by calculation and reported in milligrams/100 ml. of serum. Icteric and hemolyzed serum may be used after preparation for analysis. Urine calcium, after preparation of the specimen, may also be determined by this method.

Procedures for calcium

The following general considerations pertain to the procedures for calcium:

1. Preparation of patient: need not be fasting.
2. Preparation of blood: serum; the blood should be centrifuged and the serum obtained no later than 30 minutes after the blood is withdrawn from the patient. (If the blood stands, calcium diffuses into the cells and thus gives lower results.)
3. Preservation of serum: may be stored overnight in a refrigerator.
4. Precautions:
   a. Wash the precipitate exactly as directed in the procedure. Failure to remove interfering substances may give high results.
   b. Follow the directions *exactly* as given in the procedure.

Clark-Collip modification of Kramer-Tisdall method for calcium titration

Reagents needed

Sodium Oxalate, 0.100 N	(C-80)
Potassium Permanganate, 0.100 N	(C-81)
Ammonium Oxalate, 4%	(C-82)

Ammonium Hydroxide, Dilute (0.5%)   (C-83)
Sulfuric Acid, 1 N   (C-84)

Procedure

1. Get materials for a venipuncture. Make a venipuncture and withdraw about 8 ml. of blood. Gently expel the blood into a test tube and allow to clot. About 30 minutes after the withdrawal of blood, centrifuge the blood and pour off the serum. (If the blood is allowed to stand for a longer period of time, calcium leaves the serum and enters the cells, thus giving slightly lower results.)

2. Prepare and standardize a 0.01 N potassium permanganate solution as follows:

   a. Preparation of 0.01 N sodium oxalate: Pipet 10 ml. of 0.1 N sodium oxalate into a 100 ml. volumetric flask. Add distilled water to the 100 ml. mark. Mix. Label: 0.01 N Sodium Oxalate. This is a standard solution of exact normality. It will be used to determine the strength of approximately 0.01 N potassium permanganate, since this solution is unstable.

   b. Preparation of approximately 0.01 N potassium permanganate: Pipet 10 ml. of 0.1 N potassium permanganate into a 100 ml. volumetric flask. Add distilled water to the 100 ml. mark. Mix. Label: Approximate 0.01 N $KMnO_4$.

   c. Standardization of 0.01 N potassium permanganate: Pipet 5 ml. of 0.01 N sodium oxalate into a 125 ml. flask or similar container. Add 10 ml. of 1 N (approximate) sulfuric acid. Heat to about 90° C. by placing into a beaker containing boiling water. Using a buret, titrate with the approximately 0.01 N potassium permanganate. The titration will require about 5 ml., so add 4 ml. rather rapidly and then titrate drop by drop. The end point is reached when a single drop causes the solution to remain a faint pink color. Take the number of milliliters required and compute the factor for the 0.01 N potassium permanganate as follows.

   d. Computation of factor. The factor tells how weak or how strong the potassium permanganate solution is in comparison to an exact 0.01 N solution. If the potassium permanganate solution is weaker than 0.01 N, the factor will be less than 1.0. If the potassium permanganate solution is stronger than 0.01 N, the factor will be more than 1.0. Of course, if the potassium permanganate is exactly 0.01 N, the factor will be 1.0. Find the factor as follows: Take the number of milliliters of 0.01 N sodium oxalate that was used in the titration and divide it by the number of milliliters of potassium permanganate required to reach the end point. This is the factor, and it will be used later in the procedure.

   Example: If 4.8 ml. of potassium permanganate were needed, the factor is:

   $$\frac{5.0 \text{ (ml. of 0.01 N sodium oxalate used)}}{4.8 \text{ (ml. of potassium permanganate required)}} = 1.04$$

3. Pipet 2 ml. of serum into a 15 ml. graduated centrifuge tube (preferably a plastic tube, since the glass tubes sometimes break when centrifuged). Add 2 ml. of distilled water. Add 1 ml. of 4% ammonium oxalate. Mix thoroughly by tapping the bottom of the tube as illustrated in Fig. 54.

4. Let stand for 30 minutes in order to allow the ammonium oxalate to precipitate the calcium as calcium oxalate.

5. Centrifuge at 3000 RPM for at least 10 minutes. The precipitated calcium oxalate will then be seen as a small white precipitate in the bottom of the tube.

6. With a slow steady motion, invert the centrifuge tube, thus discarding

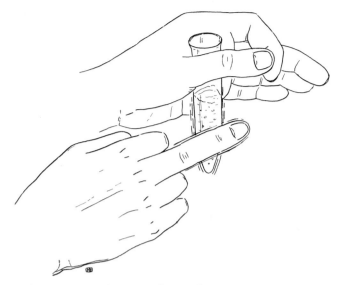

Fig. 54. Mixing the contents of a centrifuge tube.

the supernatant fluid and leaving the precipitate in the bottom of the tube. In this inverted position, place the tube on a piece of filter paper and allow to drain for a few minutes.

7. Remove any impurities from the precipitate by washing it *twice* in the following manner: Add 2 ml. of dilute ammonium hydroxide to the centrifuge tube. Suspend all the precipitate by tapping the bottom of the tube as illustrated in Fig. 54. Wash down the sides of the tube with another 1 ml. of the dilute ammonium hydroxide. Centrifuge for 10 minutes. Pour off the supernatant fluid with a slow steady motion and, with the centrifuge tube still in the inverted position, place it on a piece of filter paper to drain.

8. Add 1 ml. of 1 N (approximate) sulfuric acid. (This converts the calcium oxalate to oxalic acid.) Dissolve the precipitate by tapping the bottom of the tube. Wash down the sides of the tube with another milliliter of the sulfuric acid.

9. Get a 250 ml. beaker, fill about half full with water, and bring water to a boil. Place the centrifuge tube in this for 1 minute. (This is done because the following oxidation-reduction reaction proceeds better at a high temperature.)

10. Remove from water bath. Using a buret graduated in hundredths, titrate with the 0.01 N potassium permanganate solution until a *faint* pink color persists for 1 minute.

11. Take the number of milliliters of 0.01 N potassium permanganate used and the factor for the 0.01 N potassium permanganate and make the calculation according to the following:

$$\text{Ml. used} \times \text{Factor} \times 0.2 \times \frac{100}{2.0} = \text{Mg. of calcium/100 ml. of serum}$$

where ml. used = Ml. of 0.01 N potassium permanganate used in titration

Factor = Factor for potassium permanganate

0.2 = Amount of calcium that 1 ml. of 0.01 N potassium permanganate is equivalent to

100 = Amount of serum reported on (100 ml.)

2.0 = Amount of serum used

12. Example: If the factor for the 0.01 N potassium permanganate is

found to be 1.04, and 0.9 ml. of the potassium permanganate is used in the titration, the calcium value is found as follows:

$$\text{Ml. used} \times \text{Factor} \times \frac{\text{Calcium}}{\text{equivalent}} \times \frac{\text{Volume}}{\text{correction}} = \text{Mg./100 ml. of serum}$$

$$0.9 \quad \times \quad 1.04 \times \quad 0.2 \quad \times \quad \frac{100}{2} \quad = 9.4 \text{ mg./100 ml. of serum}$$

13. Normal values are 9.0 to 11.5, with a slight increase found in growing children. Low calcium values are of chief interest in tetany.

Bachra, Dauer, and Sobel method for determination of calcium by EDTA titration[9]

Calcium is determined by titration with disodium ethylenediaminetetra-acetate (EDTA), using cal-red* as the indicator. With urine, icteric serum, and hemolyzed serum, the calcium is first obtained as the oxalate. With clear serum (nonicteric or nonhemolyzed) the calcium is titrated directly.

Reagents needed

Potassium Hydroxide, 1.25 N	(C-85)
EDTA Solution	(C-86)
Cal-Red Indicator	(C-87)
Sodium Citrate, 0.05 M	(C-88)
Calcium Standard (1 ml.= 100 μg Ca)	(C-89)
Caprylic Alcohol	
Ammonium Oxalate, 10%	(C-90)
Hydrochloric Acid, 1 N	(C-91)
Ammonium Hydroxide, 5%	(C-92)

Procedures

1. Set up the following in 15 ml. conical centrifuge tubes:

   Standard (three tubes)
   Pipet 0.50 ml. of working standard.

   Unknown
   Pipet 0.50 ml. of serum plus 1 small drop of caprylic alcohol.
2. Proceed with one tube at a time to obtain a sharp end point. If samples remain in an alkaline medium beyond 10 minutes, the end points are not sharp.
3. Pipet 2.5 ml. of 1.25 N potassium hydroxide into the tube and mix.
4. Shake the indicator solution each time before using, to mix. Pipet 0.25 ml. of indicator solution into the tube. Mix by flipping the tube (Fig. 54).
5. *Immediately* titrate with EDTA solution until the color changes from wine-red to blue. The color change may be observed by placing the tube against a bright light.

Calculation

$$\frac{\text{Titration volume of unknown}}{\text{Titration volume of standard}} \times 0.05 \times \frac{100}{0.5} =$$

$$\frac{\text{Titration volume of unknown}}{\text{Titration volume of standard}} \times 10 \quad = \text{Mg./100 ml. (or mg.\%) Ca}$$

or

$$\frac{\text{Titration volume of unknown}}{\text{Titration volume of standard}} \times 5 \quad = \text{meq./L. calcium}$$

---

*Cal-red, or 2-hydroxy-1-(2-hydroxy-4-sulfo-1-naphthylazo)-3-naphthoic acid, may be obtained from Scientific Laboratories, Inc., Dallas, Texas.

Icteric and hemolyzed serum

There are instances when the only available specimen for analysis is either icteric or hemolyzed. Using the specimens that are either icteric or hemolyzed will give invalid results. The following treatment will enable the specimen to be used.

1. Pipet 0.50 ml. of serum into a conical tipped centrifuge tube.
2. Add 0.63 ml. of distilled water and 0.13 ml. of 10% ammonium oxalate. Mix.
3. Incubate in a 56° C. water bath for 15 minutes.
4. Centrifuge for 10 minutes at 3000 RPM.
5. Pour off the supernatant and invert the tube on a filter paper or blotter to drain.
6. Dissolve the precipitate in 0.25 ml. of 1 N HCl and add 0.25 ml. of 0.05 M sodium citrate. Mix. Refer to Fig. 54.
7. The tube is now ready for the addition of KOH (step 3 of the preceding method).
8. The procedure is carried out in the same way as with the clear serum.

Urine calcium

Calcium on a 24-hour collection of urine may be done with the serum method after the following preparation of the urine sample. If calcium determination only is to be done, the specimen may be collected in a gallon bottle containing 10 ml. of glacial acetic acid. If other tests are requested, where an acidified specimen would be undesirable, collect the specimen without the acid. Shake and mix the urine well, taking care that if there is any precipitate in the urine, none is left adhering to the walls of the bottle. Allow the urine to come to room temperature and measure the total volume in a graduated cylinder. The urine must be at room temperature, and the measurement must be accurate. Pipet 10 ml. of the well-mixed urine into a test tube and acidify to pH 1 with glacial acetic acid. Use nitrazine paper to check the pH. Proceed as follows:

1. Place the tube of acidified urine in a water bath (use a Pyrex beaker with a thermometer and beaker clamp).
2. Heat the specimen to 60° C. for 15 minutes, mixing occasionally with a stirring rod.
3. Pipet 0.50 ml. of the mixed urine into a conical tipped centrifuge tube.
4. Add 0.1 ml. of 10% ammonium oxalate. Mix.
5. Add 1 drop of methyl red indicator (0.1%). Mix.
6. With a pipet or dropper add, dropwise, 5% ammonium hydroxide (NH_4OH) until an orange color is obtained.
7. Place the tube in a boiling water bath for 20 minutes. Use the Pyrex beaker again.
8. Cool the tube to room temperature and centrifuge for 10 minutes at 3000 RPM.
9. Decant the supernatant and invert the tube on filter paper or blotter to drain.
10. Dissolve the precipitate in 0.25 ml. of 1 N HCl.
11. Add 0.25 ml. of 0.05 M sodium citrate. Mix.
12. Proceed as in step 3 of the serum procedure. The standard is set up just as it was for the serum. (Note: If less than 0.5 ml. of EDTA is used in the titration of the calcium in the urine, use a larger volume of urine—1.0 ml. or more—instead of the 0.50 ml. that was to be precipitated.) This is step 3 of the urine method.

Calculation

$$\frac{\text{Titration volume of unknown}}{\text{Titration volume of standard}} \times 10 = \text{Mg. Ca/100 ml. (or mg.\%)}$$

$$\frac{\text{Titration volume of unknown}}{\text{Titration volume of standard}} \times 5 = \text{meq. Ca/L.}$$

To calculate the mg.% or meq./L. for the 24-hour urine, the example is set, using the 0.50 ml. of urine precipitated (step 3).

$$\frac{\text{Titration volume of unknown}}{\text{Titration volume of standard}} \times 0.05 \times \frac{1}{0.50} \times \frac{\text{Urine volume}}{(24 \text{ hr.})} =$$

$$\frac{\text{Titration volume of unknown}}{\text{Titration volume of standard}} \times 0.1 \times \frac{\text{Urine volume}}{(24 \text{ hr.})} = \text{Mg. Ca/24 hr.}$$

$$\frac{\text{Titration volume of unknown}}{\text{Titration volume of standard}} \times 0.025 \times \frac{1}{0.50} \times \frac{\text{Urine volume}}{(24 \text{ hr.})} =$$

$$\frac{\text{Titration volume of unknown}}{\text{Titration volume of standard}} \times 0.05 \times \frac{\text{Urine volume}}{(24 \text{ hr.})} = \text{meq. Ca/24 hr.}$$

Calcium by flame photometry

Although calcium in serum has been successfully determined by chemical analyses and atomic absorption spectroscopy, there has been more difficulty with flame photometry. However, if the instrument purchased is suitable for calcium determinations and if care is used, accurate determinations can be produced. Glassware for the calcium determinations *must be acid-washed* in chromic acid each time before use. Glassware that is contaminated or nonchemically clean will give grossly elevated results. Standards in serum (available commercially) produce the most reliable results. Urine calcium determinations are more reliable when done by chemical analysis.

Ionized (diffusible) calcium

Determining ionized calcium is not a practical procedure for the routine laboratory. A very low ionized calcium results in tetany, causing severe muscle spasms and tremors. Therefore, a rapid method for calcium is desirable, as well as a method for determining the ionized calcium content. The following method of estimating ionized (diffusible) serum calcium is given. This differs from the McLean and Hastings[6] nomogram by utilizing the albumin and globulin ratio instead of the total protein in order to give a closer estimation of the ionized calcium value.

An explanation of the K value is as follows. Originally, a nomogram was developed from data obtained by Hopkins, Howard, and Eisenberg.[4] Total calcium, ionized (diffusible) calcium, and total serum protein with an A/G ratio of 1.8 were analyzed. The resultant factor (K) was 11.7.

Hanna, Nicholas, and Chamberlin assayed 100 thoroughly screened patients to obtain the K factor used in the following formula.[5]

By using Hanna's findings, the following constant is derived. First, the chemical equation would be:

$$\text{Ca proteinate} \longrightarrow \text{Ca}^{++} + \text{Protein}$$

Following the law of mass action, "The speed of a chemical reaction is pro-

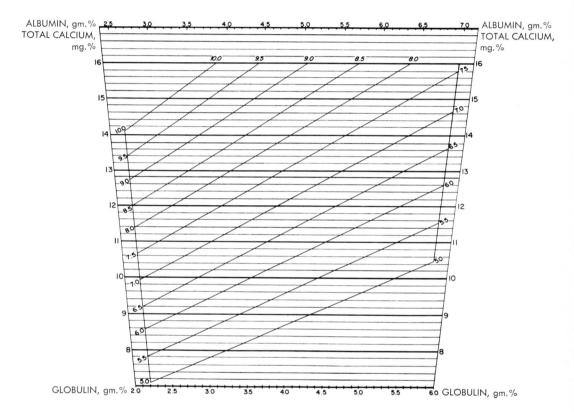

Fig. 55. Nomogram for estimating diffusible serum calcium. (From Hanna, E. A., Nicholas, H. O., and Chamberlin, J. A.: Nomogram for estimating diffusible serum calcium, Clin. Chem. **10:**235, 1964.)

portional to the active masses of the reacting substances," the following equation is:

$$\frac{\text{Ionized (diffusible) calcium} \times \text{Total protein}}{\text{Nonionized (nondiffusible) calcium}} = K$$

By assaying over 200 tests in duplicate the following values were obtained for the new K factor: Total calcium, 10.35 mg.%; ionized calcium, 6.16 mg.%; albumin, 4.40 gm.%, globulin, 3.60 gm.%, and A/G ratio, 1.22.

The following equation is set up to obtain the K factor:

$$\frac{6.16 \times 8.0}{10.35 - 6.16} = 11.8 \text{ (K value)}$$

Since the technician understands how the K value is obtained, the following formula may be used to calculate an ionized calcium:

$$\frac{11.8 \times \text{Total calcium (mg.\%)}}{11.8 + \text{Total protein (gm.\%)}} = \text{Ionized calcium (mg.\%)}$$

Normal values
5.5 to 6.6 mg.%

Using the nomogram

The nomogram shown in Fig. 55 is constructed with the K value being 11.8. The following is an example to show how the nomogram works. Patient "x" has an albumin of 4.0 gm.%, a globulin of 3.0 gm.%, and a total calcium of 10.0 mg.%. Using the nomogram, draw a line from the top line (albumin, 4.0 gm.%) to the bottom line (globulin, 3.0 gm.%). The total calcium line at 10.0 mg.% intersects the protein line, giving an ionized calcium result of 6.3 mg.%.

PHOSPHORUS

The discussion covers information significant to the student and procedure for the test.

Information significant to the student

Phosphorus is absorbed into the bloodstream from the small intestine. It is used in forming bone and in regulating the pH of blood. The normal phosphorus values are 2.4 to 4.7 mg./100 ml. of serum, with growing children having slightly higher values. An increase above the normal value is of primary concern in

Table 40. Conditions accompanied by abnormal phosphorus values

When increased	*When decreased*
Nephritis	Rickets
Healing bone fractures	Hyperparathyroidism
Hyperinsulinism	Myxedema
Hypervitaminosis	Osteomalacia
Hypoparathyroidism	Sprue
Uremia	Idiopathic steatorrhea
Pyloric obstruction	Neurofibromatosis
Starvation	Ether and chloroform anesthesia
Following Pituitrin administration	Following insulin and Adrenalin administration
	Lobar pneumonia

nephritis. Decreased values are of chief interest in rickets. Conditions in which increased or decreased phosphorus values may be expected are given in Table 40.

For the determination of phosphorus, the method of Fiske and SubbaRow is commonly used. In this method, serum is obtained. Trichloroacetic acid is added to precipitate the proteins. After filtering, a molybdate solution is added. This unites with the phosphorus to form phosphomolybdic acid. The phosphomolybdic acid is then reduced by an organic reagent to form a blue color. The intensity of blue color is proportional to the amount of phosphorus present. The depth of color is measured in a colorimeter.

Procedure for phosphorus

The following general considerations pertain to the procedure for phosphorus:

1. Preparation of patient: must be fasting.
2. Preparation of blood: serum. The serum should be obtained 30 minutes after the blood is withdrawn.
3. Preservation of serum: refrigerate.
4. Precautions: follow the directions *exactly* as given in the procedure.

Fiske-SubbaRow method[7]
Phosphates (inorganic) in serum

Reagents needed

Trichloroacetic Acid, 10%	(C-63)
Molybdate Reagent	(C-93)
Sulfuric Acid, 10 N	(C-94)
Reducing Reagent (Aminonaphtholsulfonic Acid)	(C-95)
Phosphorus Stock Standard, 0.1 mg./ml.	(C-96)

Phosphorus Working Standard (1 ml. = 0.01 mg. P)
   Using a 100 ml. volumetric flask, dilute 10 ml. of stock standard to 100 ml. with distilled water.

Procedure

Preparation of protein-free filtrate

1. Pipet 1 ml. of serum into a 15 ml. test tube.
2. Add 9 ml. of 10% TCA. Stopper and shake.
3. Allow the tube to stand for 15 minutes and then centrifuge or filter through Whatman No. 42 filter paper.

Development of color

1. Set up the following in 15 ml. test tubes:

   Blank
      a. Pipet 5.0 ml. of TCA into tube.
      b. Pipet 3.6 ml. of distilled water.

   Standards (three tubes)
      a. Pipet 4.5 ml. of TCA into each tube.
      b. Add 1.6 ml. of distilled water.
      c. Add 2.5 ml. of working standard.

   Unknown
      a. Pipet 5.0 ml. of filtrate into the test tube.
      b. Add 3.6 ml. of distilled water.
2. Add 1.0 ml. of molybdate reagent to all tubes. Mix.
3. Add 0.4 ml. of cold reducing reagent. Mix thoroughly.

4. Allow the tubes to stand for 15 minutes (use timer) for the full development of color.
5. Read against reagent blank at 660 mμ or use a filter No. 66.

Calculation

$$\frac{\text{Optical density of unknown}}{\text{Optical density of standard}} \times 0.025 \times \frac{100}{0.5} =$$

$$\frac{\text{O.D. of unknown}}{\text{O.D. of standard}} \times 5 = \text{Mg.\% phosphorus}$$

Urine phosphorus

To determine urine phosphorus, it is necessary to make a 1 to 5 or a 1 to 10 dilution with distilled water. This dilution is then treated in the same manner as the serum. The result obtained is then multiplied by the appropriate dilution factor, either 5 or 10.

Normal range
Serum 2.4 to 4.7 mg.%
Urine 0.34 to 1.0 gm./24 hr.

STUDENTS' SUMMARY FOR THE ELECTROLYTES

The significant information consists of the following:

Normal and abnormal values
Methods of analysis and synopsis of procedures
Conversion of milligrams/100 ml. to milliequivalents per liter
Conversion of milliequivalents per liter to milligrams/100 ml.
Conversion of volumes percent to millimoles per liter
Conversion of millimoles per liter to volumes percent

Normal and abnormal values

Test	Normal values	When increased	When decreased
Sodium	300 to 330 mg./100 ml. of serum	Dehydration Hypercorticoadrenalism	Addison's disease Alkali deficit
Potassium	16 to 22 mg./100 ml. of serum	Addison's disease Renal disease	Diabetes Hyperinsulinism
Chloride (as NaCl)	450 to 500 mg./100 ml. of whole blood 570 to 620 mg./100 ml. of serum	Nephritis Prostatic obstruction Eclampsia Anemia	Excessive vomiting Diarrhea Uremia Extensive burns Fevers Acute infections
CO$_2$ combining power	55 to 75 vol. %	Alkalosis: Excessive alkali therapy	Acidosis: Diabetes Nephritis Toxic conditions
pH	7.35 to 7.45	Alkalosis	Acidosis
Calcium	9.0 to 11.5 mg./100 ml. of serum	Hyperparathyroidism Hyperthyroidism Multiple myeloma	Tetany Bone disorders
Phosphorus	2.5 to 4.0 mg./100 ml. of serum	Nephritis Hypoparathyroidism	Rickets Hyperparathyroidism

Methods of analysis and synopsis of procedures

Test	Method	Synopsis of procedure
Sodium	Flame photometer	1. Obtain serum 2. Vaporize and burn serum to produce color 3. Isolate color with filter 4. Measure depth of color with photoelectric cell 5. Compare with standards
Potassium	Flame photometer	Same as for sodium above
Chloride	Whitehorn	1. Make protein-free filtrate 2. Add nitric acid and a measured excess of standard silver nitrate to precipitate chloride as silver chloride 3. Add indicator, ferric ammonium sulfate 4. Titrate excess silver nitrate with standard thiocyanate solution 5. Stop titration at end point of salmon-red color 6. Find chloride value by calculation
	Schales-Schales	1. Make protein-free filtrate 2. Add indicator, diphenylcarbazone 3. Titrate with standard mercuric nitrate solution, which removes chloride as undissociated mercuric chloride 4. Stop at end point indicated by a pale violet or light purple color 5. Find chloride content by calculation
CO_2 combining power	Van Slyke	1. Obtain plasma; if not used immediately, keep under oil to prevent loss of carbon dioxide 2. Saturate plasma with carbon dioxide from breath 3. Add saturated plasma to Van Slyke gas apparatus 4. Add alcohol to prevent foaming 5. Add lactic acid to help liberate carbon dioxide 6. Create vacuum with mercury levelling bulb to complete liberation of carbon dioxide 7. Measure carbon dioxide liberated by adjusting mercury levelling bulb 8. Calculate volumes percent of carbon dioxide
pH	pH meter	1. Obtain heparinized blood 2. Keep specimen in syringe 3. Rinse pH blood electrode with saline 4. Standardize machine with buffer solution of pH 7.0 5. Introduce blood sample into electrode 6. Make direct reading from galvanometer 7. Do at least three readings
Calcium	Clark-Collip modification of Kramer-Tisdall method	1. Obtain serum 2. Add ammonium oxalate to precipitate calcium as calcium oxalate 3. Centrifuge 4. Wash precipitate with dilute ammonium hydroxide to remove impurities 5. Add sulfuric acid to convert calcium oxalate to oxalic acid 6. Heat and titrate with standard potassium permanganate, which is reduced by oxalic acid 7. Stop titration at end point indicated by pink color of solution 8. Find calcium content by calculation

Methods of analysis and synopsis of procedures—cont'd

Test	Method	Synopsis of procedure
Calcium—cont'd	Roe-Kahn	1. Obtain serum 2. Add trichloroacetic acid to precipitate proteins 3. Filter 4. Add sodium hydroxide and trisodium phosphate to precipitate calcium as tricalcium phosphate 5. Wash precipitate with alkaline alcohol solution to remove impurities 6. Add acid molybdate and an organic reagent to form color complex with tricalcium phosphate 7. Measure in colorimeter
	Bachra, Dauer, and Sobel EDTA method	1. Obtain serum 2. Add KOH to make serum alkaline 3. Add cal-red indicator 4. Titrate with disodium ethylenediaminetetra-acetate (EDTA) 5. Calculate
Phosphorus	Fiske-SubbaRow	1. Obtain serum 2. Add trichloroacetic acid to precipitate proteins 3. Filter 4. Add molybdate solution to form phosphomolybdic acid 5. Add organic reagent that reduces phosphomolybdic acid to form a blue color complex 6. Measure in colorimeter

Conversion of milligrams/100 ml. to milliequivalents per liter

Although the information is seldom used by the average technician, student examinations usually contain questions concerning the conversion of milligrams/100 ml. to milliequivalents per liter. Consequently, a brief discussion is included here.

Milligrams/100 ml. deals with weight, whereas milliequivalents per liter deals with combining power. For example, the element calcium has a specific weight, which may be given as milligrams/100 ml. However, it also has combining power, determined by its valence, which may be expressed as milliequivalents per liter.

The following abbreviations are usually used:

$$\text{mg.} = \text{milligram}$$
$$\text{ml.} = \text{milliliter}$$
$$\text{mEq. or meq.} = \text{milliequivalent}$$

If you are asked to convert mg./100 ml. to meq. per liter, use the formula:

$$\text{meq. per liter} = \text{mg./100 ml.} \times \frac{10}{\text{equivalent weight}}$$ where 10 is used to convert 100 ml. to 1 liter

Example: Convert 325 mg. of sodium/100 ml. to meq. per liter. Equivalent weight of sodium is 23. Use the formula:

$$\text{meq. per liter} = \text{mg./100 ml.} \times \frac{10}{\text{equivalent weight}}$$
$$= 325 \times \frac{10}{23}$$
$$= 141$$

Table 41. Electrolyte conversion factors

Electrolyte	Unit	Factor	Unit
Na	mg.%	0.435	meq./L.
Na	meq./L.	2.3	mg.%
Na	meq./L.	0.0585	gm./L. as NaCl
K	mg.%	0.256	meq./L.
K	meq./L.	3.91	mg.%
K	meq./L.	0.0746	gm./L. as KCl
Cl	mg.%	0.282	meq./L.
Cl	meq./L.	3.55	mg.%
Cl	meq./L.	0.0585	gm./L. as NaCl
CO_2	vol.%	0.45	meq./L.
CO_2	meq./L.	2.24	vol.%
Ca	mg.%	0.5	meq./L.
Ca	meq./L.	2.0	mg.%
PO_4	mg.%	0.581	meq./L.
PO_4	meq./L.	1.72	mg.%

A shortcut in the above formula may be taken by first dividing 10 by 23. The number 10 divided by 23 equals 0.435; this is known as the conversion factor for sodium. The formula then becomes:

$$\text{meq. per liter} = \text{mg./100 ml.} \times \text{conversion factor}$$

Thus, to convert 325 mg. of sodium/100 ml. to meq. per liter by using the conversion factor of 0.435, we have:

$$
\begin{aligned}
\text{meq. per liter} &= \text{mg./100 ml.} \times \text{conversion factor} \\
&= 325 \times 0.435 \\
&= 141
\end{aligned}
$$

By multiplying the units in column two of Table 41, by the factor given, you may obtain the desired unit (in column four).

Conversion of milliequivalents per liter to milligrams/100 ml.

If you are asked to convert milliequivalents per liter to milligrams/100 ml., use the formula:

$$\text{mg./100 ml.} = \text{meq. per liter} \times \frac{\text{equivalent weight}}{10}$$

where the figure 10 is used to convert 1 L. to 100 ml.

Example: Convert 4.5 meq. of calcium per liter to milligrams/100 ml. The equivalent weight of calcium is 20. Use the formula:

$$
\begin{aligned}
\text{mg./100 ml.} &= \text{meq. per liter} \times \frac{\text{equivalent weight}}{10} \\
&= 4.5 \times \frac{20}{10} \\
&= 9.0
\end{aligned}
$$

Conversion of volumes percent to millimoles per liter

Gases are sometimes expressed in millimoles per liter instead of volumes percent. And another pet examination question is the conversion of volumes percent of carbon dioxide to millimoles (mM) per liter. A mole is the molecular weight expressed in grams and a millimole is one thousandth part of this.

To convert carbon dioxide in volumes percent to millimoles (mM) per liter, use this formula:

$$mM \text{ per liter} = \text{volumes percent} \times 0.446$$

Example: Convert 50 vol.% of carbon dioxide to millimoles per liter. Use the formula:

$$
\begin{aligned}
mM \text{ per liter} &= \text{volumes percent} \times 0.446 \\
&= 50 \times 0.446 \\
&= 22.3
\end{aligned}
$$

Conversion of millimoles per liter to volumes percent

To convert carbon dioxide in millimoles per liter to volumes percent, use this formula:

$$\text{volumes percent} = \text{millimoles per liter} \times 2.24$$

Example: Convert 22.3 millimoles per liter of carbon dioxide to volumes percent, using the formula:

$$
\begin{aligned}
\text{volumes percent} &= mM \text{ per liter} \times 2.24 \\
&= 22.3 \times 2.24 \\
&= 50
\end{aligned}
$$

REFERENCES

1. Annino, J. S.: Clinical chemistry: principles and procedures, ed. 2, Boston and Toronto, 1960, Little, Brown & Co.
2. Albanese, A. A., and Lein, M.: Microcolorimetric determination of sodium in human biologic fluids, J. Lab. & Clin. Med. **33:**246, 1948.
3. Lochhead, H. B., and Purcell, M. K.: Rapid determination of serum potassium employing glycine-phenol reagent, Am. J. Clin. Path. **21:**877, 1951.
4. Hopkins, T., Howard, J. E., and Eisenberg, H.: Ultrafiltration studies on calcium and phosphorus in human serum, Bull. Johns Hopkins Hosp. **91:**1, 1952.
5. Hanna, E. A., Nicholas, H. O., and Chamberlin, J. A.: Nomogram for estimating diffusible serum calcium, Clin. Chem. **10:**235, 1964.
6. McLean, F. C., and Hastings, A. B.: The state of calcium in the fluids of the body, J. Biol. Chem. **108:**285, 1935.
7. Fiske, C. H., and SubbaRow, Y.: The colorimetric determination of phosphorus, J. Biol. Chem. **66:**375, 1925.
8. Henry, R. J.: Clinical chemistry; principles and technics, New York, 1964, Hoeber Medical Division, Harper & Row, Publishers.
9. Bachra, B. N., Dauer, A., and Sobel, A. E.: The complexometric titration of micro and ultramicro quantities of calcium in blood serum, urine, and inorganic salt solutions, Clin. Chem. **4:**107, 1958.

Chapter 14

Enzymes

T he technician may use the term "enzyme" many times a day and know the tests required for enzyme studies, but what is an enzyme and what is the history concerning enzymes?

An enzyme is an organic catalyst produced by a living cell but one that acts independently of the cell. (A catalyst is a substance that will excite or accelerate a reaction, but it is not itself involved or altered by the reaction.) Most of these organic enzymes are easily destroyed by heat, acids, or alkalies. They are active only within a limited pH range, are protein in nature, and will act on only a specific or particular substance or on closely related substances. The substrate is the substance upon which the enzyme acts. Most enzyme names are obtained by adding the suffix "ase" to the substance (substrate) acted upon. Therefore lipase, amylase, protease, sucrase, uricase, and lactase act upon fat, starch, protein, sucrose, uric acid, and lactose, respectively. Upon occasion, an enzyme is named after its function rather than its substrate. Two examples of this are dehydrogenases, which bring about the removal of hydrogen, and oxidases, which bring about oxidation. The enzymes that have been known for many years still maintain their original nondescriptive names—pepsin, ptyalin, trypsin, and papain.

The word "enzyme" has not always been used to describe the catalytic reaction, nor has the reaction always been understood. We will not get too involved in a history of the enzymes, but the technician should know the basic beginnings of this field. From early times man has known of the following chemical changes that occur spontaneously: (1) the fermentation of sugar with a final product of alcohol, (2) the souring of wine, and (3) the souring of milk.

The action in each case is a result of microorganisms, growing and changing the original substance. We know now that these changes are brought about by the action of enzymes. Years ago it was thought that these reactions were bound to living organisms and their life cycles and would occur only when those were present in the substance in a living state.

Payen and Persoz (1833) precipitated a starch-digesting enzyme from a malt extract by means of alcohol. This was compared with the natural fermentation "ferments" that caused the souring of the milk or wine. This enzyme or "ferment" was given the name *diastase*. During the same period of time that Payen and Persoz were working with the starch-digesting enzyme, Beaumont found the digestive action of the gastric juice to be due to a chemical substance. However, this latter was not isolated until 1836, when Schwann isolated the substance and called it *pepsin*. Other digestive substances such as saliva and pancreatic juice were also studied at that time. Although there was great activity during this period, the newly found substances were called "ferments," not enzymes. Ferment was the term used for any agent or substance bringing about a chemical reaction in biological material. Later, Kuhne introduced the term "enzyme" as referring to a biological catalyst. Buchner (1897) finally settled some heated debates about the action of the enzymes by proving that the microorganisms used intracellular enzymes to produce their effects.

The enzymes of the blood are present in very small quantities. Because of this, they cannot be measured in the usual terms of milligrams/100 ml., but must be measured in special units. The units vary with the method of determination.

In the determination of blood enzymes, the basic principle involved is this. The enzyme is allowed to decompose a substrate. After a definite period of time, the amount of decomposition is measured. The more the decomposition, the greater is the concentration of enzyme.

This chapter considers the enzymes listed below.

> Amylase
> Lipase
> Alkaline and acid phosphatase
> Total acid and prostatic acid phosphatase
> Glutamic-oxaloacetic transaminase
> Glutamic-pyruvic transaminase

Note that all the enzymes end in -ase. The enzyme amylase is sometimes referred to as diastase.

AMYLASE

The discussion covers information significant to the student and procedures for the test.

Information significant to the student

The normal values for amylase are 80 to 150 units. Because of the variable factors involved in its determination, however, only values above 200 are considered significant. Conditions in which an increased or decreased value may be expected are listed in Table 42. Abnormal values are of primary interest in those disorders listed in italics.

A commonly used method for the determination of amylase is the procedure of Somogyi. In that method, three tubes are prepared.

The first tube contains serum, starch paste, and acid sodium chloride. The amylase in the serum will decompose the starch to reducing sugars. The acid sodium chloride is added to allow the reaction to take place at optimum conditions of pH and electrolytic content.

The second tube is a blank tube containing only the starch and acid sodium chloride. The purpose of this tube is to determine the amount of reducing substances in the starch, if any.

Table 42. Conditions accompanied by abnormal amylase values

When increased	*When decreased*
Acute pancreatitis	Cirrhosis of liver
Carcinoma of head of pancreas	Carcinoma of liver
Duodenal ulcer	Abscess of liver
Perforation of gastric ulcer	Hepatitis
Hyperthyroidism	Acute alcoholism
Mumps	Toxemias of pregnancy
Acute injury of spleen	
Renal disease with impaired renal function	
High intestinal obstruction	

The third tube is a control tube containing only the serum and acid sodium chloride. The purpose of this tube is to determine the amount of reducing substances in the serum.

All three tubes are incubated for 30 minutes to enhance the reaction. Copper sulfate is then added to each tube to stop the reactions. Sodium tungstate is added to precipitate the proteins, and the contents of each tube are filtered.

A glucose determination is run on all three filtrates. The glucose values of the blank tube and control tube are added. This, of course, is the total glucose present in the starch and serum that is *not* due to the amylase activity. When this is subtracted from the glucose value of the tube containing the starch paste and serum, the amylase activity is obtained. This is reported as units of amylase. Thus:

Units of amylase = Glucose value of tube containing starch paste and serum *minus* Glucose values of blank tube and control tube

Example:

Units of amylase = 200 mg./100 ml. − 100 mg./100 ml. = 100

Procedures for amylase

The following general considerations pertain to the procedure for amylase:

1. Preparation of patient: need not be fasting.
2. Preparation of blood: serum or plasma.
3. Preservation of serum or plasma: may be stored in a refrigerator.
4. Precautions:
   a. Temperature of water bath or incubator must not vary from figure given in procedure.
   b. Follow the *exact* directions given in the procedure.

Leitz Photrometer method

Directions for preparing the reagents are given as follows:

Reagents

Purified Cornstarch
1. In a tall 1000 ml. cylinder place 100 gm. of cornstarch (U.S.P.).
2. Add 1000 ml. of approximately 0.01 N hydrochloric acid.
3. Agitate vigorously and frequently for an hour.
4. Allow starch to settle (about 1 hour).

5. Pour off and discard the supernatant liquid.
6. Add 1000 ml. of 0.05% sodium chloride.
7. Agitate vigorously and frequently for an hour.
8. Allow starch to settle.
9. Decant and discard the supernatant liquid.
10. Wash the starch once more with 0.05% sodium chloride.
11. Either decant the supernatant liquid, after allowing the starch to settle, or filter the suspension through a Buchner funnel.
12. Spread the starch on a clean plate and allow it to dry in air, protecting it from dust.

Cornstarch Suspension 1.5%

1. In a small beaker make a thin paste of 1.5 gm. of the purified cornstarch with 5 ml. of distilled water.
2. Heat 90 ml. of distilled water to boiling.
3. Pour the starch paste into the boiling water.
4. Rinse the beaker with 5 ml. of distilled water and add the rinsings to the boiling liquid.
5. Boil for 1 minute with vigorous stirring.
6. Cover the beaker and allow to cool to room temperature.
7. Discard when starch settles out or mold appears.

Acid Sodium Chloride

1. Dissolve 10 gm. of reagent grade sodium chloride in about 800 ml. of distilled water in a liter volumetric flask.
2. Add 3 ml. of 0.01 N hydrochloric acid.
3. Dilute to volume with distilled water and mix well.

Copper Sulfate, 5%

1. Dissolve 50 gm. of reagent grade crystalline copper sulfate ($CuSO_4 \cdot 5H_2O$) in distilled water in a liter volumetric flask.
2. Dilute to volume with distilled water and mix well.

Sodium Tungstate, 6%

1. Dissolve 60 gm. of sodium tungstate ($Na_2WO_4 \cdot 2H_2O$—Folin Special) in 850 ml. of distilled water in a liter volumetric flask.
2. The solution should be neutral or slightly alkaline to phenolphthalein. If it is not, adjust by the addition of sulfuric acid or sodium hydroxide.
3. Dilute to volume with distilled water and mix well.

*Procedure**

Somogyi, M.   Proc. Exp. Biol. Med. 32, 538 (1934)

In each of two test tubes labeled "A" and "B" place:
    5 cc. of 1.5% cornstarch suspension and
    2 cc. of acid sodium chloride solution.
In a third test tube labelled "C" place:
    5 cc. of distilled water and
    2 cc. of acid sodium chloride solution
Place the tubes in a water bath at 40° C. for 10 minutes.
Add 1 cc. of serum or plasma to both Tube "A" and Tube "C".
Add 1 cc. of distilled water to Tube "B".
After mixing the contents of each tube, stopper it.
Place all three tubes in a water bath at 40° C. and leave them there for exactly 30 minutes.
Remove the tubes from the bath and quickly add to each 1 cc.. of 5% copper sulfate solution.

Mix well.

Add to each tube 1 cc. of 6% sodium tungstate solution.

Shake vigorously until foaming ceases.

Centrifuge or filter each, collecting the filtrates in correspondingly marked test tubes.

Refilter if filtrate is not clear.

Transfer 1 cc. of each filtrate to correspondingly marked Folin sugar tubes.

Add 1 cc. of distilled water to each tube.

Determine the amount of glucose in each according to the "Glucose in Blood" method, using the above diluted filtrates in place of the tungstic acid filtrates.

The number of amylase units per 100 cc. of serum or plasma is obtained by substracting the glucose values of Tube "B" (starch blank) and that of Tube "C" (serum blank) from the glucose value of Tube "A" (total reducing substances), and then multiplying the result by two.

Note: For the Blood Amylase and the Micro Glucose methods, the standards for blood glucose are used.

Somogyi method[1]

The Somogyi method is based on the measurement of time required for the amylase enzyme to convert (hydrolyze) starch to polysaccharides to glucose. The rate of speed of the conversion is proportional to the amount of amylase in the serum, urine, or fluid. Iodine is used as an indicator, yielding the following colors as the starch is converted to maltose:

Starch (deep blue) → Polysaccharides (red or violet) → Maltose (color of the iodine solution)

The end point of the reaction is an amber color. The color changes are specific enough for the test to be done visually. With experience, the technician will be able to determine, by the color of the preceding check, how much time lapse can be allowed between color checks.

Reagents needed

Starch, Sterile*
Iodine Indicator   (C-97)

Procedure

Serum

1. For each serum to be analyzed, arrange the tubes in the following manner:

Test No.	a	b
4	0	00000000
3	0	00000000
2	0	00000000
1	0	00000000

   a. Test tubes containing serum, urine, or fluid to be analyzed.
   b. Kahn tubes (eight per test) to contain the iodine indicator.
2. Sterilize the cap of the starch substrate by swabbing with 70% alcohol. With a sterile syringe and needle, remove enough starch to allow 2.0 ml. per test.
3. Place the tube containing the starch substrate into either a 37° or a 40° C. water bath.
4. Pipet into each of the Kahn tubes, 0.25 ml. of the iodine indicator.
5. Number tubes (regular size) for the tests and place in the water bath. Into each tube, pipet 2.0 ml. of starch substrate.

*May be ordered from Sigma Chemical Co., St. Louis, Mo.

6. Set timer for 40 minutes for a single test and add 1 minute for each additional test. For example, the timer would be set for 43 minutes for four tests.
7. Into the starch substrate of tube 1, pipet 0.5 ml. of serum, mix thoroughly, and *start timer*. Exactly 1 minute later, pipet into tube 2 and at exactly 1-minute intervals add the test sera to their substrate tubes until all of the tests are started.
8. After 3 minutes, remove 0.25 ml. of the substrate-serum mixture and place into the Kahn tube containing iodine indicator. Shake gently and note the color.
9. If the color is purple, wait for 3 minutes and withdraw another 0.25 ml. of mixture and add to the second iodine tube. Record the elapsed time. Continue the testing and recording of time until the end point is reached. This is an amber or reddish brown color. Test 1 minute beyond the end point to verify that the reaction is completed.

Urine

1. Urine amylase determinations should be performed on specimens collected during a timed interval. Measure and record the volume of urine and time of collection.
2. Adjust the pH to 7.0 to 7.4. If below a pH of 7.0 (acid), adjust with solid sodium carbonate. If the pH is above 7.4 (alkaline), adjust with solid potassium acid phosphate (KH_2PO_4).
3. Start with undiluted urine. If the reaction has gone past the end point in 3 minutes, dilute 1.0 ml. of urine with 4.0 ml. of 0.5% NaCl and begin again, using 0.5 ml. of diluted urine.
4. The test for urine amylase is done in the same manner as for the serum.

Calculation

The factor to be used may be found on the bottle of starch substrate. However, if you incubate the substrate at 37° C. calculate by using a factor of 1800. If the incubation is done at a temperature of 40° C. calculate with a factor of 1600. The accompanying example contains three serum specimens and one urine specimen. One of the serum specimens was quite elevated and the end point was reached before the next spot test was done. The serum may be diluted and the test started again at a later time. When checking the progress of the reaction, the time of the spot test is recorded below the previous time check. At the end point, the time recorded (underlined) is subtracted from the starting time.

	Tube 1 (serum)	Tube 2 (serum)	Tube 3 (serum)	Tube 4 (urine)
Starting time	43 min.	42 min.	41 min.	40 min.
Spot checks	40 min.	39 min.	38 min.	37 min.
	37 min.	Color beyond end point	35 min.	34 min.
	36 min.	Dilute serum and start at later time	20 min.	31 min.
			18 min.	28 min.
			15 min.	
		Starting time for diluted Tube 2:		
		24 min.		
		23 min.		
End point	35 min.	22 min.	11 min.	25 min.
	8 min.	2 min.	30 min.	15 min.

Subtracting the end point time from the starting time we have the following:

Test 1   8 minutes

Test 2   2 minutes (serum dilution: 1 ml. of serum and 2 ml. of 0.5% NaCl)

Test 3   30 minutes

Test 4   15 minutes (urine dilution: 1 ml. of urine and 4 ml. of 0.5% NaCl)

Serum calculation

$$\frac{\text{Factor of substrate}}{\text{Minutes required to obtain end point}} \times \underset{\text{(if any)}}{\text{Dilution}} = \text{Units, percent amylase}$$

Test 1 $\dfrac{1600}{8} = 200$ Somogyi units/100 ml.

Test 2 $\dfrac{1600}{2} \times 3 = 2400$ Somogyi units/100 ml.

Test 3 $\dfrac{1600}{30} = 53$ Somogyi units/100 ml.

Test 4 $\dfrac{1600}{15} \times 5 = 533$ Somogyi units/100 ml.

Urine calculation

To obtain the amount of units excreted per hour the following calculation is necessary. The value of 533 Somogyi units/100 ml. was obtained on 150 ml. of urine collected in a 2-hour period:

$$\frac{\text{Somogyi units/100 ml.}}{\text{Time of collection}} \times \frac{\text{Urine volume}}{100 \text{ ml.}} = \frac{533}{2} \times \frac{150}{100} = 399.75 \text{ or } 400 \text{ Somogyi units excreted per hour}$$

Normal values

Normal serum	80 to 150 Somogyi units/100 ml.
Borderline serum	Up to 300 Somogyi units/100 ml.
Normal urine	50 to 400 Somogyi units per hour[2]
Urine in diseases other than pancreatitis	Up to 800 Somogyi units per hour
Urine in acute pancreatitis	Above 900 Somogyi units per hour

LIPASE

The discussion covers information significant to the student and the procedure for the test.

Information significant to the student

The normal range for lipase is 0 to 1.5 Cherry-Crandall units. One unit is equivalent to 1.0 ml. of 0.05 N NaOH.

An elevated lipase value is of chief concern in acute pancreatitis. In this disease, both amylase and lipase are high. The amylase value, however, usually returns to normal after 3 days, whereas the lipase value generally takes 7 or more days to return to normal. Therefore, if the serum has not been obtained within 3 days after the attack, the lipase determination becomes the more significant diagnostic aid.

In addition to acute pancreatitis, elevated lipase values may be found in intestinal obstruction and carcinoma of the pancreas.

For the determination of lipase, the procedure of Cherry and Crandall is commonly used. In this method, serum is obtained. Two test tubes are secured. One tube is marked Patient and the other Control. One milliliter of serum is added to each tube. The control tube is heated to destroy the enzyme. A buffer solution is added to both patient and control tubes, its function being to regulate the pH and electrolyte content to optimum conditions. The substrate, olive oil, is added to each tube. The tubes are then incubated at body temperature (37.5° C.) for 24 hours. This enables the lipase to decompose the olive oil into fatty acids. Alcohol and an indicator are added. The amount of fatty acids produced in each tube is then found by titration with twentieth normal sodium hydroxide. The titration figure of the control is subtracted from the titration figure of the patient. The answer is the lipase value expressed in milliliters of twentieth normal sodium hydroxide.

Lipase value = Ml. of 0.05 N NaOH used in titration of patient *minus*
Ml. of 0.05 N NaOH used in titration of control

Example:

Lipase value = 2 ml. − 1 ml. = 1 ml. of 0.05 N NaOH

Procedure for lipase

The following general considerations pertain to the procedure for lipase.

1. Preparation of patient: must be fasting.
2. Preparation of blood: serum.
3. Preservation of serum: does *not* keep. Test must be run within 2 hours after the withdrawal of blood.
4. Precautions:
   a. Olive oil emulsion must not be rancid.
   b. Temperature of water bath or incubator must not vary from figure given in procedure.
   c. Timing of incubation must be exact.
   d. Follow the *exact* directions given in the procedure.

Cherry-Crandall method

The method of Cherry and Crandall is given below. The necessary reagents are listed and the procedure follows:

*Reagents needed**

Sodium Hydroxide, 0.05 N	(C-98)
Phosphate Buffer, pH 7.0	(C-99)
Olive Oil Substrate, 50%	(C-100)
Phenolphthalein Indicator, 1%	(C-150)
Ethyl Alcohol, 95%	

Procedure

1. The 50% olive oil emulsion should be prepared fresh every 2 weeks and stored in a refrigerator.
2. Make a venipuncture and withdraw about 7 ml. of blood. Gently expel the blood into the test tube, let clot, and then centrifuge to obtain the serum. This must be used within a few hours, since the lipase activity is affected upon long standing.
3. Get two large test tubes. Label one Patient and the other Control.

---

*May be purchased from Sigma Chemical Co., St. Louis, Mo.

4. Pipet 3.0 ml. of distilled water into each tube. Add 1.0 ml. of serum to each tube with an Ostwald-Folin pipet.
5. Destroy the enzyme in the control tube by heating in boiling water for 5 minutes. Place in room temperature water bath and cool to room temperature.
6. Add 0.5 ml. of the phosphate buffer (pH 7.0) solution to both the patient's tube and the control tube.
7. Add 2.0 ml. of the 50% olive oil emulsion to each tube.
8. Incubate both tubes for 24 hours at 37.5° C.
9. Add 3 ml. of the 95% alcohol to each tube. Add 2 drops of the phenolphthalein indicator to each tube. Mix gently.
10. Using the twentieth normal sodium hydroxide, titrate each tube to a permanent *faint* pink color. Record the amount of sodium hydroxide used for each titration.
11. Find the lipase value as follows:

Lipase value = Ml. of twentieth normal sodium hydroxide used in titration of patient's tube *minus* Ml. used in titration of control tube

Example:

Lipase value = 2.0 ml. (used for patient) *minus* 1.1 ml. (used for control)

Lipase value = 0.9 units

Normal values

0 to 1.5 units

ALKALINE AND ACID PHOSPHATASE[3,4]

The two phosphatases routinely analyzed are called alkaline and acid phosphatases according to the optimum pH at which they are measured.

The optimum pH of the alkaline phosphatase is 9.7. Alkaline phosphatase is found in the blood serum and plasma and in bone, kidney, liver, mammary gland, intestine, lung, spleen, leukocytes, seminiferous tubules, and the adrenal cortex. However, it is found chiefly in the bone and liver. Since this enzyme plays an important part in bone formation, there is an increase of activity in children. At birth, the alkaline phosphatase activity is low, rising rapidly in the first month of life, remaining highly elevated the first 2 years, and then decreasing to the normal child's range of activity.

The alkaline phosphatase increases in the blood plasma in bone disease. There have been various theories in regard to how this increased action takes place. One theory is that in the absence of normal bone synthesis, the bones' capacity for cellular activity is greater. With this greater activity there is an increased formation of phosphatase. Other explanations are given. The increased enzyme action may be one result of an overproduction of the enzyme in the bone attempting to compensate for the lesion, or there may be a forced discharge of the enzyme from the injured bone tissue. Diseases associated with this increase in the alkaline phosphatase are Paget's disease, rickets, bone atrophy, osteomalacia, osteoporosis, and bone malignancy. Moderately increased values have been found in hyperparathyroidism.

Alkaline phosphatase is also excreted into the bile by the normal liver. The serum values are usually increased in jaundice due to mechanical obstruction. Most liver diseases cause an elevation of results.

A decrease in the enzyme reaction, giving consistently low results, is found in individuals with hypophosphatasia (a hereditary bone disease), anemia, infectious hepatitis, or cretinism and in children who have an unusually early development.

The optimum pH of the acid phosphatase is 5.0. This enzyme was first discovered in male urine. Further investigation has shown the prostate gland to be extremely rich in this enzyme, thus leading to extensive investigation of tumors of the prostate. Normal blood plasma or serum contains small amounts of acid phosphatase. This may have its origin in the liver, spleen, bones, kidney, or prostate. It is present in women and children also, although the analysis for acid phosphatase is usually requested for diagnosis of prostate carcinoma.

Gutman, Tyson, and Gutman[5] (1936) first demonstrated that serum acid phosphatase levels increased significantly in many cases of metastatic prostatic carcinoma but seldom increased in the absence of metastases. (Metastasis is the transfer of diseased tissue from one part of the body to another.) However, there are three possibilities of obtaining normal results when metastasis has occurred:

1. Prostatic cells may produce very little enzyme because of very low androgen (hormone) level or because of anaplasia, which is the change of a normal cell structure to one similar to that of an embryo cell.
2. Cancer may have affected the lymph and blood channels so that the excessive amount of the enzyme cannot get into the bloodstream.
3. Castration, administration of estrogens, intensive irradiation, or radical prostatectomy inhibits the activity of the enzyme.

Women may also show elevations of acid phosphatase if they suffer from disease of any one of several organs (liver, spleen, kidney, or bone). There is an increase of the enzyme activity with carcinoma of the breast with extensive skeletal metastasis.

Since the red cells contain a high level of acid phosphatase, it is imperative that serum used for the acid phosphatase analysis contain no hemolysis.

Information significant to the student

Since alkaline phosphatase and acid phosphatase are usually determined together, they will be considered together. A brief discussion of each follows, covering information significant to the student and procedures for the test, as well as directions for calibrating a colorimeter.

Alkaline phosphatase

The normal values for alkaline phosphatase depend upon the method of determination. The values for three of the commonly used methods are listed at the top of the following page.

Table 43. Conditions accompanied by abnormal alkaline phosphatase values

When increased		When decreased
Rickets	Neurofibromatosis	Scurvy
Hyperparathyroidism	Myositis ossificans	Hypoparathyroidism
Carcinoma of bone	Obstructive jaundice	Chronic nephritis
Paget's disease	Idiopathic steatorrhea	Celiac disease
Osteomalacia	Occlusion of pancreatic duct	Osteolytic sarcoma
Multiple myeloma	Abscess of liver	

	Adults		Children	
Bodansky units	2	to 4	4	to 12
King-Armstrong units	4	to 10	10	to 20
Bessey-Lowry units	0.8 to 2.3		2.8 to 6.7	

Conditions in which an increased or decreased value may be expected are listed in Table 43. Abnormal values are of primary interest in those disorders given in italics.

For the determination of alkaline phosphatase, the three methods listed below are commonly used. A brief discussion of each follows.

Bodansky method
King-Armstrong method
Bessey-Lowry method

Bodansky method

Serum is added to sodium glycerophosphate that has been buffered to pH 8.6 in order to ensure optimum conditions of pH and electrolyte content. The mixture is incubated at 37° C. for exactly 1 hour. This allows the phosphatase enzyme in the serum to decompose the sodium glycerophosphate and liberate phosphorus.

A phosphorus determination is then run on this incubated serum and also on nonincubated serum. The phosphorus determination consists of adding trichloroacetic acid to both specimens to precipitate the proteins, adding molybdic acid to form a phosphate complex, adding a reducing agent to reduce the complex, and finally measuring the depth of color in a colorimeter.

The alkaline phosphatase units are then found by subtracting the phosphorus value of the nonincubated specimen from the phosphorus value of the incubated specimen. Thus:

Alkaline phosphatase units = Phosphorus value of incubated specimen *minus*
Phosphorus value of nonincubated specimen

Example:

Alkaline phosphatase units = 6 mg./100 ml. − 3 mg./100 ml. = 3

These units are usually reported as Bodansky units, a Bodansky unit being that amount of phosphatase which will liberate 1 mg. of phosphorus/100 ml. of serum under the conditions described above.

King-Armstrong method

Serum is added to disodium phenylphosphate that has been buffered to pH 9.0. The mixture is incubated at 37.5° C. for 30 minutes to allow the phosphatase to decompose the disodium phenylphosphate and liberate phenol. A blank containing all the above ingredients is prepared. This is not incubated.

A phenol reagent is then added to the test and the blank. The reagent forms a color complex with the liberated phenol. The depth of color is compared with a standard and measured in a colorimeter. This determines the amount of phenol present.

The nonincubated specimen (blank) subtracted from the incubated specimen (test) gives the units of alkaline phosphatase.

Alkaline phosphatase units = Phenol value of incubated specimen *minus*
Phenol value of nonincubated specimen

The report is given in King-Armstrong units, one unit being the milligrams of phenol liberated by 100 ml. of serum under the above conditions.

Bessey, Lowry, and Brock method

Serum is added to *p*-nitrophenylphosphate that has been buffered to pH 10.3 to ensure optimum conditions for reaction. The mixture is incubated at 37° C. for exactly 30 minutes. This allows the phosphatase to decompose the *p*-nitrophenylphosphate and liberate *p*-nitrophenol. The *p*-nitrophenol color is measured. Hydrochloric acid is added to decolorize the *p*-nitrophenol. The color due to serum is then measured. These units are reported as mM (millimoles) of substrate split per hour per liter of serum:

Alkaline phosphatase units or mM = *p*-Nitrophenol value of incubated serum *minus*
Decolorized value of the same specimen

Acid phosphatase

The normal values for acid phosphatase are 0 to 1 Bodansky unit or 0 to 2 King-Armstrong units. Increased values are found in the following conditions: carcinoma of the prostate, hyperparathyroidism, and acute granulocytic leukemia.

For the determination of acid phosphatase, the three methods listed below are commonly used:

Bodansky method
King-Armstrong method
Bessey-Lowry method

Bodansky method

This is exactly the same procedure as the Bodansky alkaline phosphatase procedure described above except that the buffer solution is an acid buffer of pH 5.0 rather than the alkaline buffer of pH 8.6. The acid phosphatase units are found similarly:

Acid phosphatase units = Phosphorus value of incubated specimen *minus*
Phosphorus value of nonincubated specimen

King-Armstrong method

This is exactly the same procedure as the alkaline phosphatase procedure of King and Armstrong, which has been described above, except that the buffer solution is an acid buffer of pH 5.0 instead of the alkaline buffer of pH 9.0. The acid phosphatase units are found similarly:

Acid phosphatase units = Phenol value of incubated specimen *minus*
Phenol value of nonincubated specimen

Bessey, Lowry, and Brock method, modified

This is the same procedure as for alkaline phosphatase except that an acid buffered substrate, pH 4.8, is used and serum blanks are not incubated. The *p*-nitrophenol liberated during the incubation period is measured. The nonincubated serum blanks are also measured. These units are reported either as Sigma units or as mM (millimoles):

Acid phosphatase units or mM = *p*-Nitrophenol value of incubated serum *minus*
Nonincubated serum

Procedures for alkaline and acid phosphatase

The following general considerations pertain to the procedures for alkaline and acid phosphatase:

1. Preparation of patient: must be fasting.
2. Preparation of blood: serum. *Not* hemolyzed!
3. Preservation of serum: may be kept for 2 hours by adding a small drop of toluene and storing in a refrigerator.
4. Precautions:
   a. Temperature of water bath should not vary by more than $\pm 1°$ C.
   b. Timing of incubation must be exact.
   c. Follow the *exact* directions given in the procedure.

Serum alkaline phosphatase[6]
Bessey, Lowry, and Brock method

Para-nitrophenylphosphate is colorless in solution; but upon hydrolysis the phosphate group liberates *p*-nitrophenol, which is highly colored in an alkaline solution. The rate of hydrolysis of the *p*-nitrophenylphosphate is proportional to the concentration of the enzyme present in the serum. The reaction may be shown as follows:

$$p\text{-Nitrophenylphosphate} + H_2O \xrightarrow{\text{Phosphatase}} p\text{-Nitrophenol} + H_3PO_4$$

(colorless in solution)   (colorless in acid but highly colored—yellow—in alkaline solution)

*Reagents needed**

Alkaline Buffer, 0.1 M Glycine, pH 10.5	(C-102)
Stock Substrate, *p*-Nitrophenylphosphate	(C-103)
Alkaline Buffered Substrate, pH 10.3 to 10.4	(C104)
Sodium Hydroxide, 0.02	(C105)
Hydrochloric Acid, Concentrated	

Procedure

1. Use either 16×150 mm. test tubes or spectrophotometer tubes for the test.
2. Into the *reagent blank* and *test* tubes, pipet 1.0 ml. of alkaline buffered substrate.
3. Place the tubes (blank and tests) into a 37° C. controlled water bath for 5 minutes, for the tubes and reagent to come to water bath temperature.
4. Set a timer for 30 minutes. Upon the addition of the water to the reagent blank the timer is started, and thereafter every half minute the serum is added to its tube in the water bath.
5. Pipet 0.1 ml. of distilled water to the blank and 0.1 ml. of serum to each tube at ½-minute intervals.
6. Allow the tubes to incubate until *exactly* 30 minutes after the water was added to the blank.
7. Obtain an empty test tube rack in which to place the tubes as they are taken from the water bath.
8. Have in preparation a fast-flowing 10 ml. serological pipet (blowout) with a flask of 0.02 N NaOH. This must be added at timed intervals, also. The addition of the sodium hydroxide will stop the enzyme reaction.
9. *Exactly* 30 minutes by the timer, remove the blank from the water bath, add 10 ml. of 0.02 N NaOH, and place tube into the test tube

---

*May be purchased already prepared from Sigma Chemical Co., St. Louis, Mo.

rack by the water bath. Continue at ½-minute intervals until the re-action has been stopped on all the tests.

10. Stopper the tubes with clean stoppers and mix by inverting.
11. Transfer the blank and tests to spectrophotometer tubes if these were not used during the incubation.
12. Read the tests against the reagent blank at 410 mμ wavelength.
13. Record the O.D. of the serum samples.
14. Add 0.1 ml. (2 drops) of concentrated HCl to each tube and mix by shaking tube. This removes the color due to the *p*-nitrophenol.
15. Read against the reagent blank at 410 mμ wavelength.
16. Record the O.D. of the second readings. This is the O.D. of the serum, since in an acid state the *p*-nitrophenol produces no color.
17. Subtract the second reading from the first reading where the *p*-nitro-phenol produced color. This corrected optical density is then read from a curve or table made from the curve.

Note: When a value greater than 10 mM units is obtained, repeat the test with a smaller volume of serum or a shorter incubation time. Adjust the calculations accordingly: for example, use a 15-minute incubation and multiply the result by 2 for the correct values, or dilute the serum with saline and multiply by the dilution made.

Normal values

Adult alkaline phosphatase 0.8 to 2.3 mM (millimole)
Children's alkaline phosphatase 2.8 to 6.7 mM (millimole)

Note: One millimolar (mM) unit of phosphatase activity liberates 1 milli-mole of *p*-nitrophenol per liter of serum per hour (1 mM = 0.1391 gm.). If you are using the Sigma units, these are the same as the millimolar units.

Sources of error

1. Incorrect temperature of the water bath. The temperature must not vary more than ± 1° C. With an increase in temperature of 10° C. the enzyme reaction will increase two to four times the initial value. The temperature limit of the animal enzyme is 40° to 50° C. Temperatures above this will cause a decrease in enzyme activity, and at 60° C. the enzyme is destroyed. Plant enzymes can stand a higher temperature than the animal enzyme. The animal enzymes are less stable and have a tendency to become denatured when heated in the presence of water.[3]
2. Incorrect timing of the incubation period. The timing must be exact.
3. A substrate that is either too old or has an altered pH.
4. Incorrect pipetting.
5. Improper lighting. Light may either increase the enzyme rate or in-hibit the rate of reaction. Ultraviolet rays or radium dispersion will inhibit enzyme reaction. Red or blue light will increase the reaction of the digestion enzymes such as pepsin, trypsin, and amylase.[3]
6. Glassware not chemically clean. If the glassware has been acid-washed and not thoroughly rinsed, the enzyme activity will be inhibited.
7. Violent shaking of the enzyme solutions, which will cause a denatura-tion of the protein enzyme, resulting in an inhibiting effect.
8. Separate storage, if possible, for glassware used for enzyme studies. Heavy metals such as mercury inhibit enzyme activity. Glassware used for Nessler's solution (containing mercury) should not be used for the BUN method utilizing urease. Aluminum ions inhibit peptic action, while toluene inhibits pepsin and trypsin.

TOTAL ACID PHOSPHATASE AND PROSTATIC ACID PHOSPHATASE[6]

Acid phosphatase is unstable and must be separated from the cells and refrigerated immediately. The serum must not be hemolyzed, since the red cells contain high levels of acid phosphatase. Since prostatic acid phosphatase may lose up to 50% of its activity within an hour at room temperature, 0.01 ml. of 20% acetic acid/1.0 ml. of serum is added to stabilize the enzyme.

Total acid phosphatase

The total acid phosphatase test uses the same stock substrate as the alkaline phosphatase.

Reagents needed°

Acid Buffer, 0.09 M Citric Acid, pH 4.8	(C-106)
Stock Substrate, *p*-Nitrophenylphosphate	(C-103)
Acid Buffered Substrate, pH 4.8 to 4.9	(C-107)
Sodium Hydroxide, 0.1 N	(C-108)
Acetic Acid, 20% (v/v)	(C-109)

Procedure

1. Using either 16×150 mm. test tubes or spectrophotometer tubes, set up the following test with a serum blank for each serum test to be analyzed.
2. The serum blanks are not incubated with the tests and may be read while the serum tests are incubating.
3. Into the *reagent blank* and *test* tubes, pipet 0.5 ml. of acid buffer substrate.
4. Place the tubes (blank and tests) into a 37° C. controlled water bath for 5 minutes, for the substrate to come to bath temperature.
5. Set the timer for 30 minutes. (Note: When placing the serum into the serum test tubes for incubation, it may also be added to the serum blank tube within the ½-minute interval between the tubes.)
6. Start timing at the addition of 0.2 ml. of water into the *Reagent blank*. Mix *gently* and replace the tube into the water bath.
7. At ½-minute intervals, pipet 0.2 ml. of serum into the serum test tubes. Mix *gently* and replace into the water bath.
8. Incubate for 30 minutes.
9. *Serum blanks:* To the tubes containing 0.2 ml. of serum, add 6.0 ml. of 0.1 N NaOH. Stopper and mix by inversion or mix laterally by shaking the tube gently.
   a. Obtain the optical density readings by reading the tests against a distilled water blank at wavelength of 410 mμ.
   b. Refer to the calibration chart for the acid phosphatase units.
10. *After incubating the serum tests for 30 minutes,* pipet 5.0 ml. (use a fast-flowing serological pipet) of 0.1 N NaOH into each tube at ½-minute intervals to stop the enzyme activity. The color is stable for several hours.
11. Obtain an optical density reading by reading the tests against the *reagent blank* at a wavelength of 410 mμ.
12. Determine the acid phosphatase units from the calibration chart.
13. Subtract the "unit-results" of the serum blanks from the "unit-results" of the serum tests. This is the *corrected total acid phosphatase* of the serum sample.

Note: When a value greater than 2.8 mM units is obtained, repeat the test, with a smaller volume of serum or a shorter incubation time. Adjust the calculations accordingly: for example, use a 15-minute incubation period and multiply the result by 2 for the correct value, or dilute the serum with saline and multiply by the dilution made.

°May be purchased from Sigma Chemical Co., St. Louis, Mo.

Normal values

Male total acid phosphatase 0.13 to 0.63 mM units
Female total acid phosphatase 0.01 to 0.56 mM units
Note: One millimolar (mM) unit of phosphatase activity liberates 1
millimole of *p*-nitrophenol per liter of serum per hour.

Serum prostatic acid phosphatase

Since the enzyme to be measured is highly unstable, refrigerate the blood immediately after drawing. After the clot has retracted (allow an hour) centrifuge and keep the serum at 0° to 5° C., or add 0.01 ml. of 20% acetic acid per milliliter of serum to keep it stabilized.

*Reagents needed**

Tartrate Acid Buffer, pH 4.8	(C-110)
Acid Buffer, 0.9 M Citric Acid, pH 4.8	(C-106)
Stock Substrate, *p*-Nitrophenylphosphate	(C-103)
Acetic Acid, 20% (v/v)	(C-109)

Procedure

1. Using either 16 × 150 mm. test tubes or spectrophotometer tubes, prepare two tubes as follows:
   Tube 1
       a. Pipet 0.5 ml. of stock substrate into the tube.
       b. Add 0.5 ml. of tartrate acid buffer.
   Tube 2
       a. Pipet 0.5 ml. of stock substrate into the tube.
       b. Add 0.5 ml. of acid buffer.
2. Place the tubes into the 37° C. water bath for 5 minutes.
3. Set timer at 30 minutes. Start timing with the addition of 0.2 ml. of serum into each tube. Mix *gently* and replace tube into water bath.
4. After the 30-minute incubation, add 5.0 ml. of 0.1 N NaOH to each tube. Mix either by stoppering the tube and inverting or by lateral shaking of the tube.
5. Now, since the reaction has been stopped by the addition of NaOH, the tubes are read against a distilled water blank at a 410 mμ wavelength.
6. From the calibration chart, obtain the acid phosphatase units for tubes 1 and 2.
7. Subtract the "unit-results" of tube 1 from the "unit-results" of tube 2. This is the prostatic acid phosphatase of the serum.

Normal values

Normal prostatic acid phosphatase 0.01 to 0.15 mM units
Borderline   0.15 to 0.20 mM units

Sources of error

The usual sources of error given earlier pertain to all enzymes, but two factors should be mentioned that frequently cause inaccurate results and thus misrepresent the correlation between the acid phosphatase and the prostatic acid phosphatase.

1. Care may not have been taken with the acid phosphatase determination. This enzyme is *unstable*, and correct precautions must be taken.
2. Several authors[7-9] have reported elevated total acid phosphatase and prostatic acid phosphatase after the physician has done a simple rectal palpitation of the prostate. The blood should be drawn for the phos-

---

*May be purchased from the Sigma Chemical Co., St. Louis, Mo.

phatase analysis before the examination, or a time lapse of 24 to 48 hours be allowed before drawing the blood for analysis.

Calibration of colorimeter for alkaline and acid phosphatase

The calibration may be done at room temperature. There is no incubation period in the calibration method.

Reagents needed

p-Nitrophenol, 10 mM/L.*	(C-111)
Sodium Hydroxide, 0.02 N	(C-105)

Working Standard: Discard after use—stable 1 day
    a. Into a 100 ml. volumetric flask, pipet 0.5 ml. of *p*-nitrophenol standard solution.
    b. Dilute to 100 ml. mark with 0.02 N NaOH.
    c. Stopper and mix thoroughly.

Procedure

1. Number six spectrophotometer tubes and pipet the following volumes into the tubes. Refer to Table 44.
2. Using a wavelength of 410 mμ or filter of equivalent wavelength, read the % T or O.D. of the six tubes and record results in column A. These are read against a reference blank containing 0.02 N NaOH.
3. Prepare the alkaline phosphatase curve by plotting the results in column A against the mM units of alkaline phosphatase in column B.
4. Prepare the acid phosphatase curve by plotting the results in column A against the mM units of acid phosphatase in column B.
5. If a Klett-Summerson Colorimeter is used, the Klett readings may be converted to O.D. readings by multiplying the Klett readings by $\frac{2}{1000}$. For example, a Klett reading of $310 \times \frac{2}{1000} = 310 \times 0.002 = 0.620$ O.D.
6. The calibration curve would be set up similar to this:

mM units of either the alkaline or acid phosphatase B

A chart made from the readings of the curves makes the calculations much easier and more convenient.

TRANSAMINASE

In 1940, an enzyme preparation was obtained from pig heart muscle and pigeon breast muscle. It was noted that in this preparation properties of both aspartic aminopherase and glutamic aminopherase were exhibited, thereby sug-

---

*May be purchased from Sigma Chemical Co., St. Louis, Mo.

Table 44. Phosphatase calibration

Tube No.	Working standard (ml.)	0.02 N NaOH (ml.)	A Column for scale reading % T or O.D.	B Equivalent to mM units, serum phosphatase	
				Alkaline	Acid
1	1.0	10.0		1.0	0.28
2	2.0	9.0		2.0	0.56
3	4.0	7.0		4.0	1.12
4	6.0	5.0		6.0	1.67
5	8.0	3.0		8.0	2.23
6	10.0	1.0		10.0	2.80

gesting that only one enzyme existed. It had been noted previously that the differences were related primarily to activity rather than specificity. Therefore, the name suggested for the enzyme was *transaminase*. By utilizing tissue extracts, it was shown that the transaminase is largely limited to two reactions that can be demonstrated.[10]

Reaction 1 (SGOT)

Serum glutamic oxaloacetic transaminase catalyzes the transfer of an amino group from aspartic acid to α-ketoglutaric acid to form glutamic and oxaloacetic acids:

$$l(+)\text{-Glutamic acid} + \text{Oxaloacetic acid} \rightleftharpoons \alpha\text{-Ketoglutaric acid} + l(+)\text{-Aspartic acid}$$

Reaction 2 (SGPT)

Serum glutamic pyruvic transaminase catalyzes the transfer of an amino group from alanine acid to α-ketoglutaric acid to form glutamic and pyruvic acids:

$$l(+)\text{-Glutamic acid} + \text{Pyruvic acid} \rightleftharpoons \alpha\text{-Ketoglutaric acid} + l(+)\text{-Alanine}$$

The abbreviations used to designate the enzymes that catalyze the reversible transaminase reactions serve also to monogram the main products of the equilibrium reactions:

Serum glutamic-oxaloacetic transaminase	SGOT
Serum glutamic-pyruvic transaminase	SGPT

The transaminase enzymes are found in the tissues of many organs. There are large amounts of the enzymes present in the heart muscle, skeletal muscle, brain, liver, and kidneys, in descending order of concentration. Deterioration of the organs causes a release of abnormal amounts of the transaminase enzyme into the blood. An elevated serum glutamic-oxaloacetic transaminase may be found in cases of myocardial infarction, various liver diseases, and occasionally in renal diseases.

Normally, the ratio of $\dfrac{\text{SGOT}}{\text{SGPT}}$ is 1.0 or over, with the exception of viral or infectious hepatitis, wherein the ratio is less than 1.0. Then the SGPT value is higher than the SGOT value, and both values are increased.[11,12]

SGOT and SGPT[13]

Reitman-Frankel method

The procedures for the SGOT and SGPT utilize similar conditions with the exceptions that alanine instead of aspartic acid is used in the SGPT and only a 30-minute incubation period is necessary. Since the two tests may be run simultaneously, the technician may choose either of the following incubation methods:

1. The SGOT and SGPT may be started together. Then, at the end of the 30-minute incubation period, the SGPT tubes are removed from the water bath and the hydrazine (color reagent) is added immediately. This stops the reaction and starts the color development. The tubes may sit at room temperature until the SGOT tubes have finished incubating or they may be completed.

2. The SGPT may be started 30 minutes after the SGOT.

The following method is written so that both tests may be done either simultaneously or individually.

The instrument may be calibrated and tests read at 505 mμ. It is most important that both the calibration and the test readings be done on the same wavelength.

Reagents needed*

Phosphate Buffer, 0.1 M, pH 7.4	(C-112)
SGOT Substrate, α-Ketoglutarate, 2 mM/L.; *dl*-Aspartate, 200 mM/L.	
	(C-113)
SGPT Substrate, α-Ketoglutarate, 2 mM/L.; *dl*-Alanine, 200 mM/L.	(C-114)
Color Reagent, 2,4-Dinitrophenylhydrazine, 1 mM/L.	(C-115)
Sodium Hydroxide, 0.4 N	(C-116)

Procedure

1. Including a reagent blank for the SGOT and for the SGPT, pipet 1.0 ml. of the proper substrate into each tube.
2. Place the tubes in a 37° C. water bath for 5 minutes.
3. Set the timer for 60 minutes. Start timing when 0.2 ml. of distilled water is added to the SGOT or SGPT reagent blank, whichever group is started first. Mix by swirling and replace tube in water bath.
4. At ½-minute intervals, pipet 0.2 ml. of serum into each tube. Mix by swirling. Replace tube in water bath.
5. After incubating *exactly* 30 minutes, remove the SGPT tubes from the water bath at ½-minute intervals and *immediately* add 1.0 ml. of color reagent to stop the reaction and start the color development.
6. After incubating *exactly* 60 minutes, remove the SGOT tubes from the water bath at ½-minute intervals and *immediately* add 1.0 ml. of color reagent to stop the reaction and start the color development.
7. After a minimum of 20 minutes of standing with the color reagent (hydrazine), add 10.0 ml. of 0.4 N NaOH. Stopper and mix by inverting the tubes. The final color develops in alkaline solution.
8. After standing 5 minutes, read at a wavelength of 505 mμ against the water blank. The blank tube should read very close to the same value on each run.
9. Calculate results from the calibration curve. If a value exceeds the upper limit of the curve, dilute serum with saline and multiply by the dilution made. For example, with a 1:10 dilution, multiply by 10.

*May be purchased from Sigma Chemical Co., St. Louis, Mo.

Normal range

SGOT   8 to 40 units
Doubtful 40 to 50 units

SGPT   5 to 35 units
Doubtful 35 to 45 units

Calibration curve

The standards for the calibration curve are *not* incubated. The curve may be plotted either with optical density against the activity, on linear graph paper, or with the percent transmission against the activity, on semilog paper. The units of the SGPT and SGOT are to be shown in the chart at 37° C. and 40° C. The method was presented for a 37° C. water bath, since the other enzyme tests in this chapter are calibrated for the use of a 37° C. water bath.

Reagents needed

Pyruvate Standard, 2 mM/L.   (C-117)
The remaining reagents are those used in the methods for the SGOT and SGPT.

Procedure

1. Number five spectrophotometer tubes and pipet the following volumes into the tubes. Refer to Table 45.

Table 45. Transaminase calibration

Tube No.	Pyruvate (ml.)	Substrate (ml.)	H_2O (ml.)	A O.D. % T	B SGOT		C SGPT	
					37° C.	40° C.	37° C.	40° C.
1	0	1.0	0.2		0	0	0	0
2	0.1	0.9	0.2		24	21	28	25
3	0.2	0.8	0.2		61	54	57	51
4	0.3	0.7	0.2		114	102	97	87
5	0.4	0.6	0.2		190	169	—	—

2. Add 1.0 ml. of color reagent to each tube. Mix.
3. Pipet 10.0 ml. of 0.4 N NaOH to each tube. Stopper and invert to mix.
4. Wait 5 minutes; then read against a distilled water blank, using a wavelength of 505 mμ.
5. Record the readings of the five tubes in column A.
6. Using the alkaline phosphatase as an example, plot the A column against the B or the C column.
7. A chart made from the curves drawn allows for easier and consistent calculations.

STUDENTS' SUMMARY FOR THE ENZYMES

The significant information consists of the following:
Normal and abnormal values
Methods of analysis and synopsis of procedures

Normal and abnormal values

Test	Normal values	When increased
Amylase	80–150 units	Acute pancreatitis Carcinoma of pancreas
Lipase	0–1.5 ml. of 0.05 N NaOH	Acute pancreatitis Carcinoma of pancreas
Alkaline phosphatase	0.8–2.3 mM 2–4 Bodansky units 4–10 King-Armstrong units Note: higher values in children	Disorders of bone
Acid phosphatase	Male: 0.13–0.63 mM Female: 0.01–0.56 mM 0–1 Bodansky units 0–2 King-Armstrong units	Carcinoma of prostate Extensive carcinoma with metastasis
Prostatic acid phosphatase	0.01–0.15 mM 0.15–0.20 mM (borderline)	Carcinoma of prostate
SGOT	8–40 units 40–50 units (borderline)	Myocardical infarction
SGPT	5–35 units 35–45 units (borderline)	Liver disease Viral and infectious hepatitis

Methods of analysis and synopsis of procedures

Test	Method	Synopsis of procedure
Amylase	Somogyi	1. Obtain serum 2. Prepare patient's tube containing serum and starch 3. Prepare blank tube containing starch 4. Prepare control tube containing serum 5. Add acid sodium chloride to all three tubes to control pH and electrolyte content 6. Incubate all tubes to enable amylase to decompose starch and liberate glucose 7. Add copper sulfate to stop reaction 8. Precipitate and filter off proteins 9. Run glucose levels on all three tubes 10. Amylase units equal glucose found in patient's tube minus glucose found in blank tube plus control tube
	Somogyi	1. Obtain serum 2. Prepare patient's tube containing starch substrate and place in 37° C. water bath 3. Prepare indicator tubes containing iodine 4. Add serum to starch substrate tubes 5. At timed intervals add incubated serum and starch mixture to indicator tubes 6. Obtain end point and calculate time interval of reaction
Lipase	Cherry-Crandall	1. Obtain serum 2. Add serum to patient's tube and also to control tube 3. Heat control tube to destroy enzyme 4. Add buffer solution to both tubes to control pH and electrolyte content 5. Add substrate olive oil to both tubes 6. Incubate 24 hours to enable lipase in serum to decompose olive oil and liberate fatty acids 7. Titrate both tubes with 0.05 N NaOH to find amount of fatty acid produced 8. Subtract milliliters of 0.05 N NaOH used for control tube from milliliters used for patient's tube; this is lipase value expressed in milliliters of twentieth normal sodium hydroxide

Methods of analysis and synopsis of procedures—cont'd

Test	Method	Synopsis of procedure
Alkaline phosphatase	Bodansky	1. Obtain serum 2. Add serum to sodium glycerophosphate which has been buffered to pH 8.6 to ensure optimum conditions for reaction 3. Incubate for 1 hour to decompose sodium glycerophosphate and liberate phosphorus 4. Run phosphorus determinations on incubated serum and also on some nonincubated serum 5. Alkaline phosphatase units equal phosphorus value of incubated serum minus phosphorus value of nonincubated serum; report as Bodansky units
	King-Armstrong	1. Obtain serum 2. Add serum to disodium phenylphosphate that has been buffered to pH 9.0 to ensure optimum conditions for reaction 3. Incubate for 30 minutes to allow phosphatase to decompose the disodium phenylphosphate and liberate phenol 4. Run test for phenol on incubated serum and also on some nonincubated serum 5. Alkaline phosphatase units equal phenol value of incubated serum minus phenol value of nonincubated serum; report as King-Armstrong units
	Bessey, Lowry, and Brock	1. Obtain serum 2. Add serum to p-nitrophenylphosphate that has been buffered to pH 10.3 to ensure optimum conditions for reaction 3. Incubate 30 minutes to allow phosphatase to decompose the p-nitrophenylphosphate and liberate p-nitrophenol 4. Measure the p-nitrophenol 5. Add 2 drops of hydrochloric acid to each tube to decolorize p-nitrophenol 6. Measure the decolorized specimen 7. Alkaline phosphatase units or mM equal p-nitrophenol value minus incubated serum value; report as Sigma units or mM (millimoles)
Acid phosphatase	Bodansky	1. Follow same procedure as Bodansky method for alkaline phosphatase described above except use buffer solution of pH 5.0 instead of pH 8.6 2. Acid phosphatase units equal phosphorus value of incubated serum minus phosphorus value of nonincubated serum; report as Bodansky units
	King-Armstrong	1. Follow same procedure as for King-Armstrong method for alkaline phosphatase described above except use buffer solution of pH 5.0 instead of pH 9.0 2. Acid phosphatase units equal phenol value of incubated serum minus phenol value of nonincubated serum; report as King-Armstrong units
	Bessey, Lowry, and Brock (modified)	1. Follow the same procedure as in Bessey-Lowry method for alkaline phosphatase described above but use a buffer solution of pH 4.8 to 4.9 and set up separate serum blanks that are not incubated 2. Acid phosphatase units equal p-nitrophenol value of incubated serum minus the color of the nonincubated serum; report in Sigma units or mM (millimoles)

Methods of analysis and synopsis of procedures—cont'd

Test	*Method*	*Synopsis of procedure*
Prostatic acid phosphatase	Bessey, Lowry, and Brock (modified)	1. Follow the same procedure as in Bessey-Lowry method for alkaline phosphatase described above, but use a tartrate buffered substrate of pH 4.8 2. The prostatic acid phosphatase units equal the total acid phosphatase minus the tartrate acid phosphatase value; report in Sigma units or mM (millimoles)
SGOT	Reitman-Frankel	1. Obtain serum 2. Add serum to GOT substrate 3. Incubate 60 minutes to allow transaminase to form oxalacetate 4. Add color reagent to form hydrazone 5. Measure colorimetrically 6. Report in Frankel units
SGPT	Reitman-Frankel	1. Obtain serum 2. Add serum to GPT substrate 3. Incubate 30 minutes to allow transaminase to form pyruvate 4. Add color reagent to form hydrazone 5. Measure colorimetrically 6. Report in Frankel units

REFERENCES

1. Somogyi, M.: Micromethods for estimation of diastase, J. Biol. Chem. **125**:399, 1938.
2. Sachar, L.: Simplified laboratory test for acute pancreatitis, Am. J. Clin. Path. **22**:1117, 1952.
3. Kleiner, I. S., and Orten, J. M.: Biochemistry, ed. 6, St. Louis, 1962, The C. V. Mosby Co.
4. Woodard, H. Q.: The clinical significance of serum acid phosphatase, Am. J. Med. **27**:902, 1959.
5. Gutman, A. B., Tyson, T. L., and Gutman, E. B.: Serum calcium, inorganic phosphorus and phosphatase activity in hyperparathyroidism, Paget's disease, multiple myeloma, and neoplastic disease of bones, Arch. Int. Med. **57**:379, 1936.
6. Bessey, O. A., Lowry, O. H., and Brock, M. J.: Method for rapid determination of alkaline phosphatase with 5 cubic millimeters of serum, J. Biol. Chem. **164**:321, 1946.
7. Ozar, M. B., Isaac, C. A., and Valk, W. L.: Methods for elimination of errors in serum acid phosphatase determinations, J. Urol. **74**:150, 1955.
8. Sigma Technical Bulletin 104, March, 1963, St. Louis, Sigma Chemical Co.
9. Hock, E., and Tessier, R. N.: Elevation of serum acid phosphatase following prostatic massage, J. Urol. **62**:488, 1949.
10. Sobotka, H., and Steward, C. P.: Advances in clinical chemistry, vol. 1, New York, 1958, Academic Press, Inc.
11. DeRitis, F., Coltorti, M., and Giusti, G.: An enzyme test for the diagnosis of viral hepatitis; the transaminase serum activities, Clin. chim. acta **2**:70, 1957.
12. Sigma Technical Bulletin 505, Sept., 1964, St. Louis, Sigma Chemical Co.
13. Reitman, S., and Frankel, S.: A colorimetric method for the determination of serum glutamic oxaloacetic and glutamic pyruvic transaminases, Am. J. Clin. Path. **28**:36, 1957.

Chapter 15

Special chemistry tests

Thisis chapter includes blood tests that the average technician seldom performs. Although students are not usually required to know this material, a superficial reading may prove beneficial.

The discussion covers the following.

Drugs
Carbon monoxide
Congo red test
Fibrinogen
Protein-bound iodine (PBI)
Serum iron
Osmometry

DRUGS

During the treatment of disease, the patient may take various drugs. Many of these drugs must be maintained at certain blood levels in order to be effective. If this blood level is greatly exceeded, however, the drug may have a toxic effect upon the patient. Consequently, a need has arisen for blood tests of certain drugs.

This section considers tests for the drugs listed below. Requests for these examinations are not too frequent.

Bromides
Salicylates
Sulfonamides

Bromides

Bromide is used in the treatment of epilepsy and also as a sedative. It is normally present in the blood, being found to the extent of 0.5 to 1.0 mg./100 ml. of serum. If the blood level of bromide exceeds 150 mg./100 ml., toxic symptoms may occur.

Wuth method[1]

A trichloroacetic acid protein-free filtrate is made using serum. Gold chloride is added to the filtrate producing a brown color due to the production of gold bromide. The color is obtained by the replacement of the chloride ion in the gold chloride by the bromide ion. The optical density of the brown color is directly proportional to the bromide concentration.

Reagents needed

Gold Chloride, 0.5% in water	(C-118)
Trichloroacetic Acid (TCA), 10% in water	(C-63)
Bromide Stock Standard, 20 mg./ml.	(C-119)

Bromide Working Standard
> Pipet 1.0 ml. of stock standard into a 100 ml. volumetric flask, using a volumetric pipet. Dilute to mark with 10% TCA.

Procedure

1. Pipet 2.0 ml. of serum into a tube containing 8.0 ml. of 10% TCA. Stopper and mix by inverting.
2. Allow to stand for 10 minutes; then centrifuge for 10 minutes at 3000 RPM. Filter the supernatant.
3. Prepare the following tubes:

Reagent blank
a. Pipet 5.0 ml. of 10% TCA.

Standards
a. Pipet 1.0 ml. of bromide working standard.
b. Add 4.0 ml. of 10% TCA.

Unknown
a. Pipet 5.0 ml. of filtrate.
4. Add 1.0 ml. of gold chloride solution to all tubes and mix.
5. Allow to stand for 5 minutes and read against the reagent blank at 440 mμ.

Calculation

$$\frac{\text{O.D. of unknown}}{\text{O.D. of standard}} \times 20 = \text{Mg.\% bromide}$$

Normal range

0.5 to 1.0 mg.%

Salicylates

The salt, sodium salicylate, is used in the treatment of rheumatic fever. The acid, salicylic acid, occurs in the blood during treatment, the therapeutic level being at least 35 mg./100 ml. of serum. Neither the salt nor the acid is normally present in the blood.

Trinder method[2]

The Trinder method utilizes a color reagent containing ferric nitrate, mercuric chloride, and hydrochloric acid, which precipitates the proteins and simultaneously reacts with the salicylate, giving a purple color. Plasma, serum, whole blood, urine, or cerebrospinal fluid may be analyzed by this method.

Reagents needed

Color reagent (Ferric-Mercuric Reagent)	(C-120)
Salicylate Solution, Stock, 1 mg./ml.	(C-121)
Salicylate Solution, Standard, 0.05 mg./ml.	(C-122)
Salicylate Solution, Standard, 0.20 mg./ml.	(C-123)

Procedure

1. Prepare the following tubes:

   Reagent blank

   a. Pipet 1.0 ml. of distilled water into tube.
   b. Add 5.0 ml. of ferric-mercuric reagent.
   c. Stopper and mix by inverting.

   Standards

   a. Pipet 1.0 ml. of standard, 0.05 mg./ml., into one test tube.
   b. Pipet 1.0 ml. of standard, 0.20 mg./ml., into another test tube.
   c. To both tubes, add 5.0 ml. of ferric-mercuric reagent.
   d. Stopper and mix by inverting; then filter.

   Unknown

   a. Pipet 1.0 ml. of filtrate into a test tube.
   b. Add 5.0 ml. of ferric-mercuric reagent.
   c. Stopper and mix by inverting.

2. Read against the reagent blank at a wavelength of 540 mμ.

Calculations

Calculate with the standard reading closer to the unknown.
Using the standard 0.05 mg./ml.:

$$\frac{\text{O.D. of test}}{\text{O.D. of standard}} \times 0.05 \times \frac{100}{1} =$$

$$\frac{\text{O.D. of test}}{\text{O.D. of standard}} \times 5 = \text{Mg. salicylates/100 ml.}$$

Using the standard 0.20 mg./ml.:

$$\frac{\text{O.D. of test}}{\text{O.D. of standard}} \times 0.2 \times \frac{100}{1} =$$

$$\frac{\text{O.D. of test}}{\text{O.D. of standard}} \times 20 = \text{Mg. salicylates/100 ml.}$$

The results are expressed in mg. sodium salicylate/100 ml., since the standards contain sodium salicylate. The technician may be requested to report the results as salicylic acid. This may be done by finding the molecular weight of sodium salicylate, which is 160, and the molecular weight of salicylic acid, which is 138. Divide the molecular weight 138 by the molecular weight 160 and multiply by the sodium salicylate value to obtain the salicylic acid value. Set up the formula as follows:

$$\text{Sodium salicylate} \times \frac{138}{160} =$$

$$\text{Sodium salicylate} \times 0.86 = \text{Salicylic acid}$$

or

$$\text{Salicylic acid} \times \frac{160}{138} =$$

$$\text{Salicylic acid} \times 1.16 = \text{Sodium salicylate}$$

Normal range

1 mg. or less of sodium salicylate/100 ml. of plasma

Toxic level

Above 50 mg. of sodium salicylate/100 ml. of plasma

Sulfonamides[3]

The sulfonamides are used to combat many types of infection. They found their greatest use during World War II, just prior to the advent of penicillin. There are about ten different sulfa drugs. Their optimum blood levels during therapy depend upon the particular drug, the disease, and the patient. When present in excessive amounts, they tend to crystallize out in the kidneys and may cause severe damage to these organs.

When the sulfonamides are present in the blood, the distribution between the cells and plasma is not equal. The plasma concentration is higher; oxalated whole blood should be used, therefore, since the optimum drug levels are expressed in concentration of the drug in whole blood.

Bratton-Marshall method

Whole blood is deproteinized with trichloroacetic acid, and the sulfanilamide is measured in the filtrate, by means of the diazo reaction.

Reagents needed

Trichloroacetic Acid (TCA), 5%	(C-124)
Sodium Nitrite, Working Solution B, 0.5%	(C-43)
Ammonium Sulfamate, 0.5%	(C-125)
Coupling Reagent (Naphthyl Ethylenediamine Solution)	(C-126)
Sulfanilamide, Stock Standard, 0.1 mg./ml.	(C-127)
Sulfanilamide, Working Standard, 0.001 mg./ml.	

Into a 100 ml. volumetric flask, pipet 1.0 ml. of stock standard solution and dilute to mark with 5% TCA. Stopper and mix thoroughly.

Procedure

1. Pipet 19.5 ml. of 5% TCA into a 125 ml. Erlenmeyer flask.
2. Add 0.5 ml. of oxalated whole blood to the flask, stopper, and shake to mix.
3. Filter into another Erlenmeyer flask.
4. Prepare the following tubes:

Blank

a. Pipet 3.0 ml. of 5% TCA.
b. Add 0.1 ml. of sodium nitrite.
c. Add 1.0 ml. of ammonium sulfamate solution.
d. Add 2.0 ml. of coupling reagent.
e. Stopper and mix by inverting.

Standard and unknown

a. Pipet 3.0 ml. of working standard (0.003 mg. of sulfanilamide) into a test tube.
b. Pipet 3.0 ml. of blood filtrate (0.075 ml. of blood) into the other test tube.
c. Add 0.1 ml. of sodium nitrite to each tube; mix.
d. Let stand for 3 minutes.
e. Add 1.0 ml. of ammonium sulfamate to each tube; mix.
f. Let stand for 2 minutes.
g. Add 2.0 ml. of coupling reagent.
h. Mix well.

Read against the blank with a wavelength of 540 mμ.

Dilution

If the concentration of the unknown is extremely elevated, use 1.5 ml. of filtrate and 1.5 ml. of 5% TCA. Multiply the result by 2.

Calculation

$$\frac{\text{Reading of test}}{\text{Reading of standard}} \times 0.003 \times \frac{100}{0.075} =$$

$$\frac{\text{Reading of test}}{\text{Reading of standard}} \times 4 = \text{Mg. sulfanilamide/100 ml. of blood}$$

Note: Although the use of separate calibrations for each of the sulfa compounds is preferable, it is possible to calculate the values of the various compounds. With the sulfanilamide used as a standard, the value obtained is multiplied by a factor that gives the concentration of the drug being analyzed. The factors are calculated from the ratios of the molecular weights of the various drugs to that of the sulfanilamide:

Sulfanilamide	1.00
Sulfapyridine	1.45
Sulfathiazole	1.48
Sulfamethylthiazole	1.56
Sulfadiazine	1.45
Sulfadimethylpyrimidine	1.62
Sulfaguanidine	1.35
Sulfanilylsulphanilamide	1.90
Sulfasuccinylsulphathiazole	2.06
Sulfamethazine	1.30

CARBON MONOXIDE

If carbon monoxide is inhaled, it unites with hemoglobin and thereby prevents oxygen from reaching the cells. If sufficient quantities are inhaled, death occurs due to asphyxiation (suffocation). This test may tell the physician whether or not the patient has inhaled large amounts of carbon monoxide.

Procedure (Sayers-Yant)

1. Make a venipuncture and withdraw a few milliliters of blood. Expel into a test tube containing an anticoagulant of sodium or potassium citrate. Gently invert each tube several times to dissolve the citrate. A control must be run; so draw a sample of blood from a normal person, using the same anticoagulant.
2. Using a spatula, place a small bit of pyrogallic acid in a beaker. Add an equal amount of tannic acid. Mix.
3. Get three small test tubes and label them: Patient, Positive Control, and Negative Control.
4. Pipet 2 ml. of distilled water into each tube.
5. Add 3 drops of the patient's blood to the patient's tube. Add 3 drops of normal blood to each of the other tubes. Gently mix. Bubble some illuminating gas through the positive control tube in order to saturate it with carbon monoxide.
6. Using a spatula, add a small bit of the pyrogallic and tannic acid mixture to each tube. Gently mix. Let stand 15 minutes.
7. Readings: Blood containing normal hemoglobin turns grayish brown. Blood containing carbon monoxide retains a pink color.

CONGO RED TEST

Amyloidosis is a condition characterized by the deposit of starchlike substances in the tissues. The dye Congo red has an affinity for these starchy deposits. Consequently, if a patient has amyloidosis, an injected solution of Congo red will be absorbed. Nephrosis must be ruled out, however, because this disease causes an increased elimination of the dye and therefore an apparent absorption.

Hydrochloric Acid, 0.5 N   (C-128)

Procedure (Paunz)

1. Draw 5 ml. of blood before the injection of Congo red dye. This will be used for a blank. (Note: Either use polyethylene centrifuge tubes or line regular centrifuge tubes with paraffin by immersing the tubes in a melted paraffin bath. This is to prevent the clot from adhering to the sides of the tubes when it retracts, thus preventing hemolysis. If preferred, oxalated blood may be used.
2. Ask the patient his weight. Divide the weight by 10. This is the dosage in milliliters for a 1% solution. Using sterile technique, the physician will inject the required number of milliliters of sterile Congo red into a vein, being sure to release the tourniquet prior to the injection. Note and record the time. Never use more than 18 ml. of Congo red solution.
3. Four minutes after the injection, make a venipuncture and withdraw about 12 ml. of blood. Gently expel into a test tube. Let clot.
4. One hour after the injection, make another venipuncture and withdraw about 12 ml. of blood. Gently expel into a test tube. Let clot.
5. Centrifuge the three blood specimens and obtain the serum.
6. Pipet 0.5 ml. of each serum or plasma into test tubes.
7. Add to each tube 3.0 ml. of 0.5 N HCl, to bring the pH to about 0.8. This splits Congo red from the proteins.
8. Using the fasting specimen as a blank, read the 4-minute and the 1-hour specimen at a wavelength of 590 mμ or, if using the Klett-Summerson colorimeter, use a filter No. 60.
9. In health, more than 60% of the dye remains in the serum. In amyloidosis, the dye goes into the tissues and less than 40% remains in the serum. In nephrosis, the dye leaks into the urine and less than 40% remains in the serum.

Calculation

$$\frac{\text{Absorbance of 60-minute specimen}}{\text{Absorbance of 4-minute specimen}} \times 100 = \text{Percent of dye retained in the blood}$$

FIBRINOGEN

Fibrinogen is used in the clotting of blood. The normal values range from 200 to 400 mg./100 ml. of plasma. These values are increased in infections and decreased in cirrhosis of the liver, phosphorus poisoning, and typhoid fever.

Fibrinogen screening test[4]

This method is performed by using 1 drop of blood from a finger stick. The blood is diluted with glycine-saline buffer. With the addition of the latex-antihuman fibrinogen reagent, the agglutination is compared with a normal control. The latex-antihuman fibrinogen reagent is prepared from polystyrene latex and antibody to human plasma fibrinogen. This gives a rapid and clear reaction for plasma fibrinogen levels over 100 mg.%.

*Reagents needed**

Glycine-Saline Buffer Diluent
Normal Control
Latex-Antihuman Fibrinogen Reagent

---

*These reagents, pipets, and card slides are obtained in a kit manufactured by Hyland Laboratories, Los Angeles, Calif.

Procedure

1. After obtaining a finger stick, transfer (use capillary pipet furnished) 1 drop of the patient's blood to the dropper bottle containing a measured volume of gylcine-saline buffer diluent. Cap bottle and mix well.
2. Using capillary pipets, transfer 1 drop of the diluted blood to one of the printed card slides.
3. Using another capillary pipet, transfer 1 drop of the already diluted control to another card slide.
4. To both specimens, add 2 drops of the latex-antihuman fibrinogen reagent.
5. Using separate toothpicks, mix each of the diluted specimens with the fibrinogen reagent. Carefully spread the mixed specimen over the card area within the circle.
6. Tilt the card slowly from side to side for about 15 to 20 seconds and observe for clumping.

Results

Blood specimens with plasma fibrinogen levels of 100 mg.% or less will not show agglutination in the antigen-antibody reagent. However, the specimens having fibrinogen levels within the normal range will have "clumping" comparable to that of the normal control.

Normal range

250 to 400 mg.%

Precaution

The reagent must be kept at a temperature of 2° to 10° C. (35° to 50° F.).

Fibrinogen, quantitative[5]

This method is similar to that of Reiner and Cheung[6] with the exception that fibrinogen is removed from the plasma by precipitating with calcium chloride instead of thrombin.

The method presented utilizes the materials, standards, reagents, and techniques used for the chemical determination of proteins.

Reagents needed

Physiological Saline, 0.9%	(C-34)
Calcium Chloride, 2.5%	(C-129)
Sodium Hydroxide, 0.2 N	(C-130)
Biuret Reagent	(C-33)
Protein Standard, 3 mg./ml.	(C-131)

Procedure

1. Use either a No. 3204 QBD Vacutainer Tube (EDTA) or a regular syringe and a test tube containing EDTA to collect 5 ml. of venous blood.
2. Centrifuge for 15 minutes at 3000 RPM.
3. Add 25.0 ml. of saline to an Erlenmeyer flask.
4. Pipet 1.0 ml. of EDTA plasma into the flask. Swirl to mix.
5. Add 1.0 ml. of 2.5% $CaCl_2$; thoroughly mix.
6. Let stand for 1 hour. (A firm fibrin clot will form.)
7. With a glass stirring rod, pick up the fibrin clot by twisting the clot around the glass rod, squeezing out all of the saline plasma solution. (*Note:* Small parts of the clot may have separated from the main clot. These may be found by placing the flask against a dark background.)
8. Place all of the clot in a 125 ml. Erlenmeyer flask.
9. Add about 15 ml. of saline and swirl the flask to wash the clot.
10. Carefully pour off the saline, taking care not to lose any of the clot.

11. Do three saline washings.
12. After the last washing, carefully twist the clot around a clean glass stirring rod and gently press against the side of the flask to eliminate excess saline.
13. Transfer the clot to a 15 ml. centrifuge tube. (Place the stirring rod against the lip of the test tube and gently pull the rod back away from the clot, which will slip off quite easily.)
14. Add 2.0 ml. of 0.2 N NaOH.
15. Place a marble on the tube and heat in a boiling water bath until the fibrin clot dissolves.
16. Set the tube in a room temperature water bath to cool.
17. Add 2.0 ml. of biuret reagent.
18. Stopper and mix. Let stand for 30 minutes.
19. Set up a blank and standard as follows:

   Blank
   2.0 ml. of 0.2 N NaOH
   2.0 ml. of biuret reagent. Mix.

   Standard
   1.0 ml. of protein standard, 3 mg./ml.
   1.0 ml. of 0.2 N NaOH
   2.0 ml. of biuret reagent. Mix.

20. Read the standard and test against the blank at 550 mμ.

Calculation

$$\frac{\text{O.D. of unknown}}{\text{O.D. of standard}} \times 300 = \text{Mg. fibrinogen}/100 \text{ ml.}$$

Normal values

Men   237.6 to 348.4 mg.% fibrinogen (293.0 $\pm$ 55.4)
Women   255.1 to 356.1 mg.% fibrinogen (305.6 $\pm$ 50.6)

PROTEIN-BOUND IODINE (PBI)

Ideally, the PBI analysis should be done in an isolated room away from laboratory traffic and contaminants. Precautions should be taken against iodine and mercury. Analyses with reagents containing these compounds *must* be kept away from the PBI area.

The sources of inorganic iodine available to the patient are numerous. Although the precipitate is washed, if the inorganic iodine level is very high not all may be washed clear, since some may be attached or adsorbed to the protein. Therefore, falsely elevated results will appear with no apparent clinical reason. For a list of some of the contaminants, refer to Table 46. However, bromides and meprobamate do not affect PBI results.

Two common methods for the determination of protein-bound iodine are given: the Barker, Soley, and Humphrey modification of the "dry-ash" method and a "wet-digestion" method.

A modification may be used for these two procedures. The inorganic iodine may be extracted from the serum with an ion exchange resin, Amberlite IRA-410 C.P. This may be done by using the following procedure. It is recommended that serum standards be included when this modification is employed.

1. Mix about 0.5 gm. of resin with about 4 ml. of serum and allow the tube to stand for 5 minutes; then centrifuge.
2. Proceed with the method of choice, eliminating only the washing of the precipitated protein.

Table 46. PBI contaminants[9]

Contaminants	Duration
Tincture of iodine on skin at site of puncture where blood is drawn	Specimen contaminated
Cough medicine, lozenges, vitamins, and suntan lotions containing iodine	3 to 4 days after source is removed; dosages of about 0.2 to 0.6 gm. of KI daily will increase PBI by 1.3 to 2.2 $\mu g \%$

Organic iodine compounds
1. Short duration
    I.V. pyelogram compounds
      Diodrast
      Hippuran
      Hypaque
      Neo-Iopax
      Skiodan
      Urokon
      Salpix (for salpingography)
      NeoPenil (an iodinated ester of penicillin)
	3 days to 1 week

2. Medium duration
    Gallbladder radiopaque dyes
      Telepaque
      Priodax
      Orabilex
    Therapeutic drugs
      Itrumil
      Diodoquin
	Usually disappear in 3 months but may be evident as long as 6 months

3. Long duration Lipiodol (administered intrathecally or for bronchography)	6 months to 5 years
Pantopaque (administered intrathecally or for bronchography)	6 months to 5 years
Gallbladder dye Teridax	Many years, and will cross the placental barrier, causing high values in the offspring for years
BSP dyes used for injections (Some lots contain an organic iodine)	About 1 week
Delvex (dithiazanine iodide) will increase the PBI	
Enovid and other estrogenic compounds elevate the PBI, due to the increase in the thyroxine-binding proteins of the serum	

Contaminants *lowering* the PBI value
    Mercury compounds
    Salicylates: 6 gm./day affect the results as follows
      Euthyroids—PBI decrease of 1.4 μg/100 ml.
      Hypothyroids—PBI decrease of 0.5 μg/100 ml.
      Hyperthyroids—PBI decrease of 4.2 μg/100 ml.	

Table 47. Disorders affecting the PBI

When increased	When decreased
Hyperthyroidism	Hypothyroidism
Acute thyroiditis	Cretinism
Subacute thyroiditis	Myxedema
Chronic thyroiditis	Panhypopituitarism
Hepatitis (normal 4 weeks)	(Simmonds' disease)
Pregnancy (third week)	Malnutrition
	Hypoproteinemia
	Nephrosis
	Cirrhosis

The student should be aware of some disorders affecting the functioning of the thyroid gland (see Table 47).

Normal values

4.0 to 8.0 μg/100 ml.

Barker, Soley, and Humphrey modification[7]

Iodine exists in the blood in two forms: organic (protein-bound) and inorganic. The procedures routinely used at the present time require preliminary precipitation of the protein and washing of the proteins to remove the inorganic iodine. The organic (hormonal) iodine is precipitated with the serum or plasma proteins. The organic material is destroyed by incineration in the presence of sodium carbonate, converting organic iodine to inorganic iodine. The inorganic iodine is quantitatively measured by means of the catalytic action of iodine on the reduction of ceric ammonium sulfate by arsenious acid, the yellow ceric ions being decolorized.

Equipment needed

Pyrex test tubes (15 × 125 mm.)
Marktex-Tech-Pen with heat-resistant ink
Drying oven and baskets
Muffle furnace
Spectrophotometer
Constant temperature water bath
Centrifuge

Reagents needed

Zinc Sulfate, 10%	(C-132)
Zinc Sulfate, Working Solution	(C-133)
Sodium Hydroxide, 0.5 N	(C-18)
Sodium Carbonate, 4.0 N	(C-134)
Hydrochloric Acid, 2.0 N	(C-135)
Sulfuric Acid, 7.0 N	(C-136)
Sulfuric Acid, Dilute	(C-137)
Iodine Standards:	(C-138)

    A. Concentrated Stock Standard, 100 μg/ml.
    B. Dilute Stock Standard, 0.2 μg/ml.
    C. Dilute Working Standard, 0.04 μg/ml.
    Pipet 10.0 ml. of dilute stock standard into a 50 ml. volumetric flask. Dilute to mark with double-distilled water. Stopper and mix thoroughly.

Ceric Ammonium Sulfate, 0.02 N	(C-139)
Sodium Arsenite, 0.1 N	(C-140)
Antifoam Solution	(C-141)

Procedure

Rimless, acid-washed Pyrex test tubes (15 × 125 mm.) are numbered in duplicate with a Marktex Tech-Pen. This type of ink withstands the extreme furnace temperature. For the first rack of 24 test tubes, include one set (2 tubes) of reagent blanks and two sets (4 tubes) of commercial control. For successive racks, include one set of reagent blanks and one set of either a commercial control or a pooled serum that has been assayed for quality control.

Precipitation

1. Pipet 1.0 ml. of double-distilled water into the blanks and 1.0 ml. of controls and plasma into the proper tubes. Use Ostwald-Folin pipets.
2. Add 8.0 ml. of the diluted zinc sulfate to all tubes. Use a serological pipet or, for large volumes of work, a Brewer automatic pipet is helpful.
3. The serum and zinc sulfate (diluted) are mixed either with a Vortex mixer or with glass stirring rods of 3 mm. diameter.
4. Leave the rods in the tubes and add 1.0 ml. of 0.5 N NaOH to each tube.
5. Mix the contents until they are homogeneous.
6. Remove each rod with a rotary movement, scraping off any adhering protein.
7. Place the rods on either a numbered, corrugated edging strip or a strip of paper toweling that can be discarded after use. The idea is to keep the stirring rods off the table and separated.

Washing the precipitate

1. Centrifuge the tubes for 10 minutes at 3000 RPM.
2. With the precipitate well packed by centrifugation, invert the tubes, pouring off the supernatant. Shake the tubes to dispose of the small amount of water remaining.
3. Pipet 10.0 ml. of double-distilled water into the tubes. A 5 ml. Cornwall semiautomatic pipet is very helpful.
4. Place the stirring rods into the correct tubes and homogenize the protein and water thoroughly. Leave no "lumps."
5. Centrifuge the tubes for 10 minutes at 3000 RPM.
6. The washing of the precipitate is done three times. Record when each washing is completed, so there will be no mistake in the number of times the precipitates have been washed.

Drying the precipitate

1. To each tube, add 1.0 ml. of 4 N sodium carbonate plus 1 drop of antifoam solution.
2. Mix well with the stirring rods, keeping the precipitate in the lower half of the tube.
3. Rotate each rod as it is removed, to scrape off any adhering protein.
4. Place the tubes in a slanted position in a small basket.
5. Place in a 100° C. drying oven until dry or leave overnight. An electric drying block may be used if one is available. (Note: If the antifoam solution is used, the temperature may be elevated to 110° C. for an approximate drying time of 2 hours. If the antifoam is not used, the temperature must be kept at 100° C. or the precipitate will bubble out of the tube.)

Incineration

The tubes are prepared in the following way to prevent cross-contamination.[5]

1. Tear off or cut a piece of heavy aluminum foil about 10 inches long and 4½ inches wide. Allow one sheet for each pair of tubes.

2. Place the pair of tubes at least 2½ inches from the top of the foil. The sides are then folded together and the foil is wrapped up from the bottom. The rising vapors are held within the aluminum foil cylinder, preventing contamination of other specimens.
3. Stand the foil-wrapped tubes upright in a steel bucket and incinerate for 3 hours at 600° ± 10° C.
4. Using a steel shovel, remove the tubes from the furnace and cool to room temperature.
5. Unwrap the tubes and discard the foil.

Extracting the iodide from the ash

1. Add 2.0 ml. of 2 N HCl carefully—to avoid excessive effervescence— and rotate each tube slowly while adding the acid to wash down the sides of the tubes. Allow to stand for 5 minutes, until the effervescence ceases.
2. Add 5.0 ml. of dilute H_2SO_4 to each tube.
3. Mix contents by flipping the tube.
4. Centrifuge for 10 minutes at 1700 RPM to pack the insoluble material.
Note: For adding the HCl and H_2SO_4, either a 2 ml. and 5 ml. Machlett Auto-Pipet or all-glass automatic zero buret may be used.

Determination of the iodide

1. For each unknown, number a spectrophotometer tube.
2. Treat the first ten spectrophotometer tubes as follows:
    a. Tubes 1 and 2. Pipet 3.0 ml. aliquots of the reagent blanks.
    b. Tubes 3 to 6. Keep empty for standards.
    c. Tubes 7 to 10. Pipet 3.0 ml. aliquots of the commercial control.
3. Continue to pipet a 3.0 ml. aliquot of the unknown into each tube.
4. To the tubes containing the aliquots, add 5.0 ml. of double-distilled water. A 5 ml. Cornwall pipet is accurate and time-saving for this step.
5. Treat the standards as follows:
    a. Prepare a pH-adjusting solution:
        (1) Pipet 4.0 ml. of 2 N HCl into an Erlenmeyer flask.
        (2) Add 4.0 ml. of 7 N H_2SO_4 to the flask.
        (3) Add 4.0 ml. of double-distilled (d-distilled) water and swirl flask to mix.
        (4) Add 2.0 ml. of 4 N Na_2CO_3, swirl to mix, and set aside for effervescence to cease.
    This solution will adjust the pH of the standards to equal that of the unknowns.
    b. To the "standard" spectrophotometer tubes add the following:

Tube No.	Iodine concentration of standard	Volume of working standard	Volume of water	Volume of pH solution
3	0.02 µg/ml.	0.5 ml.	4.5 ml.	3.0 ml.
4	0.04 µg/ml.	1.0 ml.	4.0 ml.	3.0 ml.
5	0.06 µg/ml.	1.5 ml.	3.5 ml.	3.0 ml.
6	0.08 µg/ml.	2.0 ml.	3.0 ml.	3.0 ml.

6. Add 0.5 ml. of 0.1 N sodium arsenite to each tube. Mix well.
7. Place tubes in a 40° C. water bath for 10 minutes.
8. Tape an Erlenmeyer flask containing ceric ammonium sulfate solution to a corner of the water bath, with the reagent below the water level. Allow 10 minutes for the reagent to come to bath temperature.
9. Set the timer for 30 minutes. Add 1.0 ml. of ceric ammonium sulfate solution to each tube at *exactly* ½-minute intervals and mix. Use a fast-flowing 1 ml. volumetric pipet.

10. *Exactly* 15 minutes later, read the tubes at exactly ½-minute intervals against a water blank at 420 mμ wavelength.

Calculations

Prepare a standard curve by plotting the O.D. readings of the standards against their iodide concentrations on linear graph paper. The 3 ml. aliquot of iodide extract used in the reading portion of the test represents 7/3 ml. of serum or plasma. By multiplying the iodide concentration of each of the standards, 0.02, 0.04, 0.06, and 0.08 μg/ml., by 7/3, one obtains values that represent 4.67, 9.33, 14.00, and 18.7 μg/100 ml., respectively. By plotting the O.D. readings against these values, the unknowns may be determined directly in μg/100 ml. of serum or plasma. If the reagent blank reading falls above the 0.0 μg/100 ml. point, determine the amount of iodide in the blank and subtract it from the unknown values to obtain the corrected values in μg/100 ml. of serum or plasma.

Wet digestion method (chloric acid)[14]

The student should be aware there are three wet digestion methods available for protein-bound iodine determinations. These are distinguished by the oxidizing agents utilized: permanganate acid, chromic acid, and chloric acid. One of the latest methods for PBI determinations is the automated method of Technicon's AutoAnalyzer, which utilizes perchloric acid as the oxidizing agent. The manual method presented is the one used by the Clinical Chemistry Laboratory of St. Lukes Hospital, St. Louis, Missouri.

This method is based on the chloric acid digestion of the precipitated protein of serum or heparinized plasma in which a small volume of chromic acid is used as a catalyst. During this period of digestion the organic iodine is oxidized to iodate. Upon the addition of arsenious acid the iodate is then reduced to iodide. Also, any excess chromate giving color is reduced to a clear solution. With the timed addition of ceric ammonium sulfate, the arsenious acid and the ceric ammonium sulfate react, reducing the ceric ions to cerous ions. This results in a loss of color as the reduction takes place. The iodide acts as a catalyst. The higher the concentration of iodide, the faster is the reaction or loss of color. This is easily observed with grossly elevated specimens.

Extreme care must be taken with reagents and prevention of contaminating materials entering the PBI area. Commercial controls or pooled serum of various concentrations must be analyzed with each group of tests. *Never* use yesterday's curve. *Always* run a set of standards and controls with each day's run.

Precaution. The digestion process must take place in a strong-drawing fume hood. If possible, the hood should have a system for washing the unit down after the digestion is completed.

Apparatus needed

Round-bottom centrifuge tubes, 40 ml.
Electrolytic beakers, 400 ml.
Cuvets (19 × 105 mm.)

Reagents needed*

Perchloric Acid, 10%	(C-203)
Chloric Acid (store in refrigerator)	(C-204)

---

*All chemicals must be of Analytical Reagent purity. Double-distilled water must be used in making all aqueous solutions.

Chromic Acid   (C-205)
Arsenious Acid, 0.2 N   (C-206)
Ceric Ammonium Sulfate, 0.04 N   (C-207)
Sulfuric Acid, 10 N with 100 mg. NaCl/ml.   (C-208)
Iodate Solution, Stock Standard, 100 μg/ml.   (C-209)
Working Iodate Standard, 0.10 μg/ml.

Using a volumetric pipet, pipet 1.0 ml. of stock standard into a 1-liter volumetric flask. Dilute to mark with double-distilled water. Mix. Prepare fresh each week!

Procedure

Precipitation of protein

1. Using a volumetric pipet, measure 3.0 ml. of serum or plasma into a 40 ml. round-bottom centrifuge tube.
2. Using a buret, slowly add 25 ml. of 10% perchloric solution while you agitate the tube.
3. Centrifuge the tubes for 30 minutes at 2000 RPM.
4. If only the PBI is to be determined, *decant and discard* the supernatant. However, for the determination of serum-soluble iodide, add an aliquot of the supernatant directly to the arsenious acid.
5. After discarding the supernatant, again add 25 ml. of 10% perchloric solution to the precipitated protein.
6. Using a glass stirring rod, resuspend the precipitate and, when the protein is homogeneous, centrifuge for 30 minutes.
7. Discard the supernatant. At this point you may either continue with the analysis or freeze the precipitated protein.

Digestion-oxidation

1. For consistent results (step 8) it is important that *exactly* 15 glass beads (5 mm.) be added to each 400 ml. electrolytic beaker. The beads are to prevent excessive bumping during the evaporation. Knowing the exact number of beads in each beaker will be invaluable when you make the visual estimation of the fluid volume remaining in each beaker.
2. Standards including the blank may be prepared at this time. Prepare four 400 ml. electrolytic beakers by adding to each:
   a. 15 beads (5 mm.)
   b. 25 ml. of chloric acid
   c. 1 ml. of chromic acid
3. The four standards are made up for each run consisting of the blank, containing no added iodate, and the following beakers, containing the given amount of working standard:
   a. 1.0 ml. which is equivalent to 0.1 μg of iodate
   b. 1.5 ml. which is equivalent to 0.15 μg of iodate
   c. 2.0 ml. which is equivalent to 0.2 μg of iodate
4. Transfer the precipitated protein to the 400 ml. beakers containing the beads. To be assured of a complete transfer of the precipitated protein from the centrifuge tube to the beaker, the following procedure is used.
   a. Divide the 25 ml. of *chloric acid* into three washings of 10, 10, and 5 ml. volumes.
   b. With a pipet, carefully add 10 ml. of chloric acid, washing down the sides of the tube. If this does not loosen the precipitate "coin," carefully rim the outside of the coin to loosen it from the centrifuge tube. The coin usually slips out easily.
   c. With the second 10 ml. wash down the sides of the tube and with a glass stirring rod (for each tube) disengage any protein clinging to the sides of the tube.
   d. The last 5 ml. of chloric acid are used to completely rinse the tube and stirring rod of any protein material.

5. Using a 5 ml. serological pipet, transfer 1.0 ml. of *chromic acid* to the beakers containing the protein precipitate but not to the blank and standards. You have already added chromic acid to these beakers.

6. Evaporate *all* of the beakers on a hot plate with a surface temperature of about 150° C. When the crackling (due to decomposition of chloric acid) ceases and the white fumes appear, pipet 0.5 ml. of chloric acid into each beaker.

7. The color of the solution will be orange, so during the process of evaporation 1 or 2 drops of chloric acid must be added from time to time in order to maintain the chromium in its *orange* quadrivalent state. This is very important, because the reduction of chromium to the green trivalent state for more than a few seconds is associated with the loss of iodine.

8. Evaporate to near-dryness, not to complete dryness or iodine may be lost. The final volume should be less than 0.5 ml. This estimation of volume is done visually, and with a standard number of beads in each beaker there is negligible volume error. Take a beaker with 15 beads, add less than 0.5 ml. of water. Use 0.4 ml. of water, tip the beaker at an angle, and you will see a small amount of liquid on either side of the beads. Until you are experienced with this type of measurement, fix a beaker with the water for guidance.

Spectrophotometry

1. Allow the beakers to cool slightly; then immediately add 10.0 ml. of distilled water to each, washing down the sides of the beaker. Swirl the beaker to effect solution (to mix thoroughly the 10.0 ml. of water and the ± 0.4 ml. of dissolved digestate).

2. Cool to room temperature.

3. Using volumetric pipets, pipet a 4.0 ml. aliquot from each beaker into its respectively numbered cuvet.

4. Pipet 2.0 ml. of 0.2 N arsenious acid and 0.5 ml. of the sulfuric-sodium chloride reagent. Mix well.

5. Place the tubes in a 30° C. controlled temperature water bath for 30 minutes. Note: Never attempt to read more than 10 tubes at a time.

6. Set a timer, and at ½-minute intervals add 0.5 ml. of 0.04 N ceric ammonium sulfate solution to each of the tubes. Mix well.

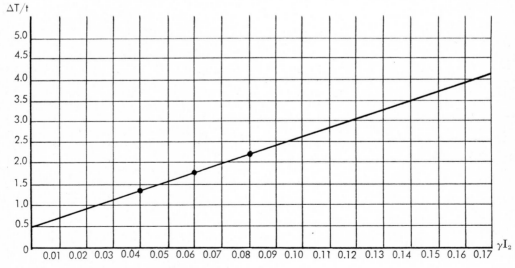

Fig. 56. Example of a PBI standard curve.

7. Using a Coleman Universal Spectrophotometer at a 420 mμ wavelength, set the water reference blank at 100% transmission. The tubes are then read at $\frac{1}{2}$-minute intervals. Each tube is read in 4- or 5-minute intervals.

Calculation

1. Calculate the rate of reaction by subtracting the spectrophotometer reading closest to 35% transmission from the reading closest to 60% transmission (T) and dividing by the time (t) interval in minutes (Table 48).
2. Construct a graph by plotting T/t against the known amounts of iodine in the aliquots of the standards (Fig. 56).
3. Read the iodine concentration in the aliquots of the unknown samples directly from the graph (see example).
4. Express the PBI in μg%.

$$\frac{I_2 \text{ concentration in aliquot}}{\text{Vol. sample} \times \text{aliquot}\%} \times 100 = \mu g\% \text{ PBI}$$

$$\frac{.047}{3 \times 0.40} \times 100 = 3.9 \ \mu g\% \text{ PBI}$$

5. Provided 3.0 ml. of serum are precipitated and a 4.0 ml. aliquot of dissolved digestate is used in the analysis, the factor 83 may be used; therefore:
   I_2 concentration in aliquote $\times$ 83 = μg% PBI

Table 48. Protein-bound iodine

Date:	4-23-65							
Time	Bl.	0.1	0.15	2.0	I	II	III	IV
4	19$\frac{1}{2}$	21$\frac{1}{4}$	21$\frac{1}{2}$	23$\frac{1}{4}$	20	22	24	21$\frac{3}{4}$
8	20$\frac{3}{4}$	24$\frac{3}{4}$	27	30	24$\frac{3}{4}$	28$\frac{1}{2}$	33	26$\frac{1}{2}$
12	22$\frac{1}{2}$	29	31$\frac{1}{2}$	38$\frac{1}{2}$	29$\frac{3}{4}$	37	45	32$\frac{1}{2}$
16	24	34$\frac{1}{4}$	38$\frac{1}{4}$	48	34$\frac{3}{4}$	45$\frac{1}{2}$	57$\frac{1}{2}$	40$\frac{1}{4}$
20	25$\frac{3}{4}$	39$\frac{1}{2}$	46	57	40$\frac{1}{2}$	55		48
24	27$\frac{3}{4}$	45	52$\frac{3}{4}$		46$\frac{1}{4}$			56
28	29$\frac{1}{4}$	50$\frac{1}{4}$			52$\frac{3}{4}$			
32	31$\frac{3}{4}$							
ΔT/t	0.46	1.33	1.77	2.25	1.50	2.25	3.06	1.95
γI$_2$					.047	.080	.117	.067
γ%					3.9	6.6	9.7	5.5
% T	31.75 20.75	50.25 34.25	52.75 31.50	57.0 30.0	52.75 34.75	55.00 37.00	57.50 33.00	56.00 32.50
$\triangle$% T	11.00	16.00	21.25	27.0	18.00	18.00	24.50	23.50
t	24	12	12	12	12	8	8	12

SERUM IRON[10]
Bothwell-Mallett method*

Iron circulates in blood plasma, bound to the β_1 globulin. The absorption of the iron occurs in the upper part of the small intestine and perhaps in the stomach. The role of iron in the body is closely associated with that of hemoglobin.

Disorders related to abnormal values are listed in Table 49.

Table 49. Disorders affecting the serum iron

When increased	When decreased
Pernicious anemia	Iron deficiency anemia
Aplastic and hemolytic anemia	Malignancy
Hemochromatosis	Uremia
Acute hepatitis	Chronic infections
Polycythemia	Nephrotic syndrome
	Extensive burns

Most methods for the analysis of serum iron are done in three basic stages.

Principle of method of determination

1. The iron is usually split from its protein by an acid (HCl). The acidified serum is allowed to stand or incubate 15 minutes to several hours (according to the method used), for the iron to separate from its protein.
2. The free iron is isolated by the precipitation of proteins with trichloroacetic acid. The tube is allowed to stand for 15 minutes for complete precipitation.
3. The color complex is developed with a 2:2'-dipyridyl at a pH range of 3 to 9. Ascorbic acid is used as the reducing agent, and the solution is buffered with saturated sodium acetate.

Reagents needed

Hydrochloric Acid, 2.0 N	(C-135)
Trichloroacetic Acid (TCA), 20%	(C-142)
Ascorbic Acid, Crystalline	
2:2'-Dipyridyl, 0.4%	(C-143)
Sodium Acetate, Saturated	(C-66,a)
Iron, Stock Standard, 100 mg./100 ml. (stable indefinitely)	(C-144)
Iron, Working Standard, 100 μg/100 ml. (stable)	

Pipet 0.5 ml. of stock standard (100 mg./100 ml.) into a 500 ml. volumetric flask. Dilute to mark with iron-free water. Stopper and mix by inverting.

Procedure

1. To the following iron-free tubes:

Blank
a. Pipet 3.0 ml. of 2 N HCl.
b. Add 4.0 ml. of double-distilled water.

Standard
a. Pipet 3.0 ml. of 2 N HCl.
b. Add 4.0 ml. of working standard (100 μg/100 ml.).

---

*Modified by the Hematology Department, Washington University School of Medicine, St. Louis, Mo.

Unknown

    a. Pipet 3.0 ml. of 2 N HCl.

    b. Add 4.0 ml. of serum.

2. Using glass stirring rods, mix all tubes thoroughly.
3. Let stand for 15 minutes.
4. Add 2.0 ml. of 20% TCA to the tubes.
5. Stir vigorously for 45 seconds.
6. Let stand for 15 minutes.
7. Centrifuge the tubes for 20 minutes at 3000 RPM (since the blank and standard have no precipitate, they will not have to be centrifuged).
8. To *each* spectrophotometer tube (blank, standard, and unknown):

    a. Pipet 6.0 ml. of supernatant.

    b. Add 30 mg. of crystalline ascorbic acid.

    c. Add 0.5 ml. of 2:2'-dipyridyl, 0.4%, to each tube.

    d. Add 2.5 ml. of saturated sodium acetate.

    e. Shake the tubes to mix thoroughly.

    f. Let stand for 5 minutes to develop color fully.

9. Read the reagent blank, standard, and unknowns against a distilled water blank at a wavelength of 520 mμ. Convert the readings to O.D.

Calculation

$$\frac{(\text{O.D. of unknown} - \text{O.D. of blank})}{(\text{O.D. of standard} - \text{O.D. of blank})} \times 100 = \mu g \ Fe/100 \ ml.$$

Normal range

Women 50 to 170 μg/100 ml.

Men   61 to 193 μg/100 ml.

OSMOMETRY*

When a solute is dissolved in a solvent, four colligative properties are affected: (1) freezing point is lowered; (2) boiling point is raised; (3) osmotic pressure is increased; (4) vapor pressure is lowered. Theoretically, any of these properties may be used to measure particle concentration in solution. Of these four properties, however, freezing point depression offers the greatest facility in terms of practical usefulness.

Osmolality has been defined as being equal to Φ n c, where Φ is the osmotic coefficient, n is the number of particles into which a molecule dissociates, and c is concentration in terms of molality. It should be kept in mind that molality describes concentration in terms of moles per kilogram of solvent, whereas molarity is in terms of moles per liter of solution. In the same way, the correct expression for the designation of solute concentration in a kilogram of solvent is osmolality, not osmolarity. For all practical purposes, however, the difference is very slight and the terms are often used interchangeably.

Osmolality is actually a measure of the concentration of particles in solution, rather than that of molecules, and is linear with respect to osmotic pressure and freezing point depression.

When 1 mole of a nonionic solute is dissolved in a kilogram of water, the freezing point is lowered by 1.858° C., termed the molal depression constant. In the case of ionizable solutes, the freezing point is dependent upon the degree of ionization and volume change. This is demonstrated by the following example. A solution of sodium chloride containing 0.910 gm./100 ml. will lower the freezing

---

*From Frankel, Sam: Osmometry in the clinical laboratory, Lab. Digest **26**:3, 1963.

point by 0.535° C. According to the ratio of 0.535/1.858, there should be 0.288 moles of a nonionic solute, expressed as 288 milliosmols (mOsM). The sodium chloride concentration, however, is only 9.10/58.5 or 0.155 molar. It is easily calculated that sodium chloride in this range of concentration supplies particles to an extent of 86% more than the number of molecules, obtained by dividing 0.288 minus 0.155 by 0.155. In other words, 100 molecules of sodium chloride, in this concentration range, reduces the freezing point to the same degree as 186 molecules of a nonionic solute, such as glucose.

The principles involved in measuring osmolality by freezing point depression are relatively simple. A solution is supercooled, that is, cooled below its freezing point. Freezing is induced by seeding the solution or, more practically, by rapidly vibrating a wire placed in the solution. The formation of ice crystals liberates heat of fusion, following which the temperature rises. The increasing temperature reaches a plateau due to the insulating effect of the slush produced and the thawing and refreezing of ice crystals. When all of the heat of fusion has been removed by the surrounding cooling bath, the temperature will begin to fall. During the period at which the temperature is constant, that is, at the plateau, the temperature is measured and converted to osmolality units.

Until recently, osmometry was considered primarily a research tool. With the improvements in modern osmometers, however, this test is now practical in any clinical laboratory. It has been suggested that routine osmolality determinations may be a valuable adjunct in the study of fluid and electrolyte balance. Many believe that osmolality offers a better evaluation of urinary excretion of solute and water load than specific gravity. There is information which indicates that tubular transfer is better represented by the number of solute particles than by weight.

Urine osmolality values are of definite application in the calculation of water clearance, in the differential diagnosis of diabetes insipidus and compulsive water drinking, for a better interpretation of concentration-dilution tests, in differentiating large and small molecule excretion, and in the evaluation of renal solute excretion in kidney disease. In addition, urine osmolality is an extremely useful tool in following patients on fluid therapy after surgery, and in estimating the state of dehydration subsequent to severe burns.

Serum osmolality measurements have been used in the determination of hypo- or hypernatremia, in the approximation of solute retention in acute renal failure, as a substitute for multiple electrolyte assays on a limited basis, and in the estimation of the concentration of material not normally assayed.

Since the major contributor of particles in serum is sodium chloride, there is a close relationship between the serum sodium level and osmolality. On the other hand, it must be remembered that osmolality is related to particle concentration; therefore, it is possible that the serum osmolality may be elevated even though the sodium level is normal or even low. A low osmolality, however, is nearly always associated with hyponatremia.

In acute renal failure the concentration of many serum constituents, such as urea, uric acid, creatinine, and phosphate, increases although in many cases the sodium level is lowered. The resulting osmolality may then be low, normal, or elevated.

In those cases where fluids are given to patients, serum osmolality serves to reflect the overall effect. The same is true in those patients subjected to hemodialysis, in which case a more rapid correlation is obtained. This becomes especially true in cases where high concentrations of drugs or other commercial products are removed by hemodialysis.

The normal value for serum osmolality has been taken to range from 280 to 300 milliosmols per kilogram of serum water. No significant differences have been observed between male and female subjects, or between serum and plasma, although any excessive amount of anticoagulant will yield a false high result. Generally, heparinized plasma is suitable, but oxalated plasma is not. In addition, according to Hendry,[11] serum separated from cells could be preserved at 4° C. for several hours without change in osmolality.

Two commonly used devices are employed to utilize serum osmolality values in conjunction with the assay of other serum constituents. In one of these devices, a calculated serum osmolality is obtained by adding the effects of sodium, urea, and glucose. This is accomplished by multiplying the sodium level in meq./L. by 1.86, dividing the urea nitrogen in mg.% by 2.8, and dividing glucose in mg.% by 18. The difference between the actual and the calculated value has been stated as 5 to 8 milliosmols, but this figure seems to be too low. If average normal values for the above-mentioned constituents are used, the following difference in actual and calculated osmolality results:

$$
\begin{array}{lrcr}
\text{Sodium} & 140 \times 1.86 & = & 260 \\
\text{Urea nitrogen} & 15 \div 2.8 & = & 5 \\
\text{Glucose} & 100 \div 18 & = & 6 \\
\hline
& & & 271 \\
\text{Actual normal} & & = & 290 \\
\text{Difference} & & = & 19 \\
\end{array}
$$

If it is assumed that Ca, Mg, and K salts yield particles to an extent of 86% more than their molecular number, these would total 21 milliosmols.

Differences of 40 to 100 milliosmols have been reported, in which case the conclusion is that there is a large quantity of material which was not assayed, and which usually indicates a poor prognosis.

A second device sometimes used to correlate serum osmolality with serum sodium is their ratio. Normally the value of this ratio falls into the range of 0.43 to 0.50, and any value below 0.43 indicates a poor prognosis.

In a study of osmolality as a routine screening test on unselected hospital patients, Stevens, Neumayer, and Gutch[12] reported that 38% of 351 cases had one or more osmolality values outside the normal range. Further, of 218 patients having normal osmolality values, only 8 had abnormal serum electrolyte levels. This would result in about 4% of unselected hospital patients who had "false negative" values if serum osmolality had been the only determination made. It was also noted that the serum sodium level was normal if the serum osmolality was normal, excepting patients with renal involvement.

The measurement of serum and urine osmolality may well become an extremely useful tool in solving difficult problems of fluid and electrolyte imbalances. It is not likely, however, that this test will ever replace multiple electrolyte determinations, although its simplicity and speed make it an ideal test for rapid approximations of the total electrolyte level.

REFERENCES

1. Wuth, O.: Rational bromide treatment; new methods for its control, J.A.M.A. **88**:2013, 1927.
2. Trinder, P.: Rapid determination of salicylate in biological fluids, Biochem. J. **57**:301, 1954.
3. Bratton, A. C., and Marshall, E. K., Jr.: New coupling component for sulfanilamide determination, J. Biol. Chem. **128**:537, 1939.
4. FI test, rapid slide test for hypofibrinogenemia, Los Angeles, Hyland Laboratories.
5. Lackland, H.: Quantitative fibrinogen, Lab. Digest **28**:3, March-April, 1965.
6. Reiner, M., and Cheung, H. L.: A practical method for the determination of fibrinogen, Clin. Chem. **5**:414, 1959.
7. Barker, S. B., and Humphrey, M. J.: Clinical determination of protein-bound iodine in plasma, J. Clin. Endocrinol. **10**:1136, 1950.
8. White, W. L.: The prevention of cross-contamination in PBI determinations, Clin. Chem. **9**:365, 1963.
9. Henry, R. J.: Clinical chemistry; principles and technics, New York, 1964, Paul B. Hoeber, Inc., Medical Book Department of Harper & Row, Publishers.
10. Bothwell, T. H., and Mallett, B.: The determination of iron in plasma or serum, Biochem. J. **59**:599, 1955.
11. Hendry, E. B.: Osmolarity of human serum and chemical solutions of biologic importance, Clin. Chem. **7**:156, 1961.
12. Stevens, S. C., Neumayer, F., and Gutch, C. F.: Serum osmolality as a routine test, Nebraska M. J. **45**:447, 1960.
13. Zac, B., Willard, H. H., Myers, G. B., and Boyle, A. J.: Chloric acid method for determination of protein-bound iodine, Anal. Chem. **24**:1345, 1952.
14. O'Neal, L. W., and Simms, E. S.: Determination of protein-bound iodine in plasma or serum, Am. J. Clin. Path. **23**:493, 1953.
15. Zac, B., Koen, A. M., and Boyle, A. J.: Normal and abnormal values of protein-bound iodine, Am. J. Clin. Path. **23**:603, 1953.

Part 3

Spinal fluid analysis

Cerebrospinal fluid is a clear, colorless fluid, having a specific gravity of 1.004 to 1.008. The fluid, being chiefly a dialysate from the blood, maintains a pH of 7.35 to 7.40 and is qualitatively similar to serum but differs in its concentration of the major constituents. The protein content is extremely low with no fibrinogen, the glucose in spinal fluid is approximately two thirds that of the blood sugar, and the chloride is about 25% higher than the plasma chloride. The total volume of cerebrospinal fluid is between 120 and 150 ml. Its location in the body is between the arachnoid membrane and the pia mater of both the brain and the spinal cord. The brain and spinal cord have three coverings: the pia mater, the arachnoid, and the dura mater.

The pia mater in the brain is attached to the cerebral cortex, passing into various fissures, and protrudes into the ventricles. In the spinal column this delicate membrane (containing many small blood vessels) is attached to the surface of the spinal cord. Outside the pia mater is the arachnoid layer, consisting of a delicate network of fibrous tissue containing many blood vessels. The network of the arachnoid is filled with spinal fluid. A bloody spinal fluid received in the laboratory may be due to a subarachnoid (beneath the arachnoid membrane, within the network of blood vessels and spinal fluid) hemorrhage. The outermost covering is a tough, thick, fibrous membrane called the dura mater. Inflammation of these coverings is known as meningitis.

The spinal fluid has three functions:

1. To protect the brain from injury by acting as a fluid buffer
2. To act as a medium of exchange for the transfer of dialyzable material between the bloodstream and the tissues of the brain and the spinal cord
3. To equalize the pressure between the brain and the spinal cord

Physical appearance of spinal fluid with various diseases

Xanthochromia. The spinal fluid is a clear yellow, showing rapid coagulation. There are no blood pigments present, but large amounts of globulin. This disorder results from a tumor pressing on the spinal cord and affecting the flow of spinal fluid. A pocket of fluid collects and stagnates, with these results. Xanthochromia may appear after a cerebral hemorrhage.

Acute meningitic infection. The fluid may appear slightly to very turbid until there is an appearance of almost pure pus.

Tuberculous meningitis. The fluid is clear, although upon standing for 12 to 24 hours, a pellicle will form. With many cases of acute meningitis, tuberculous meningitis, and suppurative meningitis a pellicle of fibrin and blood cells forms in the fluid when the specimen is allowed to stand.

Suppurative meningitis. Pellicle formation is extremely rapid. It is difficult to work with this type of material because of its speedy coagulation.

Spinal fluid contains glucose, protein, and chloride. In disease, the concentration of these materials may vary, and white cells and bacteria may also be present.

The composition of the fluid is usually altered in the following diseases: meningitis, poliomyelitis, encephalitis, and latent syphilis.

This portion of the text deals with tests on spinal fluid. The material is presented in the following chapter:

Chapter 16 Spinal fluid examination

Spinal fluid examination

The spinal fluid is obtained by making a spinal puncture. This is performed by a physician. The usual practice is to place the fluid in three sterile test tubes. The first tube goes to the bacteriology department where a smear and culture are made. The second tube goes to the hematology department where a cell count is made. The third tube goes to the chemistry department for chemical examinations and thence to the serology department for various serological tests.

The routine examination of spinal fluid consists of the following:

Smear
Culture
Cell count
Globulin
Total protein
Glucose
Chloride
Tryptophane test

SMEAR

In disease, the spinal fluid may contain the following organisms: staphylococci, streptococci, meningococci, tubercle bacilli, and influenza bacilli.

These organisms may be identified by a smear and culture. The procedures follow.

Procedure

1. Centrifuge the spinal fluid at high speed for 5 minutes.
2. Pour off and discard the supernatant fluid.
3. Using a bacteriological loop, smear some of the sediment over a glass slide.
4. Warm the bottom of the slide to "fix" the bacteria.
5. Stain with Gram's stain, using the usual gentian violet, Gram's iodine, acetone, and safranin. (If examination for tubercle bacilli is requested, make another smear and stain for AFB.)
6. Identify the organisms, using a textbook on bacteriology as a guide.
7. Report the organisms found.

CULTURE

The culture should be made while the spinal fluid is fresh. If this is not possible, store the fluid in the 37° C. incubator. This is permissible, since spinal fluid itself is a good culture medium.

In many hospitals, the routine procedure for a spinal culture begins with streaking the fluid onto the media which are listed below. (These media are usually stored in a refrigerator and should be warmed to room temperature before use.)

Blood agar plate or slant
Chocolate agar plate or slant

Procedure

1. The sediment that was used to prepare the smear may be used to make the culture. If this sediment is not available, centrifuge a sample of the spinal fluid at high speed for 5 minutes. Pour off and discard the supernatant fluid. Use the sediment for the culture.
2. Obtain a blood agar plate or slant. Warm gently over a flame.
3. Using a bacteriological loop, streak the plate or slant with the spinal fluid sediment.
4. Place in a 37° C. incubator.
5. Obtain a chocolate agar plate or slant. Warm gently over a flame.
6. Using the bacteriological loop, streak the plate or slant with the spinal fluid sediment.
7. Place the plate or slant in the CO_2 jar. Light the candle. Place the lid on the jar so that it is tightly secured. The candle, of course, will go out. This creates an increased CO_2 tenson which aids in the growth of meningococci.
8. Place the CO_2 jar in the 37° C. incubator.
9. Twenty-four hours later, examine the plates or slants for growth, make slides, and identify the organisms as directed in textbooks on bacteriology.

CELL COUNT

The spinal cell count consists of the total cell count and the differential cell count. Since the cells disintegrate rapidly, the counts should be made while the fluid is fresh—preferably within an hour following the withdrawal of fluid.

Spinal fluid often contains contagious material. Consequently, the technician should take particular care in handling the specimens. In making transfers of the fluid, it is a wise policy to use medicine droppers.

The procedures for the total cell count and the differential cell count follow.

Total cell count

The cells found in spinal fluid are usually white cells, called leukocytes. Sometimes, however, red cells produced by the puncture itself are seen. These may cause a slight increase in the count. The normal values for the total cell count are 0 to 10 cells/cu. mm. Increased values, such as 20 to 1000 cells, may be found in meningitis, encephalitis, poliomyelitis, and latent syphilis.

Procedure

1. Mix the spinal fluid thoroughly by tapping the bottom and sides of the test tube.
2. Draw the spinal fluid counting solution to the 0.5 mark and draw the spinal fluid to mark 11 in a white counting pipet, thus making a dilu-

tion of the spinal fluid of 19:20. Mix thoroughly. Transfer a small portion (2 or 3 drops) to a counting chamber, which is generally used for counting blood cells.

3. Using either the 4 mm. or the 16 mm. objective, count the cells in the *entire* ruled area. This will be the nine large squares as seen with the low power (16 mm. objective) of the microscope.

4. After the count is made, the counting chamber should be soaked in alcohol to prevent contagion.

Calculation

By counting the cells in the entire ruled area, you have counted the number in 0.9 cu.mm.° The report, however, is to be given as the number in 1.0 cu.mm. Therefore, multiply the number counted by 1.0/0.9 (or 10/9).

Example: The number of cells counted in the entire ruled area was 9. Multiplying this by 10/9, we have:

$$9 \times 10/9 = 10 \text{ cells/cu.mm.}$$

Spinal fluid counting solution (Tuerk solution)

1. Pipet 1.0 ml. of glacial acetic acid into a volumetric flask.
2. Dilute to 100 ml. with distilled water.
3. Add a few drops of alcoholic gentian violet to color.
4. Stopper and mix thoroughly.
5. Filter several times, until clear.

Differential cell count

If the total cell count is within the normal range of 0 to 10 cells/cu. mm., there is no point in making a differential cell count. If, however, the count is elevated, a differential cell count should be made.

The white cells usually found in spinal fluid are lymphocytes or segmented cells. In the following diseases, the lymphocytes usually outnumber the segmented cells: tuberculous meningitis, latent syphilis, anterior poliomyelitis, and epidemic encephalitis.

In the following diseases, the segmented cells outnumber the lymphocytes: pneumococcus meningitis, influenzal meningitis, pyogenic meningitis, and epidemic meningitis.

Procedure

1. Mix the specimen thoroughly by tapping the bottom and sides of the test tube.
2. With a medicine dropper, place a small drop of the spinal fluid on a glass slide. Using another slide as a spreader, spread the fluid over the slide as you would for a blood smear.
3. Allow to dry.
4. Stain with Wright's stain.
5. Using the oil-immersion objective of the microscope, record the number of lymphocytes and segmented cells seen while counting 100 white cells.
6. Report the percent found.

Example: 40 lymphocytes and 60 segmented cells were recorded while counting 100 white cells. Therefore, there are 40% lymphocytes and 60% segmented cells.

°The total area of the nine large squares is 9 sq. mm. Since the counting chamber is 0.1 mm. deep, this will be a volume of 0.9 cu. mm. ($9 \times 0.1 = 0.9$).

GLOBULIN

Globulin is a protein. The globulin of spinal fluid is increased in meningitis and latent syphilis.

The three most commonly used tests for globulin are listed below. The procedures follow. To prepare the reagents, take the number that follows the reagent and refer to Appendix C.

Pandy test
Ross-Jones test
Nonne-Apelt test

Reagents needed

Pandy's Reagent	(C-145)
Ammonium Sulfate, Saturated	(C-146)

Pandy test

1. Pipet 1 ml. of Pandy's reagent into a small test tube.
2. Using a medicine dropper, add a few drops of the spinal fluid.
3. If an abnormal amount of globulin is present, the solution will become *markedly* turbid.
4. Report the test as positive or negative, disregarding a faint turbidity, which may be found in normal spinal fluid.

Ross-Jones test

1. Pour about 2 ml. of a saturated solution of ammonium sulfate into a small test tube.
2. Using a medicine dropper, overlay with about 1 ml. of the spinal fluid.
3. If an abnormal amount of globulin is present, the following will take place: within a few minutes, a grayish white ring will form at the junction of the two liquids.
4. Report the test as positive or negative.

Nonne-Apelt test

1. Pour about 1 ml. of a saturated solution of ammonium sulfate into a small test tube.
2. Add about 1 ml. of the spinal fluid.
3. Mix and set aside for about 3 minutes.
4. If an abnormal amount of globulin is present, a markedly cloudy precipitate will form.
5. Report the test as positive or negative.

TOTAL PROTEIN

The normal values for total protein in spinal fluid are 15 to 45 mg./100 ml. Increased values are found in meningitis and latent syphilis.

Refer to Chapter 10 for the method for spinal fluid protein.

GLUCOSE

The normal values for glucose in spinal fluid are approximately two thirds that of the blood glucose, or 40 to 80 mg./100 ml. of fluid. Increased values may accompany brain tumors. Decreased values are seen in most types of meningitis.

The determination should be made within an hour after the withdrawal of spinal fluid, because glucose decomposes upon standing. Refer to Chapter 8 for the quantitative analysis for glucose.

CHLORIDE

The chloride is expressed in terms of sodium chloride. The normal values are 730 to 790 mg. of sodium chloride/100 ml. of spinal fluid, or 125 to 135 meq./L. Decreased values are found in acute meningitis, particularly in tuberculous meningitis.

Refer to Chapter 13 for the quantitative analysis for chloride.

TRYPTOPHANE TEST

The tryptophane test is used for tuberculous meningitis. To prepare the reagents used below, refer to Appendix C.

Procedure

1. Pour about 2 ml. of *clear* spinal fluid into a large test tube.
2. Add 15 ml. of concentrated hydrochloric acid.
3. Add 2 or 3 drops of a 2% solution of formaldehyde (C-147).
4. Mix and set aside for 5 minutes.
5. Using a medicine dropper, overlay with 2 ml. of an 0.06% solution of sodium nitrite (C-148).
6. Set aside for 3 minutes.
7. In tuberculous meningitis, a violet ring forms at the junction of the two liquids. Disregard a yellow or brown ring.

Part 4

Gastric and duodenal analysis

Gastric analysis consists of obtaining and examining the contents of the stomach after its activation by a suitable stimulant.

In health, the gastric contents are mostly water, salts, pepsin, rennin, and hydrochloric acid. In disease, the gastric contents may contain blood, bacteria, and lactic acid. The significant finding in disease, however, is a change in the hydrochloric acid content.

A decreased amount of hydrochloric acid is usually found in cancer of the stomach and in pernicious anemia. An increased amount of hydrochloric acid is generally seen in gastric ulcer.

Duodenal analysis is quite similar to gastric analysis. It consists of obtaining and examining the contents of the duodenum after its activation by a suitable stimulant.

The duodenal fluid is a colorless viscid liquid. It contains amylase, lipase, and trypsin. The concentration of these substances is usually decreased in diseases of the pancreas.

Gastric and duodenal analysis are considered in the following chapters:

Chapter 17

Gastric analysis

The discussion of gastric analysis is arranged as indicated below. A method of gastric analysis called the Diagnex test is included.

> Collection of specimens
> Free hydrochloric acid
> Total acidity
> Diagnex test
> Occult blood
> Miscellaneous tests

COLLECTION OF SPECIMENS

The stomach is stimulated to activity by one of the methods given below. Directions for inserting the tube and removing the specimens follow.

Stimulation of stomach

The following methods are used to stimulate gastric secretion:

> Ewald test meal
> Riegel test meal
> Alcohol consumption
> Histamine injection

The composition of each "test meal" is given below. The alcohol consumption method is widely used and will be the one considered in the procedure that follows.

Ewald test meal

The Ewald test meal consists of either a roll or two slices of bread and 400 ml. of water. Weak tea without cream or sugar may be substituted for the water. The meal should be well masticated. The gastric contents are removed 1 hour after the beginning of the meal.

Riegel test meal

The Riegel test meal consists of 150 gm. of mashed potatoes, 200 gm. of broiled beefsteak, and 400 ml. of bouillon. The meal should be well masticated.

Alcohol consumption

The alcohol is generally given after insertion of the tube. The usual amount is 50 ml. of a 7% solution of ethyl alcohol.

Histamine injection

Histamine is a powerful stimulant and is administered by a physician. It is usually given when the alcohol "test meal" fails to produce free hydrochloric acid. The dose depends upon the preference of the physician. Some physicians give 0.25 mg. of histamine dihydrochloride or acid phosphate (0.25 ml. of a 1:1000 dilution). Other physicians give 0.1 mg. for every 22 pounds of body weight. The injection is given *subcutaneously.*

Insertion of tube

The stomach tubes most commonly used are Rehfuss, Kaslow, and Sawyer tubes (Fig. 57). The insertion of the tube requires a bit of technique and the student should not attempt the task without the supervision of either a physician or an experienced technician. A suggested method follows.

Place an ordinary kitchen apron on the patient to prevent soiling his clothes. Give him a small emesis basin to expectorate into, if necessary. Explain that you have to insert the tube into his stomach and that his cooperation is essential. Also explain that there will be no pain but some discomfort in swallowing the tube.

Coil the tube in your left hand and take the tip of the tube in your right hand. Ask the patient to open his mouth and tilt his head back. Place the tip of the tube on the middle of the tongue and push slowly back until it is almost to the pharynx. Now tell the patient that you are going to insert it into the pharynx and that it may gag him a little but that he can help by swallowing. Thrust the tube gently but firmly into the pharynx. Tell the patient to swallow four to six times, and each time he swallows push the tube down the esophagus.

The tube should be inserted until the first mark on the tube is even with the teeth. At this point an attempt should be made to remove the stomach contents with a large syringe. If nothing can be removed, push the tube into the stomach until the second marking is even with the teeth and attempt to remove the contents. *Note:* If you think there is any danger that the tube has gone into the lungs rather than into the stomach, hold your end of the tube to your ear. If the inhalation and expiration of air can be heard, the tube is in the lungs and, of course, must be withdrawn.

Removal of specimens

The Sawyer tube is made with the syringe attached. However, with a Rehfuss or Kaslow tube, a large syringe must be attached to your end of the tube. Now continue with the steps given below.

1. Withdraw all the fasting contents of the stomach by slowly pulling back the plunger of the syringe. Transfer to a container and label: Fasting Specimen.

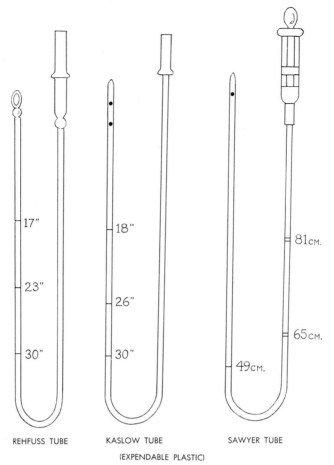

17"

23"

30"

18"

26"

30"

81cm.

65cm.

49cm.

REHFUSS TUBE   KASLOW TUBE   SAWYER TUBE

(EXPENDABLE PLASTIC)

Fig. 57. Stomach tubes.

2. Slowly inject 50 ml. of a 7% solution of *ethyl* alcohol. Record the time.
3. Fifteen minutes after the injection of the alcohol, withdraw all the available contents and transfer to another container. Label: 15-Minute Specimen.
4. Thirty minutes after the injection of the alcohol, withdraw all the available contents and transfer to another container. Label: 30-Minute Specimen.
5. Put 2 drops of Töpfer's reagent in the 15-minute specimen. Also put 2 drops of Töpfer's reagent in the 30-minute specimen. If neither specimen turns red, it means that free hydrochloric acid is absent. In such cases inform the physician, as he may wish to give a histamine injection. This, of course, is a more powerful gastric stimulant than alcohol and will produce the greatest flow of gastric juice.
6. If the histamine injection is given, withdraw specimens 15 minutes and 30 minutes after the injection and label accordingly.

FREE HYDROCHLORIC ACID

Reagents needed

Töpfer's Reagent   (C-149)
Sodium Hydroxide, 0.1 N   (C-108)

Procedure

1. Treat each specimen as follows.
2. Measure and record the volume. Remove suspended material by centrifuging or by filtering through gauze or cotton.
3. Pipet 5 ml. of the clear fluid into a small flask or beaker. Add a few drops of Töpfer's reagent. If the specimen does not turn red upon the addition of Töpfer's reagent, make a note that free hydrochloric acid is absent and titrate for total acidity as directed in the discussion of total acidity below.
4. If the gastric contents turn red when Töpfer's reagent is added, get a 2 ml. buret, graduated in hundredths, and a bottle of 0.1 N sodium hydroxide. Titrate with the 0.1 N sodium hydroxide until the red color is replaced by a canary yellow color. Record the number of milliliters of 0.1 N sodium hydroxide used. *Save the specimen,* as it will be used later to determine the total acidity.

Calculation

The report is given in degrees of acidity. The degrees of acidity are the number of milliliters of 0.1 N sodium hydroxide which *would* be required to titrate 100 ml. of gastric contents to the canary yellow color. Since only 5 ml. of gastric contents are actually used, we must multiply by 100/5:

$$\text{Free HCl in degrees of acidity} = \text{Ml. of 0.1 N NaOH used} \times \frac{100}{5}$$

Example: If 0.8 ml. of the 0.1 N sodium hydroxide was used to titrate the 5 ml. of gastric contents, the degrees of acidity are found as follows:

$$\text{Free HCl in degrees of acidity} = \text{Ml. of 0.1 N NaOH used} \times \frac{100}{5}$$

$$= 0.8 \times \frac{100}{5}$$

$$= 16$$

Normal values

The normal values are 5 to 20 degrees for the fasting specimen and 20 to 70 degrees for specimens obtained after stimulation with alcohol or histamine. Decreased values may be found in cancer of the stomach and in pernicious anemia. Increased values may be seen in gastric ulcer. The total absence of free hydrochloric acid is referred to as achlorhydria.

TOTAL ACIDITY

Reagent needed

Phenolphthalein, 1%   (C-54)

Procedure

After the free hydrochloric acid has been found in each specimen, treat each specimen as follows:

1. Add a few drops of a 1% alcoholic solution of phenolphthalein to the same specimen that was used for the free hydrochloric acid titration.
2. Continue to titrate with the 0.1 N sodium hydroxide, stopping when the mixture turns pink.
3. Record the number of milliliters of 0.1 N sodium hydroxide used.

Calculation

The report is given in degrees of acidity. The degrees of acidity are the *total* number of milliliters of 0.1 N sodium hydroxide which *would* be required to titrate 100 ml. of gastric contents to the pink color.

Name: John Smith				Date: 6-4-65
Specimen	Quantity	Free HCl	Total Acidity	Occult Blood
Fasting	20 ml.	5 degrees	15 degrees	Neg.
15 min.	15 ml.	20 degrees	50 degrees	Neg.
30 min.	10 ml.	24 degrees	70 degrees	Neg.

Fig. 58. Sample gastric analysis report.

Since only 5 ml. of gastric contents are actually used, we must multiply by 100/5.

$$\frac{\text{Total acidity in}}{\text{degrees of acidity}} = \frac{\text{Total number of ml.}}{\text{of 0.1 N NaOH used}} \times \frac{100}{5}$$

Example: If 0.8 ml. is used to titrate for free hydrochloric acid and another 1.0 ml. is used to bring the specimen to the pink color of phenolphthalein, the total number of milliliters used is 1.8 (0.8 plus 1.0 equals 1.8).

$$\frac{\text{Total acidity in}}{\text{degrees of acidity}} = \frac{\text{Total number of ml.}}{\text{of 0.1 N NaOH used}} \times \frac{100}{5}$$
$$= 1.8 \times \frac{100}{5}$$
$$= 36$$

A sample gastric analysis report is given in Fig. 58.

Normal values

The normal values are 15 to 45 degrees for the fasting specimen and 50 to 100 degrees for specimens obtained after alcohol or histamine stimulation. Decreased values may be found in cancer of the stomach and in pernicious anemia. Increased values may be seen in gastric ulcer.

DIAGNEX TEST*

The Diagnex test for gastric acidity eliminates the cumbersome task of passing a stomach tube. The patient simply swallows an indicator solution and the urine is collected and examined. The indicator, which contains quinine, functions as follows.

When free hydrochloric acid is present in the stomach, the hydrogen ions displace the quinine of the indicator. The quinine then appears in the urine where it may be observed by its fluorescent effect.

OCCULT BLOOD

In ulcers and cancer of the stomach, the gastric contents may contain occult blood. The procedures for the benzidine test and the guaiac test are given below. In interpreting the results of these tests, it must be remembered that small traces of blood may be due to injury sustained in passing the stomach tube.

Benzidine test

Reagents needed

Benzidine, Saturated, in Glacial Acetic Acid	(C-151)
Hydrogen Peroxide, 3%	(May be purchased)
Ethyl Alcohol, 95%	(May be purchased)

---

*Further information regarding this test may be obtained from E. R. Squibb & Sons, New York, N.Y.

Procedure

1. Place about 1 ml. of the filtered gastric fluid into a small test tube.
2. Add about 10 drops of a saturated solution of benzidine in glacial acetic acid. Mix.
3. Add about 10 drops of 3% hydrogen peroxide. Mix.

Reaction

A green to blue color indicates a positive reaction.

Guaiac test

Reagent needed

Guaiac Reagent
Prepare just prior to use, by placing 2 ml. of 95% ethyl alcohol and 0.2 gm. of powdered guaiac into a test tube, adding 2 ml. of 3% hydrogen peroxide, and mixing.

Procedure

1. Pour about 5 ml. of filtered gastric contents into a small test tube and add a few drops of glacial acetic acid. Mix.
2. Tilt the tube, and overlay the contents with the guaiac reagent.

Reaction

A green to blue color at the junction of the two liquids indicates a positive reaction.

MISCELLANEOUS TESTS

Some miscellaneous tests performed on gastric secretions are listed below and the procedures follow.

> Microscopic examination
> Bile
> Rennin
> Pepsin
> Tubercle bacilli
> Lactic acid
> Combined acid

Microscopic examination

Make a smear of the fasting specimen. Allow to dry and stain with Gram's stain. Examine for Boas-Oppler bacilli and sarcinae. Discussion follows.

Boas-Oppler bacilli

Boas-Oppler organisms are large gram-positive rods (Fig. 59). They are found in cancer of the stomach but must be present in large numbers to be of any significance. The presence of the bacilli indicates gastric stagnation.

Sarcinae

Sarcinae are large gram-positive cocci arranged in groups that look like bales of cotton. They may be found in ulcers but must be present in large numbers to be of any significance. Their presence also indicates gastric stagnation.

Bile

Small amounts of bile may be normally present in the gastric contents. Large amounts give the stomach secretions a yellow or green color. This usually indicates an obstruction at the beginning of the small intestine.

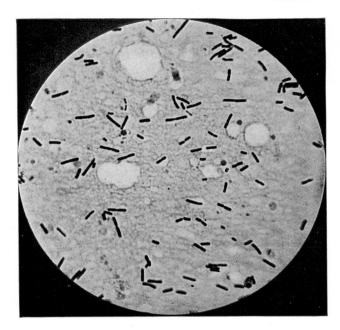

Fig. 59. Boas-Oppler bacilli. (From Levinson, S. A., and MacFate, R. P.: Clinical laboratory diagnosis, ed. 5, Philadelphia, 1956, Lea & Febiger.)

Procedure

1. Pour about 5 ml. of concentrated nitric acid into a small test tube.
2. Tilt the tube to about a 30-degree angle.
3. Using a medicine dropper, *carefully* overlay the acid with the unfiltered gastric contents.

Reaction

If bile is present, a display of colors—yellow, green, red—will form at the junction of the two liquids.

Rennin

Rennin is an enzyme produced in the stomach. Its function is to curdle milk. If the gastric secretions yield little or no rennin, an organic disease of the stomach is indicated.

Reagents needed

Phenolphthalein Indicator, 0.1%   (C-150)
Sodium Hydroxide, 0.01 N   (C-152)

Procedure (Riegel)

1. Using phenolphthalein as an indicator, neutralize 5 ml. of filtered gastric contents with 0.01 N sodium hydroxide.
2. Add 5 ml. of fresh milk to the neutralized gastric contents and place the flask in a 40° C. water bath.

Reaction

If a normal amount of rennin is present, coagulation of the milk occurs within 15 minutes. If a decreased amount of rennin is present, coagulation of the milk occurs *after* 15 minutes.

Pepsin

Pepsin is an enzyme produced in the stomach and used in the digestion of protein. If the gastric contents show little or no pepsin, an organic disease of the stomach is indicated.

Reagent needed

Hydrochloric Acid, Concentrated

Procedure (Hammerschlag)

1. Prepare a 1% solution of egg albumin in the following manner. Take 5 ml. of the white of an egg (use graduated cylinder) and place in a beaker. Add 57.6 ml. of distilled water and 2.4 ml. of concentrated hydrochloric acid. Mix and filter.
2. Get three large test tubes. Label them 1, 2, and 3. Pour 10 ml. of the 1% solution of egg albumin into each tube.
3. Into tube 1, pour 5 ml. of gastric secretion. Mix.
4. Into tube 2, pour 5 ml. of distilled water. Add 0.5 gm. of pepsin. Mix.
5. Into tube 3, pour 5 ml. of distilled water. Mix.
6. Place the three tubes in a 37° C. water bath for 1 hour.
7. Calculate the amount of albumin in each tube by the method of Esbach that is used for the quantitative determination of protein in urine.

Interpretation

1. Tube 3 represents the amount of albumin in the 1% solution of egg albumin.
2. The difference between the amounts of albumin in tube 3 and tube 2 represents the amount of albumin that would be digested by the pepsin in normal gastric secretion.
3. The difference between the amounts of albumin in tube 3 and tube 1 represents the amount of albumin digested by the pepsin in the patient's gastric secretion.
4. The figure obtained from the patient's gastric secretion (point 3 above) should be equal to or exceed the figure obtained from normal gastric secretion (point 2 above).

Tubercle bacilli

The gastric washings are sometimes examined for tubercle bacilli. This is often done in suspected cases of tuberculosis when the organisms cannot be found in the sputum. The following test is performed in the morning, before the patient has had anything to eat or drink.

Reagent needed

Physiological Saline, 0.9%   (C-34)

Procedure

1. Place a flask containing 50 ml. of physiological saline in a 37° C. water bath.
2. Pass a stomach tube as directed in discussion on collection of specimens.
3. Remove the fasting stomach contents and place in a clean container.
4. Wash the stomach with the 37° C. physiological saline by injecting and removing this solution several times.
5. Finally withdraw the solution and place it in a clean container.
6. Centrifuge the fasting stomach contents and the saline washing at high speed for 15 minutes.
7. Examine the sediment for acid-fast bacilli; if found, a guinea pig inoculation should be performed.

Lactic acid

Lactic acid is an organic acid that is formed by the activity of bacteria on carbohydrates. Stomach contents containing large amounts of lactic acid are often found in cancer of the stomach.

Simon modification of Kelling test

Reagent needed

Ferric Chloride, 10% (C-153)

Procedure

1. Obtain two large test tubes and label one Control and the other Test.
2. Pour about 20 ml. of distilled water into the Control tube and add 4 drops of a 10% solution of ferric chloride. Mix.
3. Now pour half of this solution into the Test tube and add 1 ml. of filtered gastric contents. Mix.

Reaction

Compare the Test tube against the Control tube. If lactic acid is present in large amounts the Test solution turns a deep yellow.

Combined acid

The combined acid is the total acid minus the free hydrochloric acid. Example: The total acid of a gastric specimen is 25 degrees and the free hydrochloric acid is 10 degrees. To find the combined acid:

Total acid	25 degrees
Free hydrochloric acid	10 degrees
Combined acid	15 degrees

Chapter 18

Duodenal analysis

The normal duodenal contents are colorless. Upon stimulation of the gallbladder, however, bile flows into the duodenum and gives the contents a brown, yellow, or green color. If bile fails to flow, the presence of gallstones may be suspected.

The samples of duodenal contents are usually obtained by the physician and brought to the laboratory. The method of obtaining the specimens is similar to the procedure in a gastric analysis except that the tube is allowed to pass into the duodenum. The gallbladder is then stimulated with a solution of magnesium sulfate.

An analysis of the duodenal contents consists of the tests listed below. The procedures follow.

> Amylase
> Trypsin
> Bile
> Microscopic examination

AMYLASE

The amylase of the duodenal contents is referred to as amylopsin or pancreatic amylase. The normal values depend upon the method of determination. For the procedure of Myers and Fine, which follows, the normal values are 5 to 200 units. Decreased values are found in chronic pancreatitis, pancreatic insufficiency, and fibrocystic disease of the pancreas.

Reagents needed

Sodium Carbonate, 1%	(C-154)
Starch, 1%	(C-155)
Gram's Iodine Solution	(C-156)

Procedure (Myers-Fine)

1. Test the duodenal contents with nitrazine paper. If acid, add the 1% sodium carbonate dropwise until it is alkaline.
2. Get six large test tubes. Label them 1 to 6 and place in a test tube rack.

3. Make a serial dilution of the duodenal contents by doing the following. Place 1 ml. of duodenal fluid in tubes 1 and 2. Pipet 1 ml. of distilled water into all tubes except tube 1. Take tube 2 and mix the contents by drawing them into a 1 ml. pipet and ejecting them several times. Take 1 ml. of this mixture in tube 2 and transfer to tube 3. Mix the contents of tube 3 and transfer 1 ml. to tube 4. Continue this process through the remaining tubes, discarding 1 ml. from tube 6. The number of milliliters of duodenal fluid now in each tube is given below:

Tube	1	2	3	4	5	6
Ml.	1.0	0.5	0.25	0.125	0.062	0.031

4. Add 5 ml. of the 1% starch solution to each tube. Mix. Incubate at 37° C. for exactly 30 minutes.
5. Add 10 ml. of cold water to each tube. Add 2 drops of Gram's iodine to each tube. Mix. Record the last tube in which there is a complete disappearance of blue color.

Calculation

By definition, the amylase activity equals the number of milliliters of starch solution that will be digested by 1 ml. of duodenal contents under the conditions of the above test. Therefore:

$$\text{Amylase activity} = \frac{1.00}{\text{Ml. used}} \times 5$$

where 5 is the number of milliliters of starch solution digested, and ml. used is the number of milliliters of duodenal contents in the last tube in which there is a complete disappearance of blue color.

Example: If tube 3 is the last tube in which there is a complete disappearance of blue color, the calculation is made as follows. As given in step 3, tube 3 contains 0.25 ml. of the duodenal contents. Therefore:

$$\text{Amylase activity} = \frac{1.00}{0.25} \times 5$$

$$= 20$$

Refer to Chapter 14 for Somogyi's amylase method.

TRYPSIN

Trypsin is an enzyme produced by the pancreas and used to digest protein. It is normally present in the duodenal fluid. The normal values depend upon the method of determination. For the procedure of Gross, which follows, the average tryptic activity is 2.5. Decreased values are found in chronic pancreatitis, pancreatic insufficiency, and fibrocystic disease of the pancreas.

Refer to Chapter 14 for discussion of enzymes.

Reagent needed

Acetic Acid, 1.0%   (C-157)

Procedure (Gross)

1. Prepare a casein solution by dissolving 1 gm. of pure casein in 1 liter of 0.1% sodium carbonate. Add 1 ml. of chloroform to prevent bacterial decomposition.
2. Get ten large test tubes, label them 1 to 10, and place in a test tube rack.
3. Pour 100 ml. of the casein solution into a beaker and heat to 40° C. Pipet 10 ml. into each tube.

4. Centrifuge the duodenal fluid. Take the clear fluid and pipet into each tube the amount called for below:

Tube	1	2	3	4	5	6	7	8	9	10
Ml.	0.1	0.2	0.3	0.4	0.5	0.6	0.7	0.8	0.9	1.0

5. Mix the contents of each tube. Place the tubes in a 37° C. incubator for exactly 15 minutes.
6. Remove the tubes from the incubator. Add 3 drops of 1% acetic acid to each tube, noting whether the addition of the acid causes an increased turbidity. Record the first tube which shows *no* increased turbidity upon the addition of the acid. This is the first tube in which the casein has been completely digested by the trypsin. Calculate the tryptic activity as follows.

Calculation

By definition, the tryptic activity is expressed as the effect of 1 ml. of duodenal fluid on 10 ml. of a 0.1% casein solution under the conditions of the above test. Thus:

$$\text{Tryptic activity} = \frac{1}{\text{Ml. used for digestion}}$$

Example: Tube 4 was the first tube which showed no increased turbidity upon addition of the 1% acetic acid. As noted in step 4, tube 4 contains 0.4 ml. of duodenal fluid. Therefore:

$$\text{Tryptic activity} = \frac{1}{\text{Ml. used for digestion}}$$

$$= \frac{1}{0.4}$$

$$= 2.5$$

BILE

Bilirubin is the bile pigment normally present in duodenal fluid. Its absence often indicates an obstruction in the hepatic duct or common bile duct.

Procedure

1. Bile gives the duodenal fluid a yellow or green color. Note the color and report as 1 plus, 2 plus, 3 plus, or 4 plus, depending upon the depth of color.

MICROSCOPIC EXAMINATION

A microscopic examination of the duodenal fluid may foretell of inflammation in the duodenum or biliary tract and also of the presence of parasites.

Procedure

1. Centrifuge a fresh sample of duodenal fluid.
2. Discard the supernatant (clear fluid) and place the sediment on a glass slide.
3. Look for an abnormal amount of pus cells, which indicates an inflammatory condition. A few cells are normally present.
4. In further observation of the slide, look for the cysts of amoebae, the eggs of hookworms, and for parasites such as *Giardia lamblia* and *Strongyloides stercoralis*.

Part 5

Urine analysis

The English physician and clinician Richard Bright first introduced urine examinations as a routine procedure for the physicians in Guy's Hospital (1827). Bright is known universally now for his description of chronic nephritis, Bright's disease. The physicians soon developed the analysis of urine to a fine art, and before the turn of the century many procedures were published on the macroscopic and microscopic examination of urine. Thomas Addis brought the microscopic study of the urinary sediment to a peak of perfection by the introduction of quantitative methods of study, which he felt were necessary for an accurate evaluation of renal disease.

In the 1930's physicians began to realize that too much faith had been placed upon the reading of the urinary sediment during the earlier years of medicine. When Henry Christian an authority on renal disease, stated that it was impossible to determine during life the anatomical changes in the kidney that would be found after the patient's death, the importance of the urine examination seemed to decline in popularity. With the development of new blood tests and mechanical equipment for registering various body functions, urine analysis became the "stepchild" of the laboratory.

During the last few years, however, new kidney function tests have been developed to aid the physician in determining the anatomical changes in the kidney during life, so the importance of urinary examination is again recognized. Other body malfunctions also are determined with the help of urinary studies.

Discussion of the analysis of urine is divided into the following four chapters:

Chapter 19 Routine urine examination
Chapter 20 Urine chemistry tests
Chapter 21 Pregnancy tests
Chapter 22 Special urine tests

Chapter 19

Routine urine examination

The waste materials of the blood are removed by the kidneys, passed to the bladder for temporary storage, and excreted as urine by way of the urethra. The waste materials may be separated into organic and inorganic substances. The organic portion, mostly urea, averages about 35 grams each day. The inorganic substances, largely salts, average about 25 grams each day. The waste materials of significance are listed in Table 50.

A normal person passes about 3 pints, or 1400 ml., of urine per day. An increase in amount, referred to as polyuria, occurs in diabetes. Decreases in amount called oliguria, are found in fever. The complete absence of urine, known as anuria, is seen in kidney failure.

Table 50. Waste materials in urine

Organic substances	Inorganic substances
Urea	Ammonia
Uric acid	Sulfate salts
Creatinine	Phosphate salts
	Chloride salts

In most hospitals, it is customary for a ward attendant to collect the patient's urine and deliver it to the laboratory. For examination in the physician's office, the patient may bring the urine with him or void while there. If the analysis is not made within an hour, the specimen should be preserved to prevent the growth of bacteria and the decomposition of cellular elements.

Satisfactory methods of preserving urine include use of (1) refrigeration, (2) formalin (few drops), (3) toluene (few drops), or (4) boric acid (0.1 gm./40 ml.).

A routine examination of the urine consists of the tests listed in Fig. 60. These tests are discussed on the following pages.

```
Name: Mr. John Doe                                    6-4-65

Color  . . . . . . . . . . . . . . . . . . . . . straw
Transparency  . . . . . . . . . . . . . . . . . cloudy
Reaction  . . . . . . . . . . . . . . . . . . . acid
Specific   gravity . . . . . . . . . . . . . . . 1.020
Albumin  . . . . . . . . . . . . . . . . . . . . 3+
Sugar  . . . . . . . . . . . . . . . . . . . . . negative
Acetone  . . . . . . . . . . . . . . . . . . . . negative
Microscopic   examination . . . . . . . Centrifuged specimen shows 4 to 6
                                        granular casts per high dry field
```

Fig. 60. Sample urine analysis report.

COLOR
Information significant to the student

The color of the urine often serves as a signal to notify an alert technician of urinary abnormalities. Some of these colors and their usual causes are given in Table 51.

Procedure
1. Mix urine by inverting or swirling the container.
2. Note and record the color.
3. If the color is dark amber, the urine should be shaken to produce foam. If the foam is yellow, a test for bile should be run.

Table 51. Usual causes of urinary colors

Color	*Usual cause*
Straw to amber	Urochrome, a pigment found in normal urine
Colorless	Reduced concentration
Silvery sheen or milky appearance	Pus, bacteria, or epithelial cells
Smoky brown	Blood
Black	Melanin
Port-wine	Porphyrins
Yellow foam	Bile or medications
Orange, green, blue, or red	Medications

RAPID TESTS OF THE URINE

Due to time-consuming and demanding techniques required with many of the chemical tests for urine analyses, the modern tablet, dipstick, and tape test for urinalysis are coming to the aid of the physician for a bedside check of the patient or for use in the office. These new tests are sensitive and must be used with recognition of their limitations. Each tape, dipstick, or tablet is designed for a special purpose, and if each is used according to the manufacturer's specifications and instructions, accurate results may be obtained.

The strips are made with selected cellulose of standard porosity. The tips are impregnated with chemicals that will react with various substances in the urine, producing colors that can be measured against standard color charts. Some color reactions are timed. This requirement is given in the instructions and *must* be followed exactly!

Precautions

1. When not in use, the tablets or strips must be kept in their bottles, tightly stoppered to keep out the moisture.
2. Bottles that are so marked should be placed in refrigeration.
3. If the strips (dipsticks) are kept too long in the urine or in the urine stream, the chemicals impregnated in the cellulose layer will dissolve and inaccurate results will be obtained.
4. Directions must be carefully followed when there is more than one reaction on a strip. For example, on Combistix the sections indicating pH, protein, and glucose are separated by water-impermeable barriers of plastic.

TRANSPARENCY
Information significant to the student

The transparency of urine may be classified as clear or cloudy. The degree of transparency depends upon the amount of suspended materials: the more suspended materials, the greater the cloudiness. In normal urine, the main causes of cloudiness are crystals and epithelial cells. In pathological urine, the principal causes of cloudiness are pus, blood, and bacteria.

If the urine is clear, it may inform the physician that the patient is not concentrating the urine, that is, removing metabolic waste materials. On the whole, however, this test has little significance, for both normal and pathological urine may be either clear or cloudy.

Procedure

1. Mix urine.
2. Note degree of transparency.
3. Report as clear or cloudy. Also report any abnormal contents such as clumps of mucus or pieces of tissue.

REACTION
Information significant to the student

Freshly voided urine may be either acid or alkaline, the normal pH range being 4.0 to 8.0. If allowed to stand, acid urine becomes alkaline because urea decomposes and liberates ammonia. Increased acidity of urine is found in fevers and diabetes. Increased alkalinity is seen in alkali therapy and in retention of urine.

Procedures

The reaction of urine may be found by any of the tests listed below. The procedures follow.

Neutral litmus paper test
Nitrazine paper test
pH range paper test

Neutral litmus paper test

1. Dip a piece of neutral litmus paper into the urine.
2. After the paper absorbs urine, note color of paper.
3. If the paper is pink, report Acid. If there is no color change, report Neutral. If paper is blue, report Alkaline.

Nitrazine paper test

1. Dip a piece of nitrazine paper into the urine.
2. After paper absorbs urine, note color of paper.

3. Compare with color chart that comes with the nitrazine paper.
4. Report pH value.

pH range paper test

1. Dip a piece of pH range paper into the urine.
2. After paper absorbs urine, note color of paper.
3. Compare with the color chart that comes with the pH range paper.
4. Report pH value.

DISORDERS AND THE URINE pH[1]

Tests for pH of urine should be done a short time after the specimen has been voided. As the urine stands, it will become alkaline, due to the decomposition of urea into ammonia. However, when fresh urine is persistently acid or alkaline, this may be due to one of the following disorders:

A. Consistently acid urine
1. Tuberculosis of the kidney
2. Pyrexia
3. Methyl alcohol poisoning due to the formation of formic acid
4. Metabolic disorders
   a. Phenylketonuria
   b. Alkaptonuria
5. "Metabolic" acidosis due to severe diarrhea, starvation, diabetic ketosis, uremia, and certain types of poisoning
6. "Respiratory" acidosis due to conditions in which there is CO_2 retention
B. Consistently alkaline urine
1. Certain genitourinary infections
2. "Metabolic" alkalosis due to overdosage of sodium bicarbonate, potassium citrate, or other alkalies
3. "Respiratory" alkalosis due to hyperventilation or cardiac failure
4. Bronchial carcinoma (in some cases)
5. Cushing's syndrome or hyperaldosteronism
6. The use of certain diuretics, such as Diamox and chlorothiazide, which are carbonic anhydrase inhibitors

SPECIFIC GRAVITY
Information significant to the student

Specific gravity is a term used to compare the weight of a liquid with the weight of water. For example, sulfuric acid weighs 1.840 gm./ml., whereas water weighs 1.000 gm./ml. Since sulfuric acid weighs 1.840 times as much as water, the specific gravity is 1.840.

Because of its dissolved substances, urine weighs more than water, the normal specific gravity being 1.008 to 1.030. Increased values are found in acute nephritis, fevers, and diabetes mellitus (because of the dissolved sugar). Decreased values are found in chronic nephritis and diabetes insipidus (because of the copious volume).

Measuring the specific gravity of the urine is the most convenient way of measuring the concentrating and diluting function of the kidney, meaning the ability of the kidney to produce urine of a specific gravity greater or less than 1.010.

Procedure

1. Mix the urine by inverting or swirling the container.
2. Pour into a urinometer cylinder (Fig. 61).

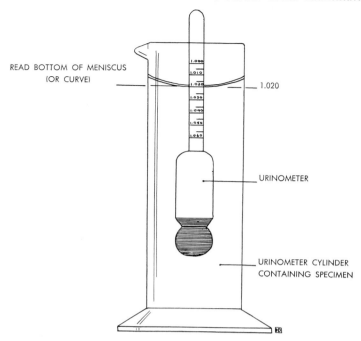

READ BOTTOM OF MENISCUS
(OR CURVE)

1.020

URINOMETER

URINOMETER CYLINDER
CONTAINING SPECIMEN

Fig. 61. Urinometer used to measure the specific gravity.

3. Place the urinometer in the urine and spin it as you would a top.
4. When it comes to rest, take the reading as indicated in Fig. 61. When the reading is taken, the urinometer must *not* be touching the sides of the cylinder.
5. Record reading.
6. If there is not sufficient urine to fill the cylinder, some laboratories report "qns" (quantity nonsufficient). The temperature-compensated hand refractometer will measure the specific gravity of a minute volume (1 to 2 drops) of urine.

Concentration tests

If the kidneys are healthy, they will remove waste materials as they accumulate. If the kidneys are diseased, however, they lose this readiness to remove waste materials. Consequently, the ability to remove waste materials can be used as a test of kidney function.

The ability of the kidneys to remove waste materials may be measured by concentration tests. The method of Mosenthal and the method of Fishberg are given on the following pages.

Mosenthal test

The Mosenthal test measures the specific gravity at various intervals and thereby determines the functional ability of the kidneys. The discussion covers the collection of specimens and the laboratory procedure.

Collection of specimens

1. The patient is told that on the day of the test, as well as the day before, he is to have a full regular diet, drinking at least a pint of fluids at each meal, and not to eat or drink between meals.

2. For the morning of the test, he is further instructed to completely empty the bladder before breakfast and to discard the urine.
3. He is then to completely empty the bladder into *separate* labelled containers at *exactly* 10 A.M., 12 NOON, 2 P.M., 4 P.M., 6 P.M., and 8 P.M.
4. Collect in a single container all the urine voided between 8 P.M. and 8 A.M.
5. Bring all specimens to the laboratory.

Laboratory procedure

1. Measure the volume of each urine specimen.
2. Determine the specific gravity of each specimen.
3. Report the volume and specific gravity of each specimen.
4. Sample report:

Specimen	10 A.M.	12	2 P.M.	4 P.M.	6 P.M.	8 P.M.	8 P.M. to 8 A.M.
Volume (ml.)	150	156	170	165	200	110	300
Specific gravity	1.017	1.020	1.014	1.022	1.012	1.010	1.018

5. Interpretation: Normal values are indicated by a fluctuation in the specific gravity of at least 7 points; that is, there is at least a 7-point difference between the lowest and the highest specific gravity. In kidney disease, the specific gravity fluctuates only a few points and the volume of the night urine (8 P.M. to 8 A.M.) is usually over 600 ml.

Fishberg test

The Fishberg test measures the specific gravity of urine at various intervals and thereby determines the functional ability of the kidneys. The discussion covers the collection of specimens and the laboratory procedure.

Collection of specimens

1. The patient is told to eat an evening meal consisting of a high-protein diet and not more than 200 ml. of fluid.
2. After the evening meal, no food or fluid is to be taken until the completion of the test on the following morning.
3. The patient is further instructed to void at will during the night. In the morning, he should empty the bladder into separate containers at 8 A.M., 9 A.M., and 10 A.M. The three specimens are then brought to the laboratory.

Laboratory procedure

1. Measure the volume of each urine specimen.
2. Determine the specific gravity of each specimen.
3. Report the volume and specific gravity of each specimen.
4. Sample report:

Specimen	8 A.M.	9 A.M.	10 A.M.
Volume (ml.)	210	190	150
Specific gravity	1.020	1.026	1.025

5. Interpretation: With healthy kidneys, at least one of the specimens has a specific gravity over 1.024. With diseased kidneys, all the specific gravities are below 1.020.

ALBUMIN
Information significant to the student

Albumin is a protein. The presence of albumin in the urine is referred to as albuminuria. There are two types of albuminuria: false and true. In false albuminuria, the albumin may be caused by excessive exercise, blood from the bladder, or vaginal discharge.

In true albuminuria, the albumin leaves the bloodstream, seeps through the kidneys, and enters the urine. True albuminuria points to a flaw in the filtering system of the kidneys and consequently aids the physician in diagnosing kidney disorders.

Tests for albumin are based on one of the following principles: (1) albumin is precipitated by heat; (2) albumin is precipitated by acids. A brief discussion follows.

If an egg is fried, the white of the egg forms a white precipitate. This is albumin. If urine is heated and albumin is present, the albumin forms a white cloud. This is the basis of the following tests:

Heat and acetic acid test
Purdy test
Osgood-Haskins test

Phosphate salts, if present, also precipitate out and form a white cloud when urine is heated. The addition of an acid, however, dissolves the salts but does not affect the albumin.

The fact that albumin is precipitated by acids is utilized in those tests listed below. The first two tests use sulfosalicylic acid, and the latter two use concentrated nitric acid.

Sulfosalicylic acid test
Exton test
Robert test
Heller test

Procedures for albumin in urine

If it is necessary to prepare any of the reagents used in the following tests, take the number that follows the reagent and refer to Appendix C.

Heat and acetic acid test	Exton test
Purdy test	Robert test
Osgood-Haskins test	Heller test
Sulfosalicylic acid test	

Heat and acetic acid test

Reagent needed

Acetic Acid, 5%   (C-158)

Procedure

1. Pour about 10 ml. of urine into a large Pyrex test tube.
2. Using a test tube holder, boil the *upper* portion over a flame as illustrated in Fig. 62. If a cloudy white precipitate forms in the heated portion, it is either phosphate salts or albumin. To decide which, proceed as follows.
3. Add a few drops of the 5% acetic acid. If the precipitate is phosphate salts, it will be dissolved by the acid. If the precipitate is albumin, however, it will not dissolve.
4. Report the test as negative, 1+, 2+, 3+, or 4+, depending upon the amount of precipitate (Fig. 63).

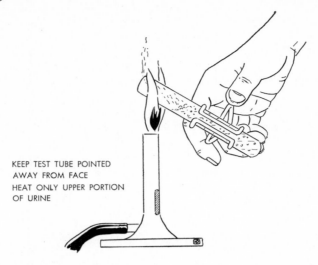

KEEP TEST TUBE POINTED
AWAY FROM FACE
HEAT ONLY UPPER PORTION
OF URINE

Fig. 62. Heating urine with a flame.

Purdy test

Reagents needed

Sodium Chloride, Saturated   (C-159)
Acetic Acid, 50%   (C-160)

Procedure

1. Pour about 5 ml. of urine into a large Pyrex test tube.
2. Add 1 ml. of the saturated solution of sodium chloride. (This prevents the precipitation of mucin, if it should be present.)
3. Add 5 to 10 drops of the 50% acetic acid. Mix.
4. Using a test tube holder, heat the *upper* portion over a flame as illustrated in Fig. 62. If a white precipitate forms, albumin is present.
5. Report the test as negative, 1+, 2+, 3+, or 4+, depending upon the amount of precipitate (Fig. 63).

Osgood-Haskins test

Reagents needed

Acetic Acid, 50%   (C-160)
Sodium Chloride, Saturated   (C-159)

Procedure

1. Pour about 5 ml. of urine into a large Pyrex test tube.
2. Add 1 ml. of the 50% acetic acid.
3. Add 3 ml. of the saturated solution of sodium chloride. (This prevents the precipitation of mucin, if it should be present.)
4. Using a test tube holder, heat the *upper* portion over a flame as illustrated in Fig. 62. If albumin is present, a white precipitate will form.
5. Report the test as negative, 1+, 2+, 3+, or 4+, depending upon the amount of precipitate (Fig. 63).

Sulfosalicylic acid test

Reagent needed

Sulfosalicylic Acid, 20%   (C-161)

Heat and acetic acid test
Purdy test
Osgood-Haskin test

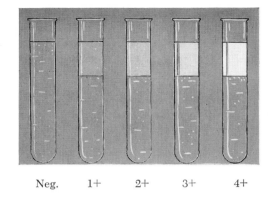

    Neg.   1+   2+   3+   4+

Sulfosalicylic acid test
Exton test

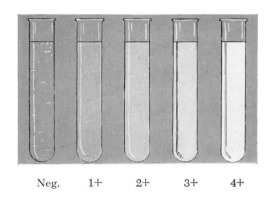

    Neg.   1+   2+   3+   4+

Robert test
Heller test

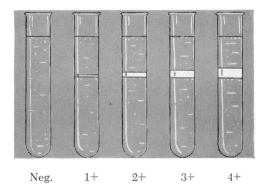

    Neg.   1+   2+   3+   4+

Fig. 63. Positive and negative results in testing for albumin.

Procedure

1. Pour about 5 ml. of urine into a test tube.
2. Add 1 drop, per milliliter of urine, of the 20% sulfosalicylic acid. Mix. If albumin is present, a white cloud will form.
3. Report the test as negative, 1+, 2+, 3+, or 4+, depending upon the amount of precipitate (Fig. 63).

Exton test

Reagent needed

Exton's Reagent (C-162)

Procedure

1. Mix equal parts of urine and Exton's reagent. If no cloudiness forms, albumin is absent.
2. If cloudiness appears, heat gently, but do not boil.
3. If cloudiness remains or increases, albumin is present.
4. Report the test as negative, 1+, 2+, 3+, or 4+, depending upon the amount of precipitate (Fig. 63). The reading should be made while the solution is warm because proteoses produce a cloud upon standing.

Robert test

Reagent needed

Robert's Reagent (C-163)

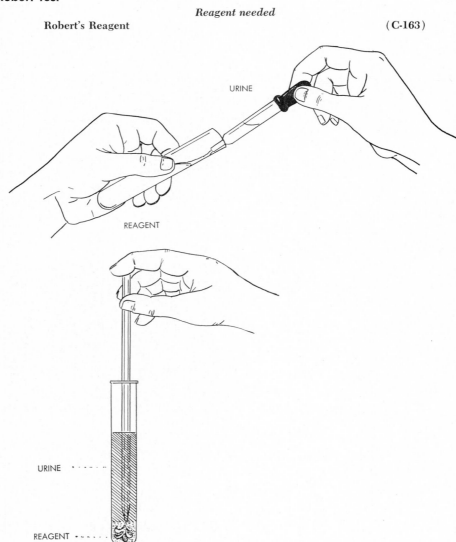

Fig. 64. Methods of overlaying reagent with urine.

Procedure

1. Follow either method A or method B:

   Method A: Pipet a few milliliters of Robert's reagent into a test tube. Tilt the tube to about a 30-degree angle. Using a medicine dropper, overlay with clear urine by allowing the urine to flow *slowly* down the sides of the test tube (Fig. 64).

   Method B: Pour about 4 ml. of urine into a test tube. Using a 1 ml. serological pipet, pipet out 1 ml. of the Robert's reagent. Place the tip of the pipet in the bottom of the test tube containing the urine. Allow the pipet to drain slowly (Fig. 64).

2. If albumin is present, within a few minutes a white ring will form at the junction between the two liquids.

3. Report the test as negative, 1+, 2+, 3+, or 4+, depending upon the amount of precipitate (Fig. 63).

Heller test

Reagent needed

Concentrated Nitric Acid

Procedure

1. Place about 3 ml. of concentrated nitric acid in a small test tube.

2. Tilt the tube to about a 30-degree angle (Fig. 64). Using a medicine dropper, overlay with urine by allowing the urine to flow *slowly* down the sides of the tube.

3. If albumin is present, within a few minutes a white ring will form at the junction between the two liquids.

4. Report the test as negative, 1+, 2+, 3+, or 4+, depending upon the amount of precipitate (Fig. 63).

SUGAR
Information significant to the student

Glycosuria means glucose in the urine. It is found in diabetes but may also occur after strenuous exercise and emotional disturbances.

The following methods are used to test for glucose:

Benedict method
Clinitest method
Galatest method
Tes-Tape method

In Benedict's method and the Clinitest method, glucose reduces copper. The reduced copper then forms a colored compound—cuprous oxide—which is readily detectable. As the particle size of cuprous oxide increases, the color of the precipitate varies from green to yellow to orange.

In the Galatest method, glucose reduces bismuth oxide to a gray or black precipitate of metallic bismuth.

In the Tes-Tape method, the color change depends upon an enzyme system reaction that is specific for glucose. The color varies from light green to deep blue.

Benedict method

Reagent needed

Benedict's Qualitative Reagent   (C-164)

Procedure

1. Place about 8 drops of urine in a test tube. (Some technicians pour a few milliliters of urine into a test tube, discard the urine by inverting the tube, and then quickly place the tube in an upright position. The amount of urine prevented from draining is about 8 drops.)
2. Add about 5 ml. of Benedict's qualitative reagent.
3. Place tube in a boiling water bath for 5 minutes. If glucose is present, it will reduce the copper in the Benedict's solution. The color will vary from green to yellow to orange, depending upon the amount of glucose present.
4. Report the test as negative, 1+, 2+, 3+, or 4+ (Plate I).

Clinitest method

Reagent needed

Clinitest Tablets*

Procedure

1. Place 5 drops of urine in a test tube.
2. Add 10 drops of distilled water.
3. Add 1 Clinitest tablet. If there is no glucose present, the solution will be blue. If glucose is present, however, the color will vary from green to yellow to orange, depending upon the amount of glucose present.
4. Report the test as negative, 1+, 2+, 3+, or 4+.

Galatest method

Reagent needed

Galatest Powder†

Procedure

1. Place a small mound (about one half the size of a dime) of the Galatest powder on a piece of white paper. Note: Keep the vial tightly closed when not in use.
2. Add a small drop of urine. If glucose is present, the powder will change color. The color will vary from gray to black. The blacker the color, the greater the concentration of glucose.
3. Report the test as negative, 1+, 2+, 3+, or 4+.

Tes-Tape method

Reagent needed

Tes-Tape‡

Procedure

1. Tear off a piece of Tes-Tape.
2. Hold one end between your thumb and index finger. Dip the other end into the urine.
3. When moist, remove from urine.
4. Continue holding tape between thumb and index finger and allow 1 minute to elapse.
5. Compare with color chart that comes with Tes-Tape.
6. Report the test as negative, 1+, 2+, 3+, or 4+.

---

*May be purchased from your local supply house or from Ames Co., Inc., Elkhart, Ind.
†May be purchased from your local supply house or from Denver Chemical Manufacturing Co., Inc., New York, N. Y.
‡May be purchased from your local supply house or from Eli Lilly & Co., Indianapolis, Ind.

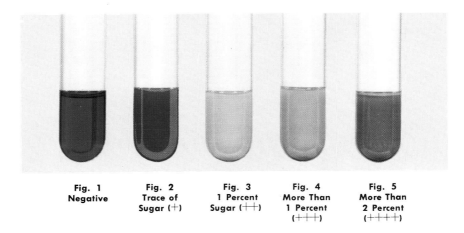

Fig. 1	Fig. 2	Fig. 3	Fig. 4	Fig. 5
Negative	Trace of Sugar (+)	1 Percent Sugar (++)	More Than 1 Percent (+++)	More Than 2 Percent (++++)

Plate I. Benedict qualitative test for sugar in urine. (From Essentials in the management of diabetes mellitus, Eli Lilly & Co., Indianapolis, Ind.)

ACETONE
Information significant to the student

When glucose is not oxidized, as in diabetes, it is believed that the body endeavors to compensate by oxidizing fats. This is referred to as abnormal fat catabolism.

During abnormal fat catabolism, diacetic acid is produced. When diacetic acid decomposes, it liberates acetone and β-oxybutyric acid:

Abnormal fat catabolism $\longrightarrow$ Diacetic acid
$\downarrow$
(Decomposition)
Acetone β-oxybutyric acid

Acetone in the urine is significant, for it often indicates acidosis—a decrease in the alkali reserve. This could mean approaching death.

Acetone may be found in the following conditions:

Prior to diabetic coma
After anesthesia
In toxemias of pregnancy
In fevers
In gastrointestinal disorders

In discussions of acetone, textbooks use various terminology, and it is well to remember the following terms: (1) the presence of acetone in the urine is frequently referred to as ketosis; (2) diacetic acid is often called acetoacetic acid; (3) the three substances—diacetic acid, acetone, and β-oxybutyric acid— are often referred to as acetone or ketone bodies.

In the presence of acetone, sodium nitroprusside forms a complex compound that is purple to red in color. This is the basis for the following tests: Acetest, acetone test (Denco), Lange test, Rothera test, and Rantzman test.

In the presence of acetone, salicylaldehyde also forms a complex compound which is purple to red in color. This is the basis of the Frommer test.

If the acetone test is positive, many laboratories run a test for diacetic acid. In diabetes, it is believed that the presence of diacetic acid is an additional indication of approaching coma.

Procedures for acetone in urine

If it is necessary to prepare any of the reagents used in the following tests, take the number that follows the reagent and refer to Appendix C.

Acetest
Acetone test (Denco)
Lange test
Rothera test
Rantzman test
Frommer test

Acetest

Reagent needed

Acetest Tablets*

---

*May be purchased from your local supply house or from Ames Co., Inc., Elkhart, Ind.

Procedure

1. Place an Acetest tablet on a piece of white paper.
2. Place a drop of urine on the tablet. If acetone is present, a lavender to purple color develops within 30 seconds. Compare with color chart that comes with the reagent.
3. Report the test as positive or negative.

Acetone test (Denco)

Reagent needed

Acetone Test (Denco)*

Procedure

1. Shake the vial containing the powdered reagent.
2. Place a small mound (about the size of a small pea) on a piece of white paper.
3. Place a drop of urine on the powder. If acetone is present, a lavender to purple color develops.
4. Report the test as positive or negative.

Lange test

Reagents needed

Glacial Acetic Acid
Ammonium Hydroxide, 28% (full-strength)
Sodium Nitroprusside, Saturated   (C-165)

Procedure

1. Pour about 5 ml. of urine into a test tube.
2. Add 5 drops of glacial acetic acid and a few drops of a saturated solution of sodium nitroprusside. Mix.
3. Tilt the tube to about a 30-degree angle. Using a medicine dropper, *slowly* overlay with 28% (full-strength) ammonium hydroxide. A purple or purplish red ring at the junction of the two liquids indicates the presence of acetone.
4. Report the test as positive or negative.

Rothera test

Reagents needed

Ammonium Sulfate
Ammonium Hydroxide, 28% (full-strength)
Sodium Nitroprusside Reagent   (C-166)

Procedure

1. Pour about 5 ml. of fresh urine into a test tube.
2. Add about 2 gm. of ammonium sulfate. Mix to saturate the urine.
3. Add 2 drops of sodium nitroprusside reagent. Mix.
4. Tilt the tube to about a 30-degree angle and, using a medicine dropper, *slowly* overlay with 28% (full-strength) ammonium hydroxide. The test is positive for acetone (or diacetic acid) if a purple to red color appears at the junction between the two liquids. The color may take up to 15 minutes to appear but must not fade. Disregard any brown or orange colors.
5. Report the test as positive or negative.

---

*This is a powder contained in a vial. It may be purchased from your local supply house or from Denver Chemical Manufacturing Co., Inc., New York, N. Y.

Rantzman test

Reagents needed

Ammonium Hydroxide, 28%
Rantzman's Reagent   (C-167)

Procedure

1. Pour about 3 ml. of urine into a test tube.
2. Add 1 ml. of Rantzman's reagent. Mix.
3. Tilt the tube to about a 30-degree angle and *slowly* overlay with 28% ammonium hydroxide. If acetone is present, a purple ring appears within a few minutes at the junction of the two liquids.
4. Report the test as positive or negative.

Frommer test

Reagents needed

Sodium Hydroxide, 40%   (C-168)
Alcoholic Solution of Salicylaldehyde, 10%   (C-169)

Procedure

1. Pour about 10 ml. of urine into a test tube.
2. Add 2 or 3 ml. of 40% sodium hydroxide.
3. Add 10 drops of a 10% alcoholic solution of salicylaldehyde.
4. Place in a 70° to 75° C. water bath for 10 minutes. If acetone is present, an intense purplish red color is formed.
5. Report the test as positive or negative.

MICROSCOPIC EXAMINATION
Information significant to the student

The microscopic examination consists of obtaining, examining, and reporting the urinary sediments. The sediments, which are examined with a microscope, are magnified either 100 or 450 times.

Knowing the type and quantity of sediments aids the physician in diagnosing diseases of the urethra, bladder, and kidneys. Some significant sediments and their usual causes are given in Table 52. The pus cells mentioned in the table are often referred to as white blood cells or WBC. The red cells are often reported as red blood cells or RBC. The casts are solidified sediments that have been forced out of urinary tubules. The *Trichomonas* is a parasite which is sometimes found in the urine of women. With the exception of *Trichomonas*, the sediments are illustrated in Fig. 65.

The manner of performing and reporting the microscopic examination varies from laboratory to laboratory. For example, some laboratories obtain the sediment by centrifuging the urine; other laboratories do not centrifuge the urine. Some laboratories report the number of sediments per low-power field (magni-

Table 52. Some significant sediments and their usual causes

Sediment	Usual causes
Pus	Inflammation of urethra, bladder, vagina, or kidneys
Red cells	Bleeding from bladder, uterus, or kidneys
Casts	Nephritis
Bacteria	Bacterial infection of urethra, bladder, vagina, or kidneys
Trichomonas	*Trichomonas* infestation of vagina

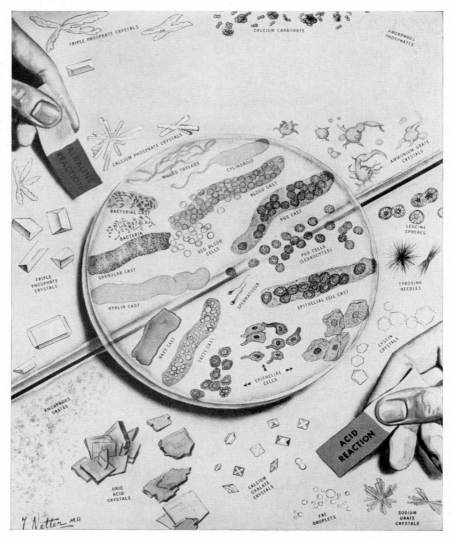

Fig. 65. Urinary sediments. (From Sharp & Dohme Seminar, November, 1940, Sharp & Dohme.)

fication 100); other laboratories report the number of sediments per high dry field (magnification 450). Some laboratories report all sediments seen; other laboratories report only the more significant sediments. In order to avoid confusion, the student should familiarize himself with the particular practices observed in his laboratory.

In performing the microscopic examination, the beginner should guard against the following sources of error:

1. Failure to see casts. If the light is too bright, casts are very difficult to see. Therefore, always lower the source of light.
2. Failure to distinguish red cells from pus cells. If you are in doubt, place a drop of 5% acetic acid on the sediment. If the cells are red cells,

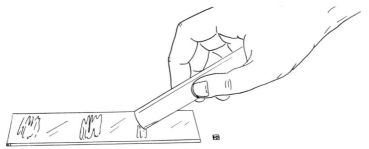

Fig. 66. Spreading urinary sediments on slide.

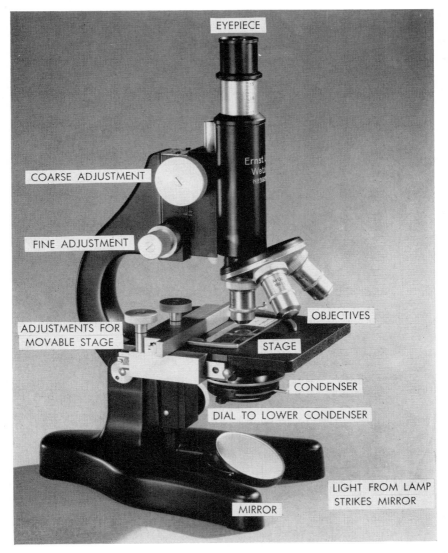

Fig. 67. Microscopic examination of urinary sediments. (Courtesy E. Leitz, Inc., New York, N.Y.)

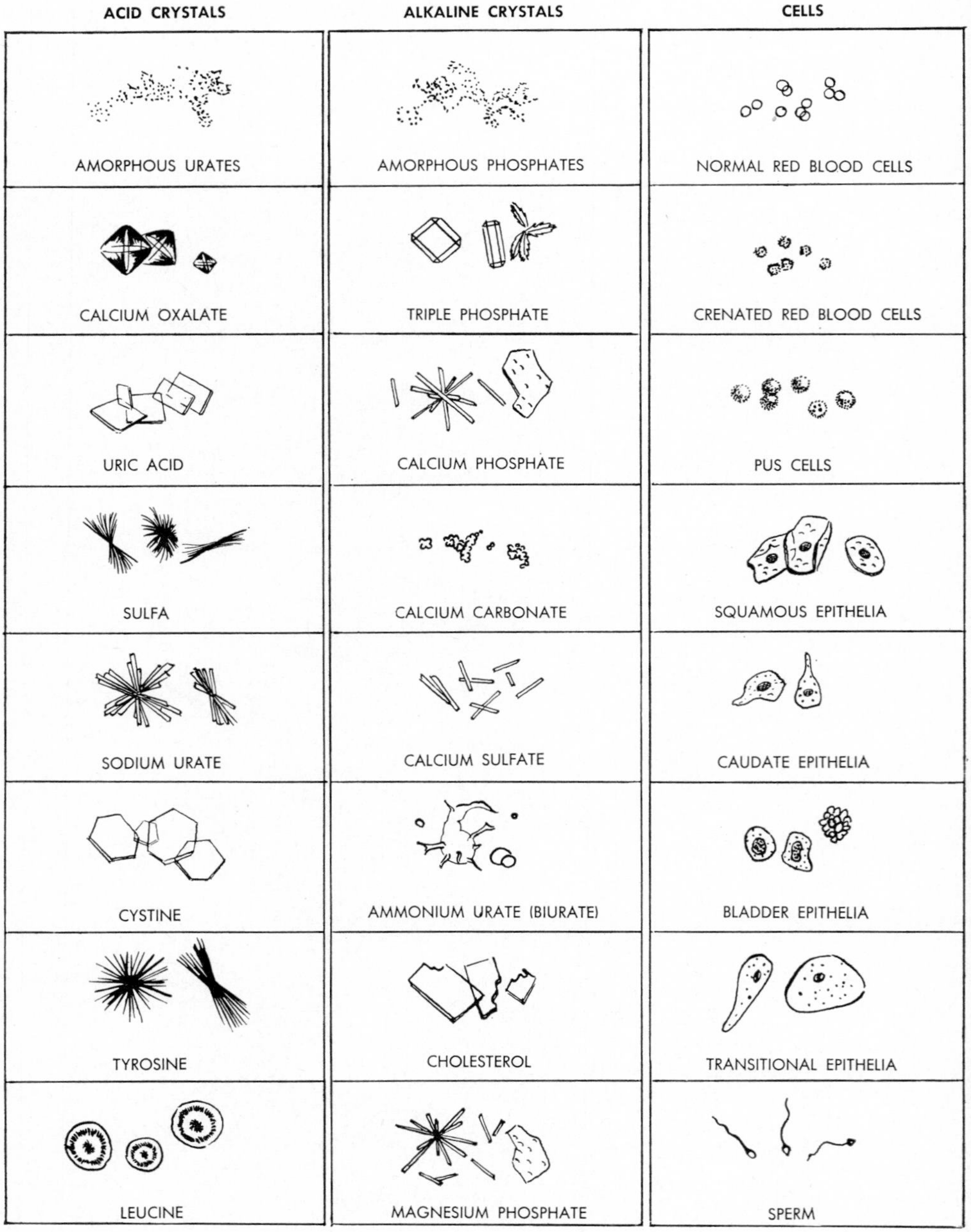

ACID CRYSTALS	ALKALINE CRYSTALS	CELLS
AMORPHOUS URATES	AMORPHOUS PHOSPHATES	NORMAL RED BLOOD CELLS
CALCIUM OXALATE	TRIPLE PHOSPHATE	CRENATED RED BLOOD CELLS
URIC ACID	CALCIUM PHOSPHATE	PUS CELLS
SULFA	CALCIUM CARBONATE	SQUAMOUS EPITHELIA
SODIUM URATE	CALCIUM SULFATE	CAUDATE EPITHELIA
CYSTINE	AMMONIUM URATE (BIURATE)	BLADDER EPITHELIA
TYROSINE	CHOLESTEROL	TRANSITIONAL EPITHELIA
LEUCINE	MAGNESIUM PHOSPHATE	SPERM

Fig. 68. Sediments found in urine. (Drawings by Robert Pribbenow and Samuel Taylor.)

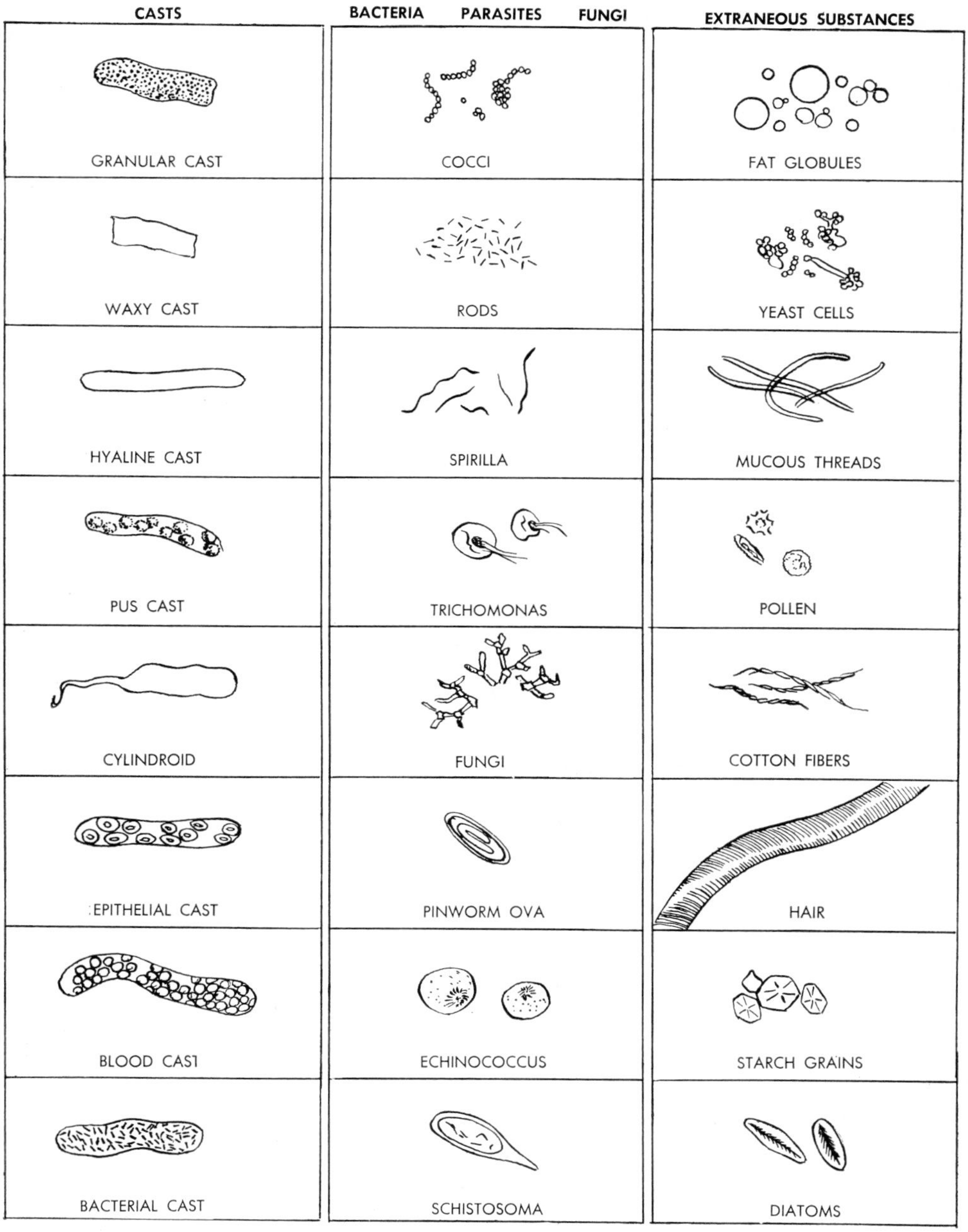

CASTS	BACTERIA PARASITES FUNGI	EXTRANEOUS SUBSTANCES
GRANULAR CAST	COCCI	FAT GLOBULES
WAXY CAST	RODS	YEAST CELLS
HYALINE CAST	SPIRILLA	MUCOUS THREADS
PUS CAST	TRICHOMONAS	POLLEN
CYLINDROID	FUNGI	COTTON FIBERS
EPITHELIAL CAST	PINWORM OVA	HAIR
BLOOD CAST	ECHINOCOCCUS	STARCH GRAINS
BACTERIAL CAST	SCHISTOSOMA	DIATOMS

Fig. 68—cont'd. For legend see opposite page.

they will hemolyze. If the cells are pus cells, it is possible to see their nuclei.

3. Failure to distinguish red cells from fat globules. The red cells are uniform in size, whereas fat globules usually come in various sizes.

A suggested procedure for the microscopic examination is given below. However, as previously mentioned, the student should follow the practices observed in his particular laboratory.

Procedure for microscopic examination

1. Mix the urine specimen by inverting or swirling the container.
2. Place about 5 ml. of urine into a test tube. Centrifuge at high speed for 5 minutes and decant the supernatant fluid.
3. The grayish white precipitate (urinary sediment) may be loosened by gently shaking or tapping the bottom of the tube.
4. Place the sediment on a glass slide. This step is illustrated in Fig. 66, where three different specimens are being placed on one slide.
5. When the sediment is on the slide, smear it over the surface of the slide with the lip of the test tube. This "spreading out" will prevent the high dry objective of the microscope from touching the sediment and eliminates the use of cover slips. (Some technicians, however, prefer to place a cover slip on the sediment.)
6. Place the slide on the stage of a microscope as illustrated in Fig. 67.
7. Lower the source of light by lowering the condenser (Fig. 67).
8. Switch the low-power (16 mm. or 10×) objective into position so that it is directly over the sediment.
9. Bring the field into focus by using the coarse and fine adjustments.
10. Using the movable stage, scan four or five fields to get a general idea of the contents.
11. Switch to the high dry (4 mm. or 45×) objective.
12. Identify the contents, using Figs. 65 and 68 as guides.
13. Make the report according to the practice in your particular laboratory.
14. Sample microscopic report: Centrifuged specimen shows 10 to 12 RBC and 0 to 2 granular casts per high dry field. Bacteria present.

STUDENTS' SUMMARY FOR THE ROUTINE EXAMINATION OF URINE

The significant information consists of the following:

> Miscellaneous information
> Normal and abnormal values
> Methods of analysis and synopsis of procedures

Miscellaneous information

1. Composition of 24-hour specimen:

> 25 gm. of inorganic substances, mostly salts
> 35 gm. of organic substances, mostly urea
> 1400 ml. of water

2. Terms for volume:

> Polyuria means an increased amount; found in diabetes
> Oliguria means a decreased amount; found in fever
> Anuria means the absence of urine; found in kidney failure

Normal and abnormal values

Test	Normal values	Abnormal values
Color	Straw to amber	Silvery sheen: due to pus, bacteria, or epithelial cells Yellow foam: due to bile or medication Smoky brown: due to blood
Reaction	pH 4.0 to 8.	Increased acidity found in fevers and diabetes Increased alkalinity found in alkali therapy and in retention of urine
Specific gravity	1.008 to 1.030	Increased in acute nephritis, fevers, and diabetes mellitus Decreased in chronic nephritis and diabetes insipidus
Albumin	None present	False albuminuria found in excessive exercise and bleeding True albuminuria found in kidney disorders
Sugar	None present	Glucose found in diabetes and after strenuous exercise or emotional disturbances
Acetone	None present	Found prior to diabetic coma, after anesthesia, in toxemias of pregnancy, in fevers, and in gastrointestinal disorders
Microscopic examination	Amorphous crystals; epithelial cells; few pus cells; miscellaneous crystals	Many pus cells found in inflammation of the urethra, bladder, vagina, or kidneys Red cells found in bleeding from bladder, uterus, or kidneys Casts found in nephritis Bacteria found in bacterial infections of urethra, bladder, vagina, or kidneys *Trichomonas* found in *Trichomonas* infestation of vagina

Methods of analysis and synopsis of procedures

Test	Method	Synopsis of procedure
Color	Observation	Mix urine and note color
Transparency	Observation	Mix urine and note whether clear or cloudy
Reaction	Litmus paper Nitrazine paper pH range paper	Dip paper into urine and note color of paper
Specific gravity (concentration)	Urinometer	Put urinometer in urine and take reading
	Fishberg	1. Collect three timed specimens of urine 2. Measure volume of each specimen 3. Put urinometer in each urine specimen and take reading
	Mosenthal	1. Collect seven timed specimens of urine 2. Measure volume of each specimen 3. Put urinometer in each urine specimen and take reading
Albumin	Heat and acetic acid	1. Heat urine 2. If white precipitate forms, add 5% acetic acid 3. If precipitate persists, albumin present
	Purdy	1. Add sodium chloride solution to urine to prevent precipitation of mucin 2. Add acetic acid to prevent precipitation of phosphates 3. Heat 4. If white precipitate forms, albumin present

Methods of analysis and synopsis of procedures—cont'd

Test	Method	Synopsis of procedure
Albumin—cont'd	Osgood-Haskins	1. Add acetic acid to urine to prevent precipitation of phosphates 2. Add sodium chloride to prevent precipitation of mucin 3. Heat 4. If white precipitate forms, albumin present
	Sulfosalicylic acid	1. Add sulfosalicylic acid to urine 2. If white cloud forms, albumin present
	Exton	1. Add Exton's reagent to urine 2. Heat gently 3. If white cloud forms, albumin present
	Robert	1. Overlay Robert's reagent with urine 2. If white ring forms, albumin present
	Heller	1. Overlay concentrated nitric acid with urine 2. If white ring forms, albumin present
Sugar	Benedict	1. Add Benedict's reagent to urine 2. Heat 3. If glucose present, the copper will be reduced to green, yellow, or orange precipitate
	Clinitest	1. Add water to urine 2. Add Clinitest tablet 3. If glucose present, the copper will be reduced to green, yellow, or orange precipitate
	Galatest	1. Add urine to Galatest powder 2. If glucose present, bismuth oxide will be reduced to gray or black precipitate
	Tes-Tape	1. Moisten Tes-Tape with urine 2. Compare with color chart
Acetone	Acetest	1. Add urine to Acetest tablet 2. If acetone present, it reacts with sodium nitroprusside to produce a lavender to purple color
	Acetone test (Denco)	1. Add urine to acetone test powder 2. If acetone present, it reacts with sodium nitroprusside to produce a lavender to purple color
	Lange	1. Add acetic acid and sodium nitroprusside to urine 2. Overlay with ammonium hydroxide 3. If acetone present, it reacts with sodium nitroprusside to produce a purple ring
	Rothera	1. Add ammonium sulfate and sodium nitroprusside to urine 2. Overlay with ammonium hydroxide 3. If acetone present, it reacts with sodium nitroprusside to produce a purple ring
	Rantzman	1. Add Rantzman's reagent to urine 2. Overlay with ammonium hydroxide 3. If acetone present, it reacts with sodium nitroprusside to produce a purple ring
	Frommer	1. Add sodium hydroxide and salicylaldehyde to urine 2. Heat 3. If acetone present, it reacts with salicylaldehyde to produce a purple color
Microscopic examination		1. Centrifuge urine 2. Examine sediment with microscope

3. Preservatives for urine:

> Refrigeration
> Formalin
> Toluene
> Boric acid

REFERENCE

1. Kark, R., Lawrence, J., Pollak, V., Pirani, C., Muehrcke, R., and Silva, H.: A primer of urinalysis, ed. 2, New York, 1963, Paul B. Hoeber, Inc., Medical Book Department of Harper & Row, Publishers.

Chapter 20

Urine chemistry tests

This chapter deals with urinary tests that are often performed in a hospital laboratory. The examinations are listed below and the procedures are given on the following pages. Quantitative analyses of some of the methods have been discussed in previous chapters, in which cases the appropriate chapter number is given for reference.

Bilirubin (bile)
Diacetic acid
Urobilinogen
Urobilin
Melanin
Occult blood
Calcium, Chapter 13
Quantitative sugar
Quantitative protein,
    Chapter 10
Bence Jones protein
Addis count
Amylase, Chapter 14
Chloride, Chapter 13

Calculi
5-Hydroxyindoleacetic acid (serotonin),
    qualitative and quantitative
Osmolality, Chapter 15
Phenylketonuria
Uric acid, Chapter 9
Urea nitrogen, Chapter 9
Creatinine, Chapter 9
Creatine, Chapter 9
Phenolsulfonphthalein (PSP)

BILIRUBIN (BILE)
Information significant to the student

Bilirubin is a red bile pigment. It is found in the urine in infectious hepatitis, obstructive jaundice, and many other liver diseases. In liver disease, bilirubin may be detected in the urine even before the blood level is elevated.

The majority of tests for bilirubin depend upon the oxidation of bilirubin to various colored compounds. Among these compounds are biliverdin, which is green, bilicyanin which is blue, and choletelin, which is yellow.

Procedures for bilirubin in urine

If it is necessary to prepare any of the reagents for the following tests, take the number that follows the reagent and refer to Appendix C.

Foam test	Gmelin test
Ictotest	Harrison test
Nitric acid test	Smith test

Foam test

Reagents needed

None

Procedure

1. Obtain two small test tubes.
2. Pour about 5 ml. of the urine that is to be tested into one tube.
3. Pour about 5 ml. of normal urine into the other tube. This will be used for a color comparison.
4. Shake both test tubes. Note the color of the foam. If the foam has a yellow color that persists for several minutes, bile may be present and one of the following tests should be run. (Certain drugs, such as Pyridium and Serenium, also impart a yellow color to the foam.)

Ictotest

Reagent needed

Ictotest Reagent Tablets°

Procedure

1. Place 5 drops of urine on a special mat that comes with the reagent.
2. Put 1 Ictotest tablet in the center of the moistened area.
3. Place 2 drops of water on the tablet so that the water just flows over the sides. If a bluish purple color appears on the mat around the tablet, the test is positive for bilirubin.
4. Report the test as positive or negative.

Nitric acid test

Reagent needed

Concentrated Nitric Acid

Procedure

1. Mix the urine by swirling or inverting the container.
2. Filter about 20 ml.
3. Allow filter paper to partially dry.
4. Place a few drops of concentrated nitric acid on the filter paper. A display of colors—yellow, green, blue—is positive for bile.

Gmelin test

Reagent needed

Concentrated Nitric Acid

Procedure

1. Carefully pour a few milliliters of concentrated nitric acid into a test tube.

°May be purchased from your local supply house or from Ames Co., Inc., Elkhart, Ind.

2. Tilt the tube to about a 30-degree angle.
3. Using a medicine dropper, overlay with urine. A band of colored rings at the junction of the two liquids is positive for bile.

Harrison test

Reagents needed

Barium Chloride, 10%   (C-170)
Fouchet's Reagent   (C-171)

Procedure

1. Pour about 20 ml. of urine into a small flask.
2. Add 10 ml. of 10% barium chloride.
3. Mix and let stand for a few minutes.
4. Filter.
5. Place a few drops of Fouchet's reagent on the filter paper. A blue to green color is positive for bile.

Smith test

Reagent needed

Iodine, Ethyl Alcohol Solution   (C-172)

Procedure

1. Pour about 5 ml. of clear urine into a test tube.
2. Tilt the tube to about a 30-degree angle.
3. Using a medicine dropper, overlay with the ethyl alcohol solution of iodine. An emerald green color at the junction of the two liquids is positive for bile.

DIACETIC ACID
Information significant to the student

As was previously mentioned, diacetic acid results from abnormal fat catabolism, which may occur in severe diabetes. Its presence in the urine may forewarn the physician of approaching coma.

Either Gerhardt's or Lindemann's test is used to test for diacetic acid. In Gerhardt's test, a reaction between diacetic acid and ferric chloride produces a red color. In Lindemann's test, a reaction between diacetic acid and iodine decolorizes the iodine.

Procedures for diacetic acid in urine

If it is necessary to prepare any of the reagents for the tests listed below, take the number that follows the reagent and refer to Appendix C.

Gerhardt test
Lindemann test

Gerhardt test

Reagents needed

Concentrated Nitric Acid
Ferric Chloride, 10%   (C-153)

Procedure

1. Pour about 5 ml. of *fresh* urine into a test tube.
2. Add 10% ferric chloride drop by drop until no further precipitation is produced.

3. Centrifuge.
4. Transfer the supernatant fluid to a test tube. Add a few more drops of 10% ferric chloride to this supernatant fluid. If no color is produced, the test is negative. If a red color is produced, however, it is due either to diacetic acid or to a drug. To decide which, proceed as follows.
5. Pour about 5 ml. of *fresh* urine into a beaker. Add 5 ml. of distilled water and 2 drops of concentrated nitric acid.
6. Boil down to 5 ml. Cool.
7. Add a few drops of the 10% ferric chloride. If *no* red color is produced, the test is *positive* for diacetic acid. The boiling drives off or oxidizes the diacetic acid but not the drug.

Lindemann test

Reagents needed

Chloroform
Acetic Acid, 30%   (C-173)
Lugol's Solution   (C-174)

Procedure

1. Pour about 10 ml. of *fresh* urine into a large test tube.
2. Add 5 drops of 30% acetic acid.
3. Add 5 drops of Lugol's solution.
4. Add 3 drops of chloroform. Shake gently.
5. The chloroform layer *does not* change color in the *presence* of diacetic acid. Consequently, if the chloroform layer does not change color, the test is positive for diacetic acid.

UROBILINOGEN
Information significant to the student

Urobilinogen is a colorless compound derived from bilirubin. Small traces are normally present in urine. Large amounts are found in liver disease, lead poisoning, hemolytic anemia, and other diseases of a hemolytic nature.

Urobilinogen is formed in the intestine by the bacterial action on bilirubin. This is reabsorbed in the small intestine and excreted partly by the kidney and partly by the liver. With hemolytic anemia, where there is an increased destruction of the red blood cells, and in parenchymal liver disease, the urinary urobilinogen is increased. With complete obstructive jaundice, there may be no urobilinogen in the urine, since bilirubin cannot reach the intestine to be changed to urobilinogen.

For the determination of urobilinogen in urine, the following methods are commonly used: (1) Ehrlich qualitative test, (2) Ehrlich semiquantitative test, and (3) Schwartz-Watson test. In all these methods, a reaction takes place between urobilinogen and Ehrlich's reagent (paradimethylaminobenzaldehyde) to produce a cherry red color. The extent of the reaction may be compared with standards.

Procedures for urobilinogen in urine

If it is necessary to prepare any of the reagents for the following tests, take the number that follows the reagent and refer to Appendix C.

Ehrlich qualitative test
Ehrlich semiquantitative test
Schwartz-Watson test

Ehrlich qualitative test

Reagent needed
Ehrlich's Reagent   (C-175)

Procedure
1. Pour about 5 ml. of *freshly* voided urine into a test tube.
2. Add 1 ml. of Ehrlich's reagent. Mix.
3. Let stand for 5 minutes. A cherry red color is positive for abnormal amounts of urobilinogen. Disregard a pink color.

Ehrlich semiquantitative test

Reagent needed
Ehrlich's Reagent   (C-175)

Procedure
1. Get five large test tubes.
2. Number them 1 to 5 and place in a test tube rack.
3. Pipet the following amounts of *freshly* voided urine and distilled water into the tubes.

Tube number	Urine	Water	Dilution
1	1.0 ml.	9.0 ml.	1:10
2	0.5 ml.	9.5 ml.	1:20
3	0.2 ml.	9.8 ml.	1:50
4	0.1 ml.	9.9 ml.	1:100
5	0.05 ml.	9.95 ml.	1:200

4. Add 1 ml. of Ehrlich's reagent to each tube.
5. Mix and let stand for 5 minutes.
6. Note color. A pink color in the first two tubes (that is, through dilutions 1:20) is normal. A pink or red color in tube 3, 4, or 5 indicates abnormal amounts of urobilinogen.
7. Report the highest dilution giving a pink or red color, stating that it is normal for the test to be positive through dilutions 1:20.
8. Example: If tubes 1, 2, 3, and 4 are pink, the report is made as follows: Test for urobilinogen is positive through dilutions 1:100. (*Note:* It is normal for the test to be positive through dilutions 1:20.)

Schwartz-Watson test

Reagents needed
Ehrlich's Reagent   (C-175)
Sodium Acetate, Saturated   (C-66a)
Sodium Acetate, Crystals
Chloroform

Procedure
1. Pipet 1.0 ml. of fresh urine into a test tube.
2. Add 1.0 ml. of Ehrlich's reagent. Mix.
3. Add 4.0 ml. of supersaturated aqueous solution of sodium acetate. Mix.
4. Test with Congo red paper. Paper reaction:
   a. If red, continue to step 5.
   b. If not red, add sodium acetate crystals (shake to dissolve) until a positive result of red is obtained.
5. Add 3.0 ml. of chloroform.
6. Mix carefully by inverting twice and releasing the stopper; then *shake vigorously.* (*Note:* If the tube is not shaken vigorously the test will produce a false positive reaction.)

7. Results
   a. *Negative*—the aqueous layer is not colored.
   b. *Positive*—the aqueous layer forms a purple-red aldehyde reaction.
   c. Note: *Porphobilinogen*° will be indicated by a red-brown aldehyde layer.
8. Results with ultraviolet light:
   a. *Uroporphyrin* and *coproporphyrin* are fluorescent in ultraviolet light.

UROBILIN
Information significant to the student

When urine stands, urobilinogen is oxidized to a brown pigment known as urobilin. Small amounts of urobilin are normally found in urine. Large amounts may be seen in diseases of the liver and in diseases of a hemolytic nature.

To determine urobilin in urine, the method of Schlesinger is commonly used. In this method, calcium chloride is added to the urine to precipitate bile. The urine is then filtered. Lugol's solution is added to the filtrate to convert urobilinogen to urobilin. A solution of zinc acetate is then added. This reacts with the urobilin to produce a green florescence.

Procedure for urobilin in urine

If it is necessary to prepare any of the reagents, take the number that follows the reagent and refer to Appendix C.

Reagents needed

Calcium Chloride, 10%	(C-199)
Lugol's Solution	(C-174)
Zinc Acetate, Saturated Alcoholic Solution	(C-200)

Procedure (Schlesinger)

1. Mix the urine and pour 12 ml. into a small flask. (Measure with a graduated cylinder.)
2. Add 3 ml. of 10% calcium chloride.
3. Mix and filter to remove any bile present.
4. Take 10 ml. of the filtrate and add a few drops of Lugol's solution.
5. Mix and add 10 ml. of a saturated alcoholic solution of zinc acetate.
6. Mix and filter. Let filtrate stand about an hour.
7. Examine in sunlight, concentrating the sunlight on the solution with a hand lens. The presence of a green florescence is positive for urobilin.

MELANIN
Information significant to the student

The word "melanin" is Greek for black. When present in the urine, melanin usually occurs as a colorless compound. Upon standing, however, it oxidizes to a black pigment which is readily discernible. Melanin is not present in normal urine but may be found in the urine of patients with melanotic tumors.

For the determination of melanin, the following methods are commonly used: (1) ferric chloride test and (2) bromine test. Both methods call for the oxidation of the colorless compound (melanogen) to the colored compound (melanin).

°Porphobilinogen is found in the urine in acute intermittent porphyria.

Procedures for melanin in urine

If it is necessary to prepare any of the reagents, take the number that follows the reagent and refer to Appendix C.

Ferric chloride test
Bromine test

Ferric chloride test

Reagent needed

Ferric Chloride, 10%   (C-153)

Procedure
1. Mix the urine and pour about 8 ml. into a small flask.
2. Add about 6 drops of 10% ferric chloride. Mix.
3. Allow to stand 30 minutes. If the solution turns black, melanin is present.

Bromine test

Reagent needed

Bromine Water   (C-176)

Procedure
1. Mix the urine and pour about 25 ml. into a small flask.
2. Add about 25 ml. of the bromine reagent. Mix.
3. Allow to stand 30 minutes. If the solution turns black, melanin is present.

OCCULT BLOOD
Information significant to the student

Occult blood is hidden blood; that is, blood which has dissolved or hemolyzed. When it occurs in the urine, the condition is referred to as hemoglobinuria. It may be found in the following disorders, all of which are accompanied by excessive red cell destruction: transfusion reactions, severe burns, and various chemical poisonings.

For the detection of occult blood, the following tests are commonly used: (1) benzidine test, (2) orthotoluidine test, (3) guaiac test, and (4) Hematest. The principle of these tests is as follows. The hemoglobin of the blood reacts with peroxide to liberate oxygen. The liberated oxygen then reacts with an organic reagent to produce a colored compound.

Procedures for occult blood in urine

If it is necessary to prepare any of the reagents, take the number which follows the reagent and refer to Appendix C.

Benzidine test
Orthotoluidine test
Guaiac test
Hematest

Benzidine test

Reagents needed

Hydrogen Peroxide, 3%
Benzidine, Saturated, in Glacial Acetic Acid   (C-151)

Procedure

1. Mix the urine and pour about 2 ml. into a test tube.
2. Add 3 ml. of a saturated solution of benzidine in glacial acetic acid. Mix.
3. Add 1 ml. of 3% hydrogen peroxide. Mix. A green to blue color indicates a positive reaction.

Orthotoluidine test

Reagents needed

Hydrogen Peroxide 3%
Orthotoluidine Reagent   (C-177)

Procedure

1. Place about 1 ml. of urine in a test tube.
2. Add 1 ml. of the orthotoluidine reagent.
3. Add about 10 drops of 3% hydrogen peroxide. Mix. A green to blue color is a positive reaction.

Guaiac test

Reagents needed

Glacial Acetic Acid
Guaiac Reagent   (C-178)

Procedure

1. Pour about 5 ml. of urine into a test tube.
2. Add a few drops of glacial acetic acid.
3. Mix. Tilt the tube to about a 30-degree angle and slowly overlay with the guaiac reagent. A green to blue color at the junction of the two liquids is a positive reaction.

Hematest

Reagent needed

Hematest Tablets°

Procedure

1. Place a piece of filter paper (which comes with the reagent bottle) on a clean surface.
2. Place a Hematest tablet on the filter paper.
3. Place a large drop of urine on the tablet so that the urine just flows over the sides. If a blue color appears on the filter paper around the tablet, the test is positive for occult blood.

CALCIUM
Information significant to the student

Calcium is normally present in the urine. Increased amounts are found in hyperparathyroidism. Decreased quantities are observed in hypoparathyroidism.

A quantitative test for calcium is given in Chapter 13.

The qualitative test of Sulkowitch, however, is commonly used. In this test, a solution of ammonium oxalate is added to the urine. If calcium is present in excessive amounts, it drops out of solution as a heavy white precipitate of calcium oxalate.

°May be purchased through your local medical supply house or ordered directly from Ames Co., Inc., Elkhart, Ind.

Procedure for calcium in urine

If it is necessary to prepare the reagent, take the number that follows the reagent and refer to Appendix C.

Reagent needed

Sulkowitch Reagent   (C-179)

Procedure (Sulkowitch)

1. Pour 5 ml. of urine into a test tube.
2. Add 5 ml. of the Sulkowitch reagent.
3. Mix by inverting the tube several times.
4. Allow to stand 3 minutes.
5. If a fine white cloud appears, the calcium content is normal.
6. If no white cloud appears, the calcium content is decreased.
7. If a heavy white milky precipitate forms, the calcium content is increased.
8. Report the calcium content as Normal, Decreased, or Increased.

QUANTITATIVE SUGAR
Information significant to the student

A quantitative urinary sugar test may aid the physician in determining the severity of a diabetic case and also in following its course during treatment.

For the quantitative determination of sugar in urine, the method of Benedict is commonly used. In this test, the following takes place. Urine, containing glucose, is slowly added to 5 ml. of a copper solution of known strength. The amount of urine required to cause complete reduction of the copper is recorded. This figure is then used in a formula to calculate the percent of glucose present.

Procedure for quantitative sugar

If it is necessary to prepare the reagent, take the number that follows the reagent and refer to Appendix C.

Reagents needed

Sodium Carbonate
Benedict's Quantitative Reagent   (C-180)

Procedure (Benedict)

1. Get a 250 ml. beaker and half fill with water. Heat to boiling.
2. Pipet *exactly* 5 ml. of Benedict's *quantitative* reagent into a large Pyrex test tube. Add 1 to 2 gm. of sodium carbonate. Mix.
3. Place the tube in the boiling water and allow the solution to come to a boil.
4. Get a 1 ml. serological pipet having 100 graduations or a buret. Pipet out exactly 1 ml. of urine and add it drop by drop to the boiling Benedict's solution until the blue color completely disappears (Fig. 69). Take the pipet or buret reading and make the calculation as follows.

Calculations

The Benedict's solution is made so that 1.0 ml. of a 1% glucose solution will exactly neutralize the 5 ml. of Benedict's solution. If you wish to check the strength of the Benedict's solution, proceed as follows. Using the analytical balance, weigh out 1.000 gm. of glucose. Transfer to a 100 ml. volumetric flask and add distilled water to the 100 ml. mark. Mix. Use this 1% glucose solution in place of the urine and continue as in the procedure. It should require 1.0 ml. If it does not, take the

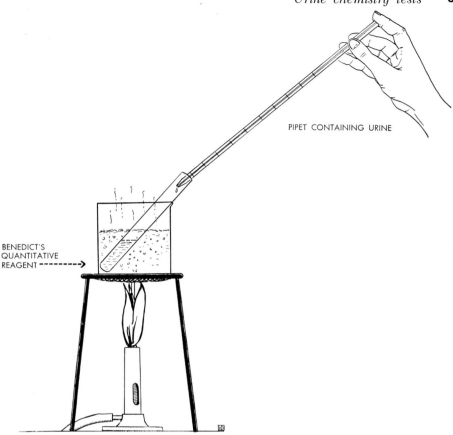

PIPET CONTAINING URINE

BENEDICT'S
QUANTITATIVE
REAGENT - - - - - - - - ->

Fig. 69. Quantitative test for urinary sugar.

number of milliliters required and substitute that figure in the formula
for the 1.0 shown here (milliliters required for neutralization). To find
the percentage of glucose in the urine, use this formula:

$$\frac{1.0 \text{ (ml. required for neutralization)}}{\text{ml. used in titration}} \times 1\% = \% \text{ glucose in gm./100 ml.}$$

5. Example: If 0.5 ml. of urine is used in the titration, we have:

$$\frac{\text{Ml. required for neutralization}}{\text{Ml. used in titration}} \times 1\% = \% \text{ glucose}$$

$$\frac{1.0}{0.5} \times 1\% = 2\% \text{ glucose}$$

QUANTITATIVE PROTEIN
Information significant to the student

A quantitative protein determination may be of some help to the physician
in following the course of a kidney disease.

For the quantitative determination of protein in urine, the following methods
are commonly used: (1) Esbach's method, (2) Tsuchiya's method, (3) Exton's
method, and (4) Kingsbury's method. The first two methods call for the precipitation of the protein by an acid. The amount of precipitation is then measured in

an Esbach tube. The latter two methods also call for the precipitation of the protein by an acid, but the amount of precipitation is then compared with a set of standards.

Procedures for quantitative protein

If it is necessary to prepare the reagents for the tests given below, take the number that follows the reagent and refer to Appendix C.

Esbach method
Tsuchiya method
Exton method
Kingsbury method

Esbach method

Reagents needed

Hydrochloric Acid, 5%   (C-181)
Esbach's Reagent   (C-182)

Procedure

1. Acidify the urine with the 5% hydrochloric acid to pH 5.
2. Filter.
3. Fill the Esbach tube to "U" mark with the filtered urine.
4. Add the Esbach reagent to the "R" mark.
5. Close the tube with a rubber stopper and invert several times to mix.
6. Place in an upright position for 24 hours.
7. Read off the height of the coagulation. This will be the number of grams per 1000 ml. of urine. To obtain percentage, divide reading by 10.

Tsuchiya method

Reagents needed

Hydrochloric Acid, 5% (v/v)   (C-181)
Tsuchiya's Reagent   (C-37)

Procedure

1. Acidify the urine with 5% hydrochloric acid, to pH 5.
2. Filter.
3. Fill an Esbach tube to the "U" mark with the filtered urine.
4. Add the Tsuchiya reagent to the "R" mark.
5. Close the tube with a rubber stopper and invert several times to mix.
6. Place in an upright position for 24 hours.
7. Read off the height of the coagulation. This will be the number of grams per 1000 ml. of urine. To obtain percentage, divide reading by 10.

Exton method

Reagents needed

Acetic Acid, 5%   (C-158)
Exton's Reagent   (C-162)
Exton's Standard Tubes*

Procedure

1. Acidify the urine with 5% acetic acid to a pH 5.
2. Place 3 ml. of the acidified urine in a test tube that is the same size as the Exton standard tubes.

---

*May be purchased from a local medical supply house.

3. Add 3 ml. of Exton's reagent. Mix.
4. Let stand 5 minutes.
5. Warm gently—but do not boil.
6. Compare with a set of Exton's standard tubes, giving report in mg., of protein/100 ml. of urine.

Kingsbury method

Reagents needed

Sulfosalicylic Acid, 3%   (C-183)
Kingsbury's Standard Tubes*

Procedure

1. Filter the urine and place 2.5 ml. in a test tube that is the same size as the Kingsbury standard tubes.
2. Add 7.5 ml. of 3% sulfosalicylic acid.
3. Mix and let stand for 5 minutes.
4. Compare with Kingsbury's standard tubes, giving the report in mg. of protein/100 ml. of urine.

BENCE JONES PROTEIN
Information significant to the student

This protein, discovered by Bence Jones, has the following peculiar characteristics: it precipitates out at a temperature of about 50° C., partially or completely disappears at 100° C., and then reappears upon cooling to room temperature. Its presence in the urine is considered a significant diagnostic aid in multiple myeloma, a malignant tumor of the bone marrow.

Procedure

1. Get a bottle of 5% acetic acid and a centigrade thermometer.
2. Pour about 10 ml. of the urine into a test tube.
3. Place the thermometer and the test tube containing the urine in a beaker of water.
4. Heat gently and watch both the thermometer and the urine.
5. Bence Jones protein is present if *all* the three following conditions are met: (a) At about 50° to 60° C., a white cloud will appear which turns into a white precipitate and usually clings to the sides of the tube. (b) Upon the addition of a few drops of 5% acetic acid and further heating to the boiling point, the precipitate will partially or completely disappear. (c) If the urine is filtered while hot, using a heated funnel and test tube, the white cloud will reappear as the solution cools to room temperature. (*Note:* If a heated funnel and tube are not used, a false positive may be read.)

ADDIS COUNT
Information significant to the student

The Addis count is an estimate of the number of casts, red cells, and white cells in a 12-hour specimen of urine. The normal values are given below. In nephritis, the normal values are greatly exceeded.

Casts	0 to 5000
Red cells	0 to 1,000,000
White cells	0 to 1,000,000

---

*May be purchased from a local medical supply house.

Procedure
Instructions to the patient

The patient is given a clean jar containing 0.5 ml. of formalin, with the
following instructions:

1. On the day of the test, eat a normal breakfast.
2. Throughout the day and night, continue your normal diet, with the
   following exception: *Do not drink anything* or eat extra fruit.
3. At 8:00 P.M. completely empty the bladder and discard the urine.
4. Collect all urine from 8:00 P.M. to 8:00 A.M.
5. Void at 8:00 A.M. and add this to the collection.
6. Bring specimen to the laboratory.

Laboratory procedure

1. Mix the urine specimen *thoroughly*.
2. Pour into a large graduate and measure the amount. Record the volume
   in milliliters.
3. Mix urine again. Pipet *exactly* 10 ml. of the mixed urine to a centrifuge
   tube and centrifuge for 6 minutes at 1800 RPM (medium speed).
4. Pipet out *exactly* 9.0 ml. and discard, thus leaving 1.0 ml. of urine
   containing the sediment.
5. Mix the sediment thoroughly by tapping the bottom sides of the tube.
6. Get a blood-counting chamber. Use a white cell pipet and transfer a
   sample of the sediment to the counting chamber. Do this in the same
   manner as you would for a white cell count.
7. Place the counting chamber on the stage of a microscope, bring into
   focus with the low power (16 mm. objective), and switch to high dry
   power (4 mm. objective).
8. Now count the casts, red cells, and white cells in the *entire* ruled area
   (9 sq. mm.). This represents a volume of 0.9 cu.mm., or 0.0009 ml.

Calculation

Calculate the number excreted in the 12-hour specimen:

$$\text{Number} = n \times \frac{V_1}{V_2} \times \frac{V_3}{V_4}$$

where n = Number counted in 0.0009 ml.
V_1 = Volume of 12-hour specimen
V_2 = Volume of urine centrifuged
V_3 = Volume of mixed sediment used
V_4 = Volume of counting chamber

Example: The 12-hour specimen measured 1000 ml., and 10 casts were
counted in the entire rule area (in 0.0009 ml.).

$$\text{Number} = n \times \frac{V_1}{V_2} \times \frac{V_3}{V_4}$$

$$= 10 \times \frac{1000}{10} \times \frac{1.0}{0.0009}$$

$$= \frac{1000}{0.0009}$$

$$= 1,111,111 \text{ casts in 12-hour specimen}$$

STUDENTS' SUMMARY

The significant information consists of the following:

Normal and abnormal values
Methods of analysis and synopsis of procedures

Normal and abnormal values

Test	Normal values	When increased
Bilirubin (bile)	None present	Infectious hepatitis Obstructive jaundice
Diacetic acid	None present	Severe diabetes
Urobilinogen	Small trace	Liver disease Lead poisoning Hemolytic anemia
Urobilin	Small trace	Liver disease Lead poisoning Hemolytic anemia
Melanin	None present	Melanotic tumors
Occult blood	None present	Transfusion reactions Severe burns Chemical poisoning
Calcium	Normally present	Hyperparathyroidism
Quantitative sugar	None present	Diabetes
Quantitative protein	None present	Kidney disease
Bence Jones protein	None present	Multiple myeloma
Addis count	Casts: 0–5000 Red cells: 0–1 million White cells: 0–1 million	Nephritis

Methods of analysis and synopsis of procedures

Test	Method	Synopsis of procedure
Bilirubin (bile)	Foam test	1. Shake urine 2. If foam yellow, bilirubin may be present
	Ictotest	1. Place urine on mat 2. Add Ictotest tablet 3. Add 2 drops of water 4. If bilirubin present, mat around tablet turns bluish purple
	Nitric acid test	1. Filter urine 2. Add concentrated nitric acid to filter paper 3. If bilirubin present, it is oxidized to yellow, green, and blue compounds
	Gmelin	1. Overlay concentrated nitric acid with urine 2. If bilirubin present, it is oxidized to form a band of colored rings
	Harrison	1. Add barium chloride solution to urine 2. Filter 3. Add Fouchet's reagent to filter paper 4. If bilirubin present, paper turns green or blue
	Smith	1. Overlay urine with iodine solution 2. If bilirubin present, an emerald green ring will form
Diacetic acid	Gerhardt	1. Add ferric chloride to *fresh* urine 2. Centrifuge 3. Add more ferric chloride 4. If red color produced, diacetic acid or drugs present 5. To decide which: add acid to *fresh* urine, boil to remove diacetic acid, and add ferric chloride 6. If no red color produced, test positive for diacetic acid
	Lindemann	1. Add acetic acid, Lugol's solution, and chloroform to *fresh* urine 2. Shake gently 3. If diacetic acid present, chloroform layer does not change color

Methods of analysis and synopsis of procedures—cont'd

Test	Method	Synopsis of procedure
Urobilinogen	Ehrlich qualitative	1. Add Ehrlich's reagent to *fresh* urine 2. If urobilinogen present, cherry red color produced
	Ehrlich semi-quantitative	1. Make graded dilutions of *fresh* urine 2. Add Ehrlich's reagent 3. Report highest dilution giving pink color
	Schwartz-Watson	1. Add Ehrlich's reagent to fresh urine; mix 2. Add sodium acetate; mix 3. Add chloroform; mix 4. If urobilinogen present, aqueous layer becomes purple-red
Urobilin	Schlesinger	1. Add calcium chloride to urine to precipitate bile 2. Filter 3. Add Lugol's solution to convert urobilinogen to urobilin 4. Add zinc acetate solution 5. Examine in sunlight 6. If urobilin present, a green florescence produced
Melanin	Ferric chloride test	1. Add ferric chloride to urine 2. If melanogen present, it is oxidized to black melanin
	Bromine test	1. Add bromine reagent to urine 2. If melanogen present, it is oxidized to black melanin
Occult blood	Benzidine test	1. Add benzidine solution to urine 2. Add hydrogen peroxide 3. If occult blood present, it liberates oxygen that oxidizes benzidine to green or blue compound
	Orthotoluidine test	1. Add orthotoluidine reagent to urine 2. Add hydrogen peroxide 3. If occult blood present, solution turns green or blue
	Guaiac test	1. Add acetic acid to urine 2. Overlay with guaiac reagent 3. If occult blood present, a green or blue ring produced
	Hematest	1. Place urine on Hematest tablet 2. If occult blood present, a blue color will appear around tablet
Calcium	Sulkowitch	1. Add Sulkowitch reagent to urine to precipitate calcium as calcium oxalate 2. If calcium present in excessive amounts, a heavy white precipitate produced
Quantitative sugar	Benedict	1. Titrate 5 ml. of Benedict's quantitative reagent with urine 2. Record number of milliliters of urine used 3. Find percent glucose by calculation
Quantitative protein	Esbach	1. Acidify urine and pour into Esbach tube 2. Add Esbach reagent 3. Let stand 24 hours 4. Read off grams of proteins/1000 ml. of urine
	Tsuchiya	1. Same as above except use Tsuchiya's reagent in place of Esbach's reagent
	Exton	1. Acidify urine 2. Add Exton's reagent 3. Warm gently 4. Compare with Exton's standards

Methods of analysis and synopsis of procedures—cont'd

Test	Method	Synopsis of procedure
Quantitative protein —cont'd	Kingsbury	1. Filter urine 2. Acidify 3. Compare with Kingsbury's standards
Bence Jones protein	Bence Jones	1. Heat urine and watch urine and thermometer 2. Bence Jones protein present if precipitate forms at about 50° to 60°C., disappears at 100°C., and reappears upon filtration and cooling to room temperature
Addis count	Addis	1. Using blood-counting chamber and microscope, count casts, red cells, and white cells in representative sample of 12-hour specimen of urine 2. Calculate number present in 12-hour specimen

AMYLASE

The normal values for urinary amylase (or diastase) depend upon the method of determination. Greatly increased values are found in acute pancreatitis. See Chapter 14 for procedure.

CHLORIDE

The average person excretes 10 to 15 gm. of chloride (expressed as sodium chloride) per day. Decreased values may be found in acute infections, severe diarrhea, nephritis with edema, and dehydration conditions. See Chapter 13 for procedure.

CALCULI

Calculi, the Latin word for stones, are formed by the crystallization of salts. Their formation is often started by an infection in the urinary system and is enhanced by sedentary habits and the presence of urinary salts that are difficult to dissolve, two of the chief offenders being calcium oxalate and calcium phosphate. In mild cases, the stones may be passed in the urine; in severe cases, surgery is essential.

Procedure

To perform the various tests, follow the procedures given in Table 53.

Reagents needed

Ammonium Molybdate Solution
> Dissolve 3.5 gm. of ammonium molybdate in 75 ml. of water. Add 25 ml. of concentrated nitric acid and mix.

Hydrochloric Acid, 10% (v/v)
> Add 10 ml. of concentrated hydrochloric acid to 90 ml. of water. Mix.

Sodium Cyanide, 5%
> Weigh 25.0 gm. of sodium cyanide and transfer to a 500 ml. volumetric flask. Add 1 ml. of concentrated ammonium hydroxide. Dissolve and dilute to volume with water.

Sodium Nitroprusside, 5%
> Weigh 5.0 gm. of sodium nitroprusside (nitroferricyanide) and transfer to a 100 ml. volumetric flask. Dissolve and dilute to volume with water. Mix. Store in a brown bottle.

Table 53. Analysis of urinary calculi

Stone	Physical characteristics	Procedure	Positive results
Urates or uric acid	1. Multiple, smooth, round, without luster 2. Single stones may have bumpy surface, miniature craters 3. Crushed stones are yellow	1. Pulverize stone 2. Place in small evaporating dish 3. Add several drops of concentrated nitric acid 4. Heat gently and evaporate to dryness 5. Add 2–3 drops of concentrated NH_4OH	Deep yellow, orange-red, or crimson, turning purple with NH_4OH, or bluish violet
Phosphates	1. Rather large compact balls 2. Also appear as large friable masses 3. Color: clay or chalky 4. Note: white color, porous, corallike formations are usually calcium oxalate, *not* phosphate	1. Pulverize stone 2. Use microscope slide instead of evaporating dish 3. Add 4–5 drops of ammonium molybdate solution 4. Warm slide over flame	Distinct yellow precipitate forms. This is $(NH_4)_3PO_4 \cdot 12MnO_3$
Carbonate	Same appearance as phosphate	1. Pulverize stone 2. Use a dark background for easier visibility 3. Place a larger quantity of stone on a slide 4. Add 8–10 drops of 10% HCl	Foaming effervescence
Oxalates	1. Smooth luster or 2. Irregular, buff-colored stone with elaborate crystalline structure 3. Occasionally the structure may appear loose and porous	1. Pulverize stone 2. Mix with an equal portion of resorcinol 3. Add 3 drops of concentracted H_2SO_4	Dark blue-green color
Cystine	1. Pale yellow or white granules 2. Appearance similar to calcium oxalate	1. Pulverize stone 2. Add 1 drop of NH_4OH and 1 drop of NaCN 3. Wait 5 minutes 4. Add 2–3 drops of sodium nitroprusside	Upon standing, a beet-red color may change to orange-red

5-HYDROXYINDOLEACETIC ACID (SEROTONIN)

Carcinoid syndrome with its various symptoms can be confused with other disorders. In 1954, it was proposed that carcinoid tumors secreted a large volume of serotonin, which might account for the variety of symptoms such as chronic diarrhea, cutaneous flushes, valvular disease of the heart, and respiratory distress. Since 5-hydroxyindoleacetic acid (5-HIAA) is a urinary metabolite of serotonin (5-hydroxytryptamine), the measurement of the 5-HIAA is now a diagnostic procedure.

Nitrosonaphthol reagent and nitrous acid are added to urine, and if 5-HIAA is present a purple color is produced. Some medications, however, interfere with the reactions. If a rose color or a color not quite purple is observed, a check for medication should be made. A positive test is a definite purple—no other color.

The patient should be off all medication for 72 hours before the urine is collected. Excessive eating of bananas may result in a false positive. Following are drugs that affect the test.

False positives	*False negatives*
Aspirin	Chlorpromazine groups
Phenacetin	Phenergan
Thorazine Spansules	Promethazine HCl
	Mephentermine sulfate
	Thorazine
	Compazine
	Pacatal
	Trilafon
	Sparine
	Azulfidine
	Pamine

5-Hydroxyindoleacetic acid (5-HIAA), qualitative

Reagents needed

Sulfuric Acid, 2 N	(C-184)
Nitrosonaphthol Reagent, 0.1%	(C-185)
Sodium Nitrite, 2.5%	(C-186)
Ethylene Chloride (Fisher, purified)	
Hydrochloric Acid, Concentrated	
Nitrous Acid Reagent	

Mix just before using! Pipet 0.2 ml. of 2.5% sodium nitrite into a test tube. Add 4.8 ml. of 2 N sulfuric acid. Mix.

Procedure

1. Acidify either a 24-hour specimen or a random urine specimen to pH 3 with concentrated HCL.
2. Pipet 1.0 ml. of urine into test tube.
3. Add 0.5 ml. of nitrosonaphthol solution. Mix.
4. Add 0.5 ml. of nitrous acid reagent. Mix.
5. Let stand for 10 minutes.
6. Add 5.0 ml. of ethylene chloride. Shake vigorously!
7. Centrifuge for 5 minutes at 3000 RPM.
8. A purple color in the upper urine layer indicates a positive reaction which should be further investigated.

5-Hydroxyindoleacetic acid (5-HIAA), quantitative

Reagents needed

Sulfuric Acid, Dilute (1 N)	(C-84)
Nitrosonaphthol Reagent, 0.1%	(C-185)
Sodium Nitrite, 0.5%	(C-187)
Ethylene Dichloride (Fisher, purified)	
5-HIAA Standard, 10 mg./100 ml.	(C-188)
Nitrous Acid Reagent	

Mix just before using! Pipet 1.0 ml. of 0.5% sodium nitrite into a test tube. Add 10.0 ml. of 1 N sulfuric acid. Mix.

Procedure

1. Collect a 24-hour urine specimen and carefully measure the volume.
2. Set up the following tubes:

Reagent blank

a. Pipet 1.0 ml. of distilled water into a test tube.
b. Add 2.0 ml. of 1 N sulfuric acid.
c. Add 1.0 ml. of nitrosonaphthol reagent.
d. Stopper tube and mix.

Standard

a. Pipet 1.0 ml. of standard into a test tube.
b. Add 2.0 ml. of 1 N sulfuric acid.
c. Add 1.0 ml. of nitrosonaphthol reagent.
d. Stopper tube and mix.

Unknown

a. Pipet 1.0 ml. of urine into test tube.
b. Add 2.0 ml. of 1 N sulfuric acid.
c. Add 1.0 ml. of nitrosonaphthol reagent.
d. Stopper tube and mix.

Unknown urine blank (A urine blank is set up for each unknown.)

a. Pipet 1.0 ml. of urine into test tube.
b. Add 2.0 ml. of 1 N sulfuric acid.
c. Add 1.0 ml. of *distilled water.*
d. Stopper tube and mix.

3. To all tubes add 2.0 ml. of nitrous acid reagent. Mix.
4. Let stand 20 minutes.
5. Add 10.0 ml. of ethylene dichloride and shake vigorously.
6. Centrifuge for 5 minutes at 3000 RPM.
7. Pipet 5.0 ml. of aqueous layer into a cuvette and read against the reagent blank at 520 mμ wavelength.

Calculations

$$\frac{\text{O.D. of unknown} - \text{O.D. of urine blank}}{\text{O.D. of standard}} \times 10 = \text{Mg./100 ml.}$$

$$\text{Mg./100 ml.} \times \frac{\text{24-hour urine volume}}{100} = \text{Mg./24 hr.}$$

Normal range

Normal urinary output is less than 14 mg./24 hr. Elevated values are found in certain types of metastasizing carcinoid.

OSMOLALITY

Osmometry provides an accurate and fast means of determining the total solute concentration of urine and serum (Chapter 15). The normal range for serum is 275 to 295 mOs/kg. The measurement of urine and serum solute concentrations may be of considerable diagnostic significance to the physician when working out special problems with disturbances of fluid and electrolyte balance or urinary excretion.

PHENYLKETONURIA[1]

Phenylketonuria is an inherited disorder of phenylalanine metabolism, which will cause severe mental retardation. This disorder usually appears between the second and sixth week of the infant's life. The urines of all infants are now usually tested for phenylpyruvic acid weekly up to the age of 6 months, if they have convulsions, severe diaper rashes, or eczema. Normal children are checked either biweekly or monthly during this period of 6 months. Phenylketonuria is diagnosed by the excess phenylpyruvic acid found in urine or serum. Urine will also contain phenylacetic and phenyllactic acid.

By early treatment with diets low in phenylalanine, mental defects may be avoided or corrected. If undetected, abnormal metabolism of the amino acid (phenylalanine) will impair the normal development of the brain.

Qualitative methods
Ferric chloride method

Reagents needed

Sulfuric Acid, Dilute (1 N)   (C-84)
Ferric Chloride, 5%   (C-189)

Procedure

1. Place 5.0 ml. of fresh urine into a test tube and acidify with 2 drops of diluted sulfuric acid.
2. Add 5 drops of 5% ferric chloride solution. Mix.
3. Positive result: solution turns to a bluish green.

Note: The ferric chloride method has been used also for determination of acetoacetic acid. Positive result: solution turns to red. Other substances may interfere with the test.

Phenistix test

The reagent strip reacts rapidly with the phenylketones in urine, the color of the strip changing from gray to a distinctive blue-gray. The strip is either dipped into a fresh specimen of urine or pressed against the wet diaper. Within ½ minute the color is developed on the strip and it is then compared with the color scale whose reference points are zero and 15, 40, and 100 mg./100 ml. of phenylketone.

Reagents on the strip

Ferric Ammonium Sulfate
    Supplies the ferric ions, which react with phenylpyruvic acid in a properly acidified medium
Cyclohexylsulfamic Acid
    Provides the optimum acidity for the above reaction
Magnesium Sulfate
    The magnesium ions are incorporated to prevent the urine phosphates from interfering with the color reaction.

Procedure

1. Dip the test strip in fresh urine and remove immediately, or press against a wet diaper to moisten.
2. At the end of ½ minute compare the color against the reference points on the color chart.

Note: The only other substance giving a typical blue-gray color of phenyl-pyruvic acid in a 30-second interval is β-imidazolepyruvic acid. This is excreted in the urine due to the deficiency of the enzyme, histidine α-deaminase, a rare disorder of children. Substances not affecting Phenistix are as follows:

Phenylacetate	Thymol
Phenyllactate	Toluene
Phenylalanine	Baby powders
Pyruvate	Baby oils
Lactate	Antiseptics
Tyrosine	Homogentisic acid
Tryptophane	Acetoacetic acid

URIC ACID

The urine of the average person contains about 250 to 750 mg. of uric acid per day. Increased amounts are found after an attack of gout. (Chapter 9.)

UREA NITROGEN

The normal urine urea nitrogen is 6 to 17 gm./24 hr. Decreased values may be found in acute nephritis, acidosis, and cirrhosis of the liver. Increased values may be seen in febrile conditions. (Chapter 9.)

CREATININE

The normal range for urine creatinine is 1.0 to 1.8 gm./24 hr. Creatinine excretion is decreased in disorders associated with muscular atrophy and muscular weakness. It increases with increased tissue catabolism, as in fever. (Chapter 9.)

CREATINE

The 24-hour urine specimen of the average person contains 0 to 200 mg. of creatine. Increased values are found in fever, malnutrition, and pregnancy. (Chapter 9.)

PHENOLSULFONPHTHALEIN (PSP)

Phenolsulfonphthalein is a harmless dye. When injected into the body, the dye is removed by the kidneys and excreted in the urine. If the kidneys are healthy, they will remove 60 to 85% of the dye within 2 hours. If the kidneys are diseased, however, they will remove less than 60%. The test is considered a reliable index of the functioning ability of the kidneys.

Procedure (Rowntree-Geraghty)

The discussion covers the collection of specimens and the laboratory procedure.

Collection of specimens

The nurse and physician usually have the task of instructing the patient, injecting the dye, and collecting the urine specimens. This consists of the following:

1. The patient is told not to take any stimulants (coffee, tea, or tobacco) for 2 hours prior to the test and also during the test.
2. The patient is given two glasses of water to drink and told to void 20 minutes later and discard the urine.
3. Exactly 1 ml. (6 mg.) of sterile phenolsulfonphthalein is then injected *intramuscularly* and the time noted and recorded.
4. Exactly 1 hour 10 minutes after the injection, the urine is collected and labelled: 1-Hour Specimen.
5. Exactly 2 hours 10 minutes after the injection, the urine is collected and labelled: 2-Hour Specimen.
6. The two specimens are then brought to the laboratory.

Reagents needed

Sodium Hydroxide, 10% (2.5 N)   (C-13)
    For method B
PSP Stock Standard, 120 mg./500 ml.   (C-190)
Working Standard, 1.2 mg./500 ml.
    Pipet 5.0 ml. of stock standard into a 500 ml. volumetric flask, add 1.0 ml. of 10% NaOH and dilute to mark with distilled water. Mix thoroughly.

Procedure

1. Measure and record the volume of each specimen.
2. Add 10% sodium hydroxide dropwise to each specimen until the maxi-

mum red color is brought out. About 5 ml. are usually required. The dye is colorless in acid urine and red in alkaline urine. Check the pH. It should be higher than 9.0.

3. Dilute the urines according to volumes, as follows:
   a. If the volume is less than 50 ml., dilute to 250 ml. with water.
   b. If the volume is between 50 ml. and 450 ml., dilute to 500 ml. with water.
   c. If the volume is above 450 ml., dilute to 1000 ml. with water.
4. Mix each specimen.
5. Determine the percent of dye in each specimen by one of the two following methods:
   Method A. Compare with Dunning standards representing known percentages of the dye.
   Method B. Compare in a photoelectric colorimeter.
   Filter about 10 ml. of urine. Pipet 6.0 ml. of filtered urine into a cuvette and 6.0 ml. of diluted working standard into another cuvette. Read against a water blank at 520 mμ.

Calculation

$$\frac{\text{O.D. of unknown}}{\text{O.D. of standard}} \times 1.2 = \text{Mg. PSP in specimen}$$

Note: If diluted urine volume is 250 ml., divide by 2. If diluted urine volume is 1000 ml., multiply by 2.

The sum of the mg. PSP in the two specimens is the total PSP excreted. Since 6 mg. are usually injected, calculate the percent excreted as follows:

$$\frac{\text{Total mg. PSP}}{6} \times 100 = \% \text{ excreted}$$

Normal values

1-hour specimen 40 to 60%
2-hour specimen 20 to 25%
Total excretion 60 to 85%

Decreased values indicate decreased functioning ability of the kidneys.

REFERENCE

1. Kark, R., Lawrence, J., Pollak, V., Pirani, C., Muehrcke, R., and Silva, H.: A primer of urinalysis, ed. 2, New York, 1963, Paul B. Hoeber, Inc., Medical Book Department of Harper & Row, Publishers.

Chapter 21

Pregnancy tests

The blood and urine of pregnant women contain a chemical substance that is known as the gonadotropic hormone. When this hormone is injected into female mice, rats, or rabbits, the ovaries of the animals become enlarged and bloody. This is the principle of the pregnancy test.

In addition to normal pregnancy, the hormone may be present in the following conditions: cancer of the ovary, beginning of menopause, abnormal pregnancies, abortions, and cystlike moles. The hormone may also be present in men with malignant tumors of the testes. Consequently, the preganancy test may be used not only to reveal an early pregnancy, but also to help diagnose a pathological condition.

The physician may request a pregnancy test by any of the following expressions:

> A-Z test (for Aschheim-Zondek, who developed the first test)
> Friedman test (for a research worker who first used rabbits)
> *Rana pipiens* test (for the male frog)
> *Xenopus laevis* test (for the female frog)
> Rabbit test
> Frog test
> Immuno-plate test

Usually the physician is not interested in the method employed in performing the pregnancy test. However, it is a good policy to report the method with your results.

The more commonly used pregnancy tests are listed below and the procedures are given on the following pages.

> Immuno-plate test
> Male frog test
> Female frog test
> Rabbit test
> Mouse test
> Rat test

IMMUNO-PLATE PREGNANCY TEST[1]

This gel-diffusion procedure is a simple, rapid, and minimal-cost test done on urine specimens. It is based on an immunological reaction that gives results similar to those obtained by the usual animal test.

Urine contains high levels of chorionic gonadotropin from 6 weeks after the last normal menstrual cycle through the first trimester of pregnancy. This is the hormone previously described as injected into the animal. A rapid concentration based on the Yale technique[2] makes it possible to use a specimen obtained at any time of the day, although the first morning specimen would have the highest concentration. A measured amount of urine is placed in a well in an agar plate containing an antiserum to human chorionic gonadotropin. As this concentrate (urine) diffuses into the gel, a zone of precipitation is produced, the diameter of which is related to the concentration of the hormone in the specimen.

Reagents and supplies needed[*]

1. Disposable plastic plates, each containing anti-human chorionic gonadotropic serum in agar, with sodium azide 0.1% as a preservative. Each plate should be individually sealed in a plastic envelope and consist of three wells: one for a positive control, and two for the urine test.
2. A plastic vial containing 24 capillary pipets and 2 rubber bulbs.
3. A vial containing 0.5 ml. of Positive Control (200 IU of human chorionic gonadotropin per milliliter in a buffered saline with sodium azide 0.1% for a preservative).
4. Dropper bottle containing 1 ml. of eluting fluid (dilute ammonium hydroxide containing bromthymol blue).
5. Dropper bottle containing 2.5 ml. of adsorbent suspension (kaolin in acetic acid-acetate buffer). An excess is provided to facilitate mixing before use.

Procedure

1. Pipet 2.0 ml. of clear urine into a small tube (12 × 75 mm.).
2. Mix adsorbent suspension by shaking vigorously. Add 2 drops to the urine and mix well.
3. Mix frequently for 2 minutes; then centrifuge sufficiently (about 5 minutes) to pack kaolin particles.
4. Discard supernatant fluid by inverting the tube. Either shake off the last drop or remove with absorbent tissue.
5. Add 1 drop of eluting fluid and bring kaolin into suspension, either by flicking the tube with the finger (Fig. 54) or by using a vibrator.
6. Centrifuge for 5 minutes. Do not discard supernatant.
7. Using a capillary pipet, fill one well of the *immuno-plate* with the supernatant until level with the agar surface.
8. Fill one well of each plate used, to the level of the agar surface, with the Positive Control.
9. In the third well, use a urine specimen from a nonpregnant person.
10. Place the plastic cover on the plate and incubate at 37° to 40° C. for 4 to 5 hours.
11. Examine plate for zones of precipitation around wells, using indirect (reflected) or oblique light against a dark background as when observing slide or tube agglutination tests. A zone, halo, or ring of precipitation appears as a translucent circular area around a well, faint

---

[*]These materials may be purchased in a kit form from the Hyland Laboratories, Los Angeles, Calif., or be obtained from your local dealer.

but sharply demarked at its outer edge. A magnifying device such as a hand lens will be helpful in recognizing the zone.

12. A halo or ring of precipitation of any diameter, either smaller or larger than the one produced by the Positive Control, is a positive reaction.

Precautions

1. Refrigerate urine until it is tested or freeze the specimen if it is to be stored for a prolonged time.
2. Refrigerate the immuno-plates but do *not* store in freezer. Do not use the plates if the agar gel is dry or shrunken excessively.
3. The eluting fluid is an alkaline pH (blue or greenish blue). If it appears acid (yellow) do not use the fluid, because the proper elution of chorionic gonadotropin from the kaolin adsorbent will occur *only* if the elute is alkaline.
4. The wells should be completely filled but not overfilled, since there will be a deposit formation on the surface of the agar that could be mistaken for a positive reaction.

Reactions

1. With a rapid-reacting positive specimen, distinct zones of precipitation may show before 4 hours of incubation.
2. After the first trimester, pregnant women frequently excrete too little of the hormone for a positive result to be detected.
3. False positive results may be found in nonpregnant patients with chorio-epithelioma or hydatidiform mole. With these two disorders chorionic gonadotropin is usually excreted.

MALE FROG TEST

The most commonly used male frog is the species *Rana pipiens*. If the test is positive, the frog gives off sperm cells. These can be seen with the microscope. The discussion of the male frog test includes the following:

> Purchase and storage of male frogs
> Instructions to the patient
> Procedure for the male frog test

Purchase and storage of male frogs

The male frogs may be purchased from various supply houses.*

Upon delivery, the frogs should be given access to water and a day or two to recover from the plane trip. They should then be placed in an enamel pan containing about ¼ inch of water and stored in the refrigerator at a temperature of 36° to 40° F. The water should be changed daily with water that has been stored in the refrigerator and is therefore the same temperature as the water in the frog pan.

Instructions to the patient

Since some drugs will give false positive results, the patient is told to refrain from using medicines or drugs for 2 days prior to the test. She is also told that it is useless to run the test unless she has missed her period by at least 14 days, and also that pregnancies which have progressed beyond the third month usually give negative results.

---

*The names and addresses of several supply houses are E. G. Steinhilber Co., Oshkosh, Wis.; Quivira Specialties, Topeka, Kan.; and New York Scientific Supply Co., New York, N. Y.

Procedure for the male frog test

If it is necessary to prepare any of the reagents, take the number that follows the reagent and refer to Appendix C.

1. Remove two frogs from the refrigerator and place in separate containers, such as mayonnaise jars, with perforated lids. Check the frogs to make sure they are males. Male frogs have an unusually large thumb on the forelimb. Also check the frog's urine under the microscope to make certain that no sperm cells are present. Before making the injection, give the frogs at least ½ hour at adjust to room temperature.
2. If serum is to be used, obtain a 20 ml. syringe and collect 20 ml. of blood. Allow to clot—a process that takes about 30 minutes. Centrifuge to obtain the serum and then go to step 4 below. (Step 3 deals with the concentration of urine.)
3. If urine is to be used, concentrate it as follows: Mix the urine. Pour about 50 ml. into a cylinder jar. (A suitable cylinder jar is a discarded

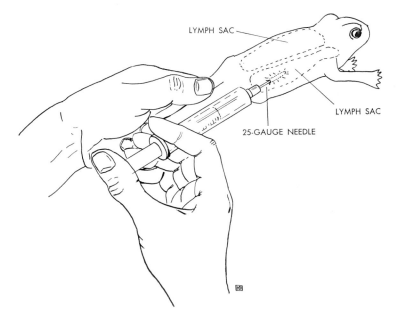

LYMPH SAC

LYMPH SAC

25-GAUGE NEEDLE

Fig. 70. Technique of injecting a frog.

1. Obtain a 10 ml. syringe and a 25-gauge hypodermic needle. Attach the needle to the syringe.
2. Draw up the desired amount of serum or urine concentrate.
3. Grasp the legs of the frog firmly with the left hand and place the frog on a flat surface such as a table.
4. Hold the needle at about a 10-degree angle and push it into the lymph sac. When the needle has entered the skin, adjust it so that you can plainly see the impression of the needle beneath the skin. (This is important because many beginners plunge the needle into the organs of the frog and the ensuing injection of fluid often kills the frog.)
5. Slowly inject the serum or urine into the frog. When the injection is completed, wait about 30 seconds before withdrawing the needle.

olive jar whose 50 ml. level can be noted with a marking pencil.) Add
0.6 ml. of 20% hydrochloric acid. Mix. Add 5 ml. of 20% acid washed
kaolin (may be purchased from a medical supply house). Mix. Allow
the precipitate to settle out to about the 15 ml. mark. Pour off the
supernatant fluid. Pour the precipitate—containing the hormone—into
two separate test tubes. Equalize the contents of the test tubes and
centrifuge at high speed for 5 minutes. Pour off the supernatant fluid.
Add 2 drops of phenolphthalein indicator (C-54) to each tube. Add
2.5 ml. of 0.1 N sodium hydroxide (C-108) to each tube. Using a
wooden applicator stick, mix the white precipitate thoroughly with
the pink fluid. Centrifuge both tubes at high speed for 5 minutes. Pour
the fluids—containing the hormone—into a medicine glass. Using a
medicine dropper or pipet, add the 20% hydrochloric acid dropwise
until the solution just turns yellow. (Usually 1 or 2 drops are enough.)
Mix.

4. Slowly inject 3 ml. of serum or 2 ml. of urine concentrate into the lymph
   sac of each frog (see Fig. 70 with directions for injection). Some technicians weigh the frogs and inject 1 ml. of serum for each 10 gm. of
   the frog's weight.

5. Place the frogs back in their jars and wait 3 hours. Usually the frogs
   will urinate within this period. If not, wait until they urinate. Sometimes a frog can be induced to urinate by placing a hand inside the jar
   and squeezing his head.

6. Using a medicine dropper, place a sample of each frog's urine on a
   slide. Spread it out thin so that it will not touch the high dry objective
   of the microscope. Examine with the high dry (4 mm. or 45×) objective of the microscope. A positive test is indicated by the presence
   of many motile sperm cells, as shown in Fig. 71. If no sperm cells are
   seen, centrifuge the urine and examine the sediment. If either one or
   both of the frogs yield sperm cells, the test is reported as positive.

7. Any frogs that were used in a positive test should not be used again.
   Frogs that were used in a negative test, however, may be used again.
   These should be placed in a pan of water for a day before returning to
   the refrigerator.

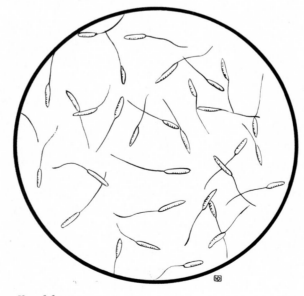

Fig. 71. Sperm cells of frog.

FEMALE FROG TEST

The most commonly used female frog is the species *Xenopus laevis.* If the test is positive, the frog deposits eggs. These can be seen with the naked eye. The discussion of the female frog test includes the following:

Purchase and storage of female frogs
Instructions to the patient
Procedure for the female frog test

Purchase and storage of female frogs

The female frogs may be purchased from various supply houses.*

The frogs may be kept in large glass jars or tanks containing about 3 inches of water. The water should be changed at least twice a week and the frogs fed liver or worms twice a week. They should not be fed, however, for 24 hours before a test, because they may regurgitate food. This makes it difficult to see the eggs.

Instructions to the patient

The patient is given the same instructions as in the preceding male frog test.

Procedure for the female frog test

1. Serum or concentrated urine may be used. If serum is to be used, get a 20 ml. syringe and withdraw about 20 ml. of blood. Allow to clot, which takes about 30 minutes. Centrifuge to obtain the serum. If urine is to be used, concentrate it by the kaolin method described in step 3 for the male frog test.
2. Inject 3 ml. of serum or 2 ml. of concentrated urine into two frogs, as illustrated in Fig. 70.
3. Place the frogs in separate jars on an elevated wire mesh (½-inch size) platform. Any eggs dropped will pass through the wire mesh into the jar.
4. Look for eggs before closing the laboratory and again the next morning. If eggs are found in either jar, the test is positive.
5. Frogs participating in a negative test may be used again after 1 week's rest. Frogs participating in a positive test may be used again after 4 weeks' rest.

RABBIT TEST
Friedman test

1. Instruct the patient to refrain from drugs for 2 days prior to the test and to bring a morning specimen of urine to the laboratory. The specific gravity should be measured, and if it is not over 1.020, another specimen should be requested with the suggestion that the patient drink no fluids the night before the collection.
2. Obtain a female rabbit that weighs over 4 pounds and is more than 16 weeks old. The rabbit should be isolated from all other rabbits for at least 9 weeks before the test. (Many laboratories use virgin rabbits that have been raised specifically for pregnancy tests.)

---

*The names and addresses of several supply houses are Jay E. Cook, Box 302, Baltimore, Md.; Louis C. Herring Co., Orlando, Fla.; and California Xenopus Laevis Exchange, Studio City, Calif.

3. If necessary, warm the urine specimen to room temperature. Mix the urine specimen.
4. Wrap the body of the rabbit in a towel to prevent movement.
5. Moisten a piece of cotton with acetone and rub the outer surface of the rabbit's ear. This makes the veins stand out.
6. Select a large vein and *slowly* inject 15 ml. of the urine.
7. Put the rabbit in a container for 48 hours.
8. To determine the results: Some technicians kill the rabbit and look at the ovaries, whereas others perform an operation on the rabbit, look at the ovaries, and then close the incision.
9. If you wish to kill the rabbit, moisten a piece of cotton with chloroform. Hold the cotton to her nose.
10. If you decide to operate, give an anesthetic of Nembutal and perform the operation.
11. If the ovaries of the rabbit are enlarged and bloody, the test is positive. If the ovaries are normal, the test is negative.

MOUSE TEST
Aschheim-Zondek test

In the Aschheim-Zondek test, a morning specimen of urine is filtered and acidified with acetic acid. Five female white mice, each weighing 5 to 7 gm., are subcutanteously injected as follows:

Mouse	Urine injection
1	0.20 ml.
2	0.25 ml.
3	0.30 ml.
4	0.35 ml.
5	0.40 ml.

Four days after the injection, the mice are killed with illuminating gas, an abdominal incision is made, and the ovaries are examined with a hand lens. If the ovaries of all the mice are small and pale, the test is negative. If any of the ovaries are greatly enlarged and contain yellow or blue pigmentation, the test is positive.

RAT TEST
Kelso method

In the method of Kelso, female rats weighing 30 to 65 gm. are used. The rats should be 3 to 6 weeks old.

A subcutaneous injection of 4 ml. of urine is made into the rat. After a period of 24 hours the animal is killed, an abdominal incision is made, and the ovaries are examined. If the ovaries are small and pale, the test is negative. If the ovaries are enlarged and bloody, the test is positive.

REFERENCES

1. Hyland HCG immuno-plate pregnancy test, Los Angeles, 1963, Hyland Laboratories.
2. Hon, E. H.: A manual of pregnancy testing, Boston, 1961, Little, Brown & Co.

Chapter 22

Special urine chemistry tests

$\mathbf{T}$his chapter considers tests which the average technician seldom performs. In fact, the average technician can probably work a lifetime without running one third of the tests discussed on the following pages.

The examinations of this chapter are grouped under the following headings:

Drugs
Poisons
Carbohydrates
Additional urinary tests

DRUGS

At times, the physician may wish to know whether certain drugs used in therapy are being utilized or simply excreted in the urine. At other times, he may wish to know if the patient has taken drugs without his knowledge. This section considers tests for some of the more commonly used drugs. Those discussed are listed below and the procedures are given on the following pages.

Acetanilid   Morphine
Antipyrine   Phenolphthalein
Chloral hydrate   Quinine
Iodine   Salicylic acid and acetylsalicylic acid

Many of the following tests call for the use of a separatory funnel to separate waste fluids from ether or chloroform. If in an emergency you do not have a separatory funnel available, the two liquids may be separated by using the barrel of a 10 or 20 ml. syringe. The technique is illustrated in Fig. 72.

In ether extractions of blood or aqueous solutions, the ether layer will be on top. In chloroform extractions, the chloroform layer will be on the bottom.

Acetanilid

Acetanilid relieves pain and reduces fever. It is used in the treatment of neuralgia and rheumatism.

351

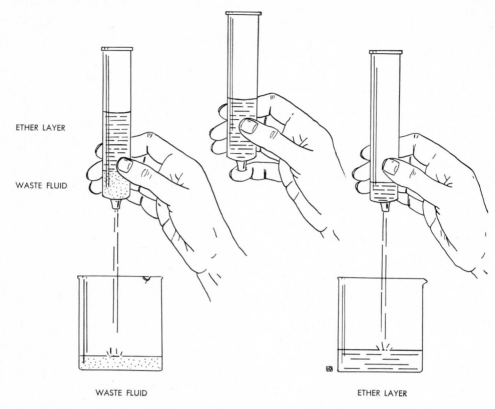

ETHER LAYER

WASTE FLUID

WASTE FLUID

ETHER LAYER

Fig. 72. Using the barrel of a syringe to separate ether from waste fluid.

Yvon method

Reagents needed

Chloroform
Mercurous Nitrate

Procedure

1. Mix urine and pour about 15 ml. into a separatory funnel.
2. Add about 15 ml. of chloroform, stopper, and shake.
3. Allow to stand until the two layers are separated.
4. Carefully allow the bottom chloroform layer to run out into a 100 ml. beaker.
5. Gently boil down this chloroform layer to about 4 ml.
6. Add about 0.5 gm. of mercurous nitrate. If acetanilid is present, a green color will form.

Antipyrine

Antipyrine relieves pain and reduces fever. It is used in the treatment of neuralgia and rheumatism.

Fieux method

Reagents needed

Sulfuric Acid, Concentrated
Sodium Metaphosphate
Sodium Nitrate, Saturated

(C-210)

Procedure

1. Mix urine and pour about 20 ml. into a small flask.
2. Add 1 ml. of concentrated sulfuric acid and 2 gm. of sodium meta-phosphate.
3. Mix and filter.
4. Add 5 drops of a saturated solution of sodium nitrate to the filtrate. If antipyrine is present, a green color will be produced.

Chloral hydrate

Chloral hydrate is used as a hypnotic in tetanus, insomnia, labor, mania, and many other conditions.

Todd-Sanford method

Reagents needed

Hydrochloric Acid, Concentrated
Ether
Benedict's Qualitative Reagent   (C-164)

Procedure

1. Mix urine and transfer 100 ml. to a 250 ml. beaker.
2. Boil off 75 ml., leaving 25 ml. Cool.
3. Add 5 ml. of concentrated hydrochloric acid and mix.
4. Transfer to a separatory funnel.
5. Add 15 ml. of ether and shake well.
6. Separate the two layers, saving the ether layer (top) in a small beaker.
7. Using a hot plate, evaporate the ether just to dryness. Allow to cool.
8. Add 5 ml. of distilled water and mix.
9. Run a qualitative Benedict test for glucose on this solution. If the glucose test is positive, chloral hydrate is present in the urine.

Iodine

Iodine may be found in the urine after treatment with iodides.

Todd-Sanford method

Reagents needed

Sulfuric Acid, Concentrated
Nitric Acid, Concentrated
Chloroform

Procedure

1. Mix urine and measure 5 ml. into a small test tube.
2. Add 4 drops of concentrated sulfuric acid and mix.
3. Add 4 drops of concentrated nitric acid and mix.
4. Add 2 ml. of chloroform and shake well. If iodine is present, the chloroform layer will become a pink to reddish violet color.

Morphine

Morphine is a form of opium used to relieve pain.

Todd-Sanford method

Reagents needed

Ammonium Hydroxide, Concentrated
Ether
Sulfuric Acid, Concentrated
Formalin

Procedure

1. Mix urine and measure 15 ml. into a small beaker.
2. Add ammonium hydroxide until the urine is alkaline to litmus or nitrazine paper.
3. Transfer to a separatory funnel, add 15 ml. of ether, and shake well.
4. Separate the two layers, collecting the ether layer (top) in a small beaker.
5. Using a hot plate, evaporate the ether just to dryness.
6. Cautiously pipet 1 ml. of concentrated sulfuric acid into a test tube; add 1 drop of formalin to this test tube and mix.
7. Add a few drops of this mixture to the ether residue in the beaker. If morphine is present, a color will be produced, which changes from red to violet to blue.

Phenolphthalein

Phenolphthalein is sometimes used as a purgative.

Reagent needed

Ammonium Hydroxide, Concentrated

Procedure

1. Add about 5 ml. of concentrated ammonium hydroxide to about 25 ml. of urine. If phenolphthalein is present, a pink to red color will be produced.

Quinine

Quinine has many uses, but it is probably best known for its effectiveness in the prevention and treatment of malaria. It is also used to reduce fever and to stimulate uterine contraction in labor.

Todd-Sanford method

Reagents needed

Ammonium Hydroxide, Concentrated	
Ether	
Ethyl Alcohol, 10%	
Sulfuric Acid, 10%	(C-193)
Iodine, Ethyl Alcohol Solution	(C-172)

Procedure

1. Mix urine and add ammonium hydroxide dropwise until the urine is alkaline.
2. Transfer 100 ml. to a separatory funnel, add 15 ml. of ether, and shake well.
3. Separate the two layers, collecting the ether layer (top) in a small beaker.
4. Using a hot plate, evaporate the ether just to dryness.
5. Add 2 ml. of 10% alcohol, 1 drop of 10% sulfuric acid, and 1 drop of an ethyl alcohol solution of iodine. Mix.
6. Heat gently and allow to cool. If quinine is present, green crystals will form.

Salicylic acid and acetylsalicylic acid

Salicylic acid and acetylsalicylic acid (aspirin) are used to relieve pain and reduce fever.

Siebold-Bradbury method

Reagents needed

Potassium Carbonate
Lead Nitrate, Saturated (C-201)
Ferric Chloride, 10% (C-153)

Procedure

1. Mix urine and add potassium carbonate until the urine is alkaline to litmus or nitrazine paper.
2. Measure 25 ml. into a small flask.
3. Add 25 ml. of a saturated solution of lead nitrate, mix, and filter.
4. To the filtrate, add about 5 drops of a 10% solution of ferric chloride. If salicylic acid or acetylsalicylic acid is present, a violet color will be produced.

POISONS

This section considers tests for the toxic substances, arsenic and mercury. Although salts of these elements are used in certain medications, arsenic and mercury are usually considered industrial poisons. More detailed discussions may be found in texts on toxicology.

Arsenic
Reinsch test

Reagents needed

Hydrochloric Acid, Concentrated
Copper Foil
Ethyl Alcohol
Ether

Procedure

1. Mix urine and transfer 40 ml. to a small beaker.
2. Add 10 ml. of concentrated hydrochloric acid and mix.
3. Add a 1-inch square of clean copper foil and boil for a few minutes. If arsenic is present, a gray or bluish film is deposited on the copper. To confirm the presence of arsenic, proceed with steps 4, 5, and 6.
4. Allow to cool. Remove the copper foil and dip successively into water, alcohol, and ether. Allow to dry.
5. Roll up the foil like a cigarette and insert in a glass tube.
6. Gently heat over a Bunsen burner. The arsenic will sublime to the cooler parts of the tube. The crystals may be seen with a magnifying glass and will appear as eight-sided figures.

Mercury
Reinsch test

Reagents needed

Hydrochloric Acid, Concentrated
Copper Foil
Ethyl Alcohol
Ether

Procedure

1. Mix urine and pour 40 ml. into a small beaker.
2. Add 10 ml. of concentrated hydrochloric acid and mix.
3. Place a 1-inch square of copper foil in the acidified urine and warm to 50° C.

4. Set aside overnight. If mercury is present, it will be deposited on the copper foil as a bright lustrous mirror. To confirm the presence of mercury, proceed with steps 5, 6, and 7.
5. Remove the copper foil and dip successively into water, alcohol, and ether. Allow to dry.
6. Roll up the foil like a cigarette and insert in a glass tube.
7. Heat gently over a Bunsen burner. If mercury is present, it will be deposited on the cooler portion of the glass tube. It can be seen with a magnifying glass and will appear as fine metallic globules.

CARBOHYDRATES

This section considers tests for lactose, levulose, galactose, and pentose, as well as a fermentation test for glucose, and a phenylhydrazine test.

Lactose

Shortly before and shortly after the birth of a baby, a woman's urine may give false positive tests for glucose. This is often caused by the presence of lactose, which reacts similarly to glucose. The two sugars may be distinguished by a test introduced by Max Rubner.

Rubner test

Reagents needed

Lead Acetate
Ammonium Hydroxide, Concentrated

Procedure

1. Mix the urine and measure 10 ml. into a large test tube.
2. Add 3 gm. of lead acetate, shake, and filter.
3. Bring the filtrate to a boil, add 2 ml. of concentrated ammonium hydroxide, and boil again. If lactose is present, the solution turns brick-red and a red precipitate forms. If glucose is present, the solution also turns red but the precipitate is yellow.

Levulose

Levulose is often referred to as fructose. Levulose reacts similarly to glucose but may be distinguished from it by the following test of Seliwanoff.

Seliwanoff test

Reagents needed

Ethyl Alcohol
Seliwanoff's Reagent: Place 0.05 gm. of resorcinol in a 125 ml. Erlenmeyer flask. Add 60 ml. of distilled water and 30 ml. of concentrated hydrochloric acid. Mix.

Procedure

1. Mix the urine and place 5 drops in a small test tube.
2. Add 5 ml. of Seliwanoff's reagent and boil for not more than 30 seconds.
3. Centrifuge, pour off the fluid, and add 3 ml. of ethyl alcohol. Mix. If levulose is present, a bright red color will be produced.

Galactose

Galactose may be found in the urine of nursing infants having disturbances of the digestive tract. It may be distinguished from other sugars (with the exception of lactose) by the following mucic test.

Mucic test

Reagent needed

Nitric Acid, Concentrated

Procedure

1. Mix the urine and pour 50 ml. into a small beaker.
2. Add 10 ml. of concentrated nitric acid and boil until the volume is reduced to about 10 ml.
3. Add 10 ml. of water and let stand overnight. If galactose (or lactose) is present, a fine white precipitate will form.

Pentose

Pentose may be found in the urine when the diet is rich in fruit juices, grapes, prunes, and plums. It has no pathological significance.

Tauber test

Reagents needed

Tauber's reagent: Dissolve 1 gm. of benzidine in 25 ml. of glacial acetic acid. Mix.

Procedure

1. Mix the urine and pipet 0.5 ml. into a test tube.
2. Add 2.5 ml. of Tauber's reagent and boil vigorously for 2 minutes.
3. Cool by immersing tube in cold water.
4. Add 5 ml. of distilled water and mix. If pentose is present, a pink to red color is produced. Disregard any yellowish brown color.

Glucose

Fermentation test

The fermentation test may be used to distinguish glucose from lactose and pentose. When glucose and yeast are mixed, fermentation occurs and carbon dioxide is given off. This, however, does not occur with lactose and pentose.

Reagents needed

Fresh Yeast
Glucose, 5%

Procedure

1. Place a small test tube in an inverted position in each of three large test tubes (see Fig. 73).
2. Label these tubes as follows: Test, Positive Control, and Negative Control.
3. *Test:* Boil the urine to be tested. Cool. Pour 25 ml. of the urine into a small beaker and add one third of a cake of fresh yeast. Make an emulsion by mixing thoroughly. Pour into the tube labelled Test. Stopper and slowly invert so that the small tube becomes *completely* filled.
4. *Positive Control:* Pour 25 ml. of 5% glucose into a small beaker and add one third of a cake of fresh yeast. Make an emulsion and pour into the tube labelled Positive Control. Stopper and slowly invert so that the small tube becomes *completely* filled.
5. *Negative Control:* Make an emulsion with 25 ml. of water and the remaining third of the yeast cake. Pour this into the tube labelled Negative Control. Stopper and slowly invert so that the small tube becomes *completely* filled.
6. Plug the three tubes with cotton and place in a 37° C. incubator for 2 hours.

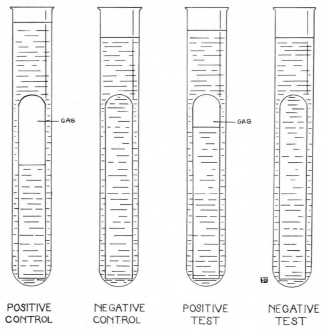

Fig. 73. Reading the results in a fermentation test.

7. Remove the tubes from the incubator. The tube labelled Positive Control should contain gas in the small tube (Fig. 73), whereas the tube labelled Negative Control should not contain gas in the small tube. If this is not so, repeat the test with fresh yeast. If this is so, look at the tube marked Test. If this tube contains gas in the small tube, the test is positive for glucose. However, if this tube does not contain gas, the test is negative for glucose.

Phenylhydrazine test
Kowarsky test as modified by Blumel

The phenylhydrazine test helps to distinguish glucose from other sugars occurring in urine. When sugars are treated with osazone, they form characteristic crystalline structures.

Reagents needed

Phenylhydrazine
Acetic Acid, Glacial
Sodium Chloride, Saturated

Procedure

1. Place 5 drops of pure phenylhydrazine in a large test tube.
2. Add 10 drops of glacial acetic acid and 1 ml. of a saturated solution of sodium chloride. Mix.
3. Add 4 ml. of urine and 4 ml. of distilled water. Mix.
4. Add about 4 glass beads to prevent bumping and boil until the volume is lowered to about 2 or 3 ml. Allow to cool for 30 minutes.
5. Using a medicine dropper, place a sample of the sediment on a glass slide and examine with the low-power (16 mm.) objective of the microscope. If glucose is present, yellow needlelike crystals (usually arranged in clusters) may be seen. These crystals are phenylglucosazone.

ADDITIONAL SPECIAL URINARY TESTS

This section contains information on the following additional urinary tests:

Beta-oxybutyric acid   Porphyrins

Calcium, quantitative test   Porphobilinogen

Diazo substances   Proteoses

Hemosiderin   Sulfates

Hippuric acid synthesis   Titratable acidity

Indican   Total solids

17-Ketosteroids   Vitamin C

Mucin

Beta-oxybutyric acid

Beta-oxybutyric acid is a reduction product of diacetic acid. When found in the urine, it is usually accompanied by both diacetic acid and acetone and, like these, its presence indicates the abnormal catabolism of fats.

Hart method

Reagents needed

Acetic Acid, Glacial

Hydrogen Peroxide, 3%

Ammonium Hydroxide, Concentrated

Sodium Nitroprusside, Saturated (freshly prepared)   (C-165)

Procedure

1. Mix urine. Pour 20 ml. into a small beaker. With a marking pencil, mark the level to which the urine comes (the 20 ml. level). Add 20 ml. of distilled water and a few drops of glacial acetic acid. Drive off any acetone or diacetic acid by boiling down to the 20 ml. level.
2. Add 10 ml. of distilled water. Mix. Get two large test tubes. Label No. 1 and No. 2. Pour 10 ml. of the mixture into each tube. Add 1 ml. of 3% hydrogen peroxide to tube 1. (This oxidizes any beta-oxybutyric acid present to diacetic acid and acetone.) Add none to tube 2. Warm gently and allow to cool.
3. To each tube add 10 drops of glacial acetic acid and 10 drops of a freshly prepared concentrated solution of sodium nitroprusside. Mix both tubes by inversion.
4. Using a medicine dropper, overlay both tubes with concentrated ammonium hydroxide. If tube 1 shows a reddish purple ring at the junction of the two liquids, the test is positive for beta-oxybutyric acid. Tube 2 should show no ring.

Calcium, quantitative test

The urine of the average person contains 50 to 300 mg. of calcium per day. Increased values may be found in hyperparathyroidism, whereas decreased values are seen in rickets.

Wang method

Reagents needed

Trichloroacetic Acid (TCA), 20%   (C-142)

Sodium Acetate, 20%   (C-194)

Ammonium Hydroxide, 10% (w/v)   (C-195)

Acetic Acid, 10% (v/v)   (C-51)

Sulfuric Acid, 2 N   (C-184)

Ammonium Oxalate, 0.1 M   (C-196)

Potassium Permanganate, 0.01 N (C-81 diluted 1 to 10)

Wash Solution: Place 80 ml. of distilled water in a large flask; add 80 ml. of ether and 80 ml. of alcohol; then add 5 ml. of ammonium hydroxide. Mix.

Procedure

1. Collect a 24-hour specimen of urine from the patient. Measure and record the volume. Mix. Pour about 100 ml. into a flask. Add 25 ml. of the 20% trichloroacetic acid. Add 2 gm. of acid washed charcoal. Shake well and set aside for 15 minutes.
2. Filter. Pipet 5 ml. of the filtrate into a 15 ml. centrifuge tube. Add 1 ml. of the 20% sodium acetate solution. Mix by tapping the bottom side of the tube. Add 1 ml. of the 0.1 M ammonium oxalate solution. Mix again.
3. Adjust the acidity to pH 5 as follows. Find the approximate pH with nitrazine paper. If above pH 5, add the 10% acetic acid dropwise until the solution is green to bromcresol green or pink to methyl red. If below pH 5, add the 10% ammonium hydroxide dropwise until the solution is green to bromcresol green or pink to methyl red. Mix again and place in the refrigerator overnight.
4. The next morning, centrifuge for 15 minutes at high speed. With a steady deliberate motion, invert the tube, thus discarding the supernatant fluid and leaving the precipitate in the bottom of the tube. Keep the tube in an inverted position, place on a piece of filter paper, and let drain for a few minutes.
5. Wash the precipitate *twice* as follows. Add 2 ml. of the wash solution (preparation given above). Mix well by tapping the bottom sides of the tube. Wash down the inside of the tube with another 2 ml. of the wash solution. Centrifuge for 15 minutes.
6. With a steady deliberate motion, invert the tube, thus discarding the supernatant fluid and leaving the precipitate in the bottom of the tube. Keep the tube in an inverted position, place on a piece of filter paper, and let drain for a few minutes.
7. Place the tube (right side up) in an oven at 85° to 100° C. for 1 hour. This removes organic solvents.
8. Add 2 ml. of the 2 N (approximate) sulfuric acid. Mix to dissolve the precipitate. Place in a boiling water bath for 2 minutes. Remove from water bath. Titrate while hot (over 70° C.) with the 0.01 N potassium permanganate. The end point is a faint pink color that persists for at least 1 minute. Record the milliliters of permanganate used.

Calculations

One milliliter of the 0.01 N potassium permanganate is equivalent to 0.2 mg. of calcium. Therefore:

$$\frac{\text{Mg. of calcium}}{\text{(24-hour specimen)}} = \frac{\overset{\text{Ml. of urine}}{\text{(24-hour specimen)}}}{4} \times 0.2 \times \frac{\text{Ml. of KMnO}_4}{\text{used}} \times \text{Factor}$$

Where,
   a. The 4 is the ml. of urine used in the test (5 ml. of a 4 to 1 mixture of urine and 20% trichloroacetic acid).
   b. The factor is a number telling how strong or how weak the potassium permanganate solution is in comparison to an exact 0.01 N KMnO$_4$ solution. The factor is determined in preparing the solution.

Sample calculation: If the 24-hour specimen measured 1000 ml., the number of milliliters of 0.01 N potassium permanganate used was 2, and the factor is 1.0, the calculation is performed as follows:

$$\frac{\text{Mg. of calcium}}{\text{(24-hour specimen)}} = \frac{1000}{4} \times 0.2 \times 2 \times 1.0 = 100 \text{ mg.}$$

Diazo substances

Diazo substances are unknown substances that give a color reaction with Ehrlich's diazo reagent. They may appear in the urine in febrile conditions, measles, typhoid fever, and tuberculosis.

Reagents needed

Ehrlich's Diazo Reagent   (C-197)
Ammonium Hydroxide

Procedure

1. Pipet 2.0 ml. of urine into a small test tube and add 2.0 ml. of Ehrlich's diazo reagent. Shake well.
2. Using a medicine dropper, overlay with 2.0 ml. of full-strength (28%) ammonium hydroxide. If a red ring appears at the junction of the two liquids, the test is positive for diazo substances. Disregard a yellow or orange color.

Hemosiderin

Hemosiderin is a pigment derived from hemoglobin. It may be found in the urine in hemolytic anemia and other conditions associated with the presence of hemoglobin.

Ham method

Reagent needed

Aqueous Solution of Ammonium Sulfide, 30%

Procedure

1. Mix the urine, pour about 6 ml. into a test tube, and centrifuge.
2. Place a drop of the sediment on a glass slide.
3. Add a drop of 30% aqueous solution of ammonium sulfide and mix with the sediment, using an applicator stick.
4. Examine with the low-power (16 mm.) objective of the microscope. If hemosiderin is present, it will appear as jet-black granules of various sizes. The granules may be separate or may be included in epithelial cells or casts.

Hippuric acid synthesis

This is a liver function test based on the principle that a healthy liver will convert benzoic acid to hippuric acid. The latter is then excreted in the urine. When the liver is not functioning properly, however, this process of conversion and excretion is decreased.

Quick's method

Reagents needed

Sodium Benzoate
Oil of Peppermint
Ammonium Sulfate
Glacial Acetic Acid
Hydrochloric Acid, Concentrated
Congo Red Indicator   (Table 11)
Phenolphthalein Indicator   (C-54)
Sodium Hydroxide, 0.2 N   (C-130)

Procedure

1. The patient is instructed to eat a light breakfast. One hour after breakfast, he is told to empty the bladder and discard the urine. He is then

given a dose of 6 gm. of sodium benzoate dissolved in 30 ml. of water and flavored with a little oil of peppermint. This is followed with a half glass of water.

2. Collect all urine voided within the next 4 hours. Ask the patient to empty the bladder at the end of the 4-hour period and add this to the collection.

3. Measure the volume of urine. If the volume is 150 ml. or less, it does not have to be boiled down. However, if the volume is more than 150 ml., acidify with a few drops of glacial acetic acid and boil down to 150 ml.

4. Add 5 gm. of ammonium sulfate for each 10 ml. of urine. Stir to dissolve. Filter.

5. Add concentrated hydrochloric acid to the filtrate until the indicator Congo red turns blue (pH 3.0). Usually about 2 ml. are needed. Stir for several minutes to aid crystallization. Place in the refrigerator for 1 hour.

6. Using a Buchner filter and suction, filter off the crystalline hippuric acid. Wash the container with ice-cold distilled water and pour the washings into the Buchner filter. Wash the precipitate several times with ice-cold distilled water.

7. Carefully transfer the precipitate and filter paper to a beaker. Add enough distilled water to cover and heat gently to dissolve the crystals. Add a few drops of phenolphthalein indicator and titrate to a permanent pink color with 0.2 N sodium hydroxide. Record the milliliters of sodium hydroxide used.

Calculations

One milliliter of the 0.2 N sodium hydroxide is equivalent to 0.0358 gm. of hippuric acid. Therefore:

Ml. of NaOH used $\times$ 0.0358 = Gm. of hippuric acid

Some hippuric acid, however, still remains in solution. To correct for this, take your answer obtained above and add 0.1 gm. for each 100 ml. of urine used. If you wish to express the hippuric acid in terms of benzoic acid, multiply your corrected answer by 0.68.

Normal values

The normal values are 3 gm. or more of benzoic acid in 4 hours or, if sodium benzoic acid is given intravenously, the normal value is at least 1 gm. of benzoic acid in 1 hour.

Indican

Indican is a product of putrefaction. Small amounts are normally present in the urine. Large amounts are found in heavy-protein diets and in diseases involving stagnation of the intestinal contents, such as cancer of the stomach, peritonitis, and prolonged constipation.

Obermayer method

Reagents needed

Chloroform
Ferric Chloride
Hydrochloric Acid, Concentrated
Preparation of the indican reagent before using: Weigh 0.5 gm. of ferric chloride on the analytical balance and dissolve in 250 ml. of concentrated hydrochloric acid. Mix.

Procedure

1. Mix urine specimen and pipet 5.0 ml. into a large test tube.
2. Pipet 5.0 ml. of the indican reagent into the tube and mix by inverting the tube several times.
3. Add about 3 ml. of chloroform and mix by inverting several times. If abnormal amounts of indican are present, the chloroform layer will become a deep blue color.

17-Ketosteroids

17-Ketosteroids are metabolites of hormones produced by the adrenal cortex, testes, and ovaries. They are characterized by a ketone group attached to C-17 and are excreted as compounds conjugated with glucuronic and sulfuric acids. In a 24-hour specimen of urine, the normal values are 5 to 15 mg. for women and 9 to 22 mg. for men. For adults, decreased values may be found in hypopituitarism, male hypogonadism, Addison's disease, and myxedema, and increased values may occur in adrenocortical carcinoma and hyperplasia of the suprarenal cortex.

17-Hydroxycorticosteroids

The term 17-hydroxycorticosteroids refers to metabolites from cortisol and other 21-carbon steroids having a hydroxyl group at C-17. The normal range of excretion is 2 to 6 mg./24 hours for women and 3 to 10 mg./24 hours for men.

Mucin

Mucin is the chief constituent of mucus, the watery secretion that covers mucous membranes. Small amounts of mucin are found in normal urine. Increased amounts are present in inflammations of the urinary and vaginal tracts.

Reagent needed

Acetic Acid, Glacial

Procedure

1. Mix urine and transfer 3 ml. to a small test tube.
2. Add 3 ml. of water and mix.
3. Add 0.5 ml. of glacial acetic acid and mix gently. If mucin is present, a white cloud will form.

Porphyrins

The porphyrins are complex organic compounds. Small amounts may be found in normal urine. Increased amounts are found in porphyria, a metabolic disease in which prophyrins are retained in pathological quantities in the blood and other tissues and in feces and urine. Urine containing increased amounts of porphyrins usually turns dark red upon standing.

The two porphyrins of interest to the technician are coproporphyrin and uroporphyrin.

Reagents needed

Acetic Acid, Glacial
Ethyl Ether
Hydrochloric Acid, 5% (v/v)   (C-181)

Procedure

1. Mix the urine, pour 25 ml. into a separatory funnel, and add 10 ml. of glacial acetic acid.

2. Extract the mixture twice with 50 ml. portions of ether, saving the *waste fluids* from the extractions, since they will be used later in the procedure.
3. Combine the two ether extractions and wash with 10 ml. of 5% hydrochloric acid, saving the *washings*.
4. Examine the *washings* under ultraviolet light. If there is a strong fluorescence, the test is positive for coproporphyrin.
5. Examine the urinary *waste fluids* (which resulted from the above ether extractions) under ultraviolet light. If there is a strong red fluorescence, the test is positive for uroporphyrin.

Porphobilinogen

Porphobilinogen is a precursor of uroporphyrin. It is found in the urine in porphyria.

Reagents needed

Ehrlich's Reagent, Modified: Dissolve 0.7 gm. of paradimethylaminobenzaldehyde in a mixture of 100 ml. of distilled water and 150 ml. of concentrated hydrochloric acid. Mix well and store in a brown bottle.
Hydrochloric Acid, Concentrated
Sodium Acetate, Saturated   (C-66a)
Chloroform

Procedure

1. Obtain a fresh sample of urine and acidify to pH 4 or 5 with concentrated hydrochloric acid, using nitrazine paper as an indicator.
2. Pipet 3 ml. of the urine into a large test tube and add 3 ml. of the modified Ehrlich's reagent. Mix by inversion.
3. Add 6 ml. of saturated sodium acetate and mix.
4. Add 3 ml. of chloroform and mix thoroughly.
5. Let settle for a few minutes. If the water fraction (upper layer) is red, the test is positive for porphobilinogen. If the chloroform fraction (lower layer) is red, it indicates the presence of urobilinogen or indole.

Proteoses

Proteoses are intermediate products in the digestion of proteins. Under normal conditions, proteoses are not found in the urine. They may be present, however, in cancer, osteomalacia, pneumonia, diphtheria, and atrophy of the kidneys.

Reagents needed

Acetic Acid, 5%   (C-158)
Trichloroacetic Acid, 10%   (C-63)

Procedure

1. Acidify the urine with 5% acetic acid, using nitrazine paper as an indicator. Mix.
2. Pour 10 ml. of the acidified urine into a small beaker and bring to a boil.
3. Filter the urine while it is still hot in order to remove any albumin or globulin that may be present.
4. Allow the filtrate to cool.
5. Add several drops of 10% TCA to the filtrate. If proteoses are present, a white cloud will form.

Sulfates

The normal values for total urinary sulfates in a 24-hour period are 0.6 to 1.2 gm. Increased values are found in acute fevers. Decreased values are seen in conditions associated with decreased metabolic activity.

Folin method

Reagents needed

Hydrochloric Acid, Concentrated
Barium Chloride, 5%   (C-202)

Procedure

1. Collect a 24-hour specimen of urine. Mix. Pour 50 ml. into a 250 ml. flask. Add 4 ml. of concentrated hydrochloric acid. Mix. Place a watch-glass or small beaker over the mouth of the flask and boil gently for ½ hour.
2. Cool the flask in cold water. Add sufficient distilled water to make the total volume equal 150 ml. Mix. Without stirring the solution, add dropwise 10 ml. of a 5% solution of barium chloride. This precipitates the sulfur as barium sulfate. Set aside for 1 hour.
3. Weigh a Gooch crucible on the analytical balance. Handle crucible with tongs. Record the weight. Shake the solution and then filter it through the weighed Gooch crucible. Wash the precipitate with 200 ml. of cold distilled water. Dry in an oven. Ignite, cool, and weigh.

Calculations

a. To obtain the weight of the barium sulfate, subtract the weight of the crucible before filtering from the weight of the crucible after ignition.
b. To find the weight of sulfur in this amount of barium sulfate, use the following formula:

$$\text{Weight of sulfur} = \text{Weight of BaSO}_4 \times \frac{32.064}{233.402}$$

where 32.064 is the atomic weight of sulfur and 233.402 is the atomic weight of barium sulfate.

c. To find the amount of sulfur in the 24-hour specimen, use this equation:

$$\frac{\text{Weight of sulfur}}{\text{in 24-hour specimen}} = \frac{\text{Weight of sulfur}}{\text{in sample}} \times \frac{\text{Ml. of 24-hour specimen}}{\text{Ml. used in test}}$$

Sample calculations: A 24-hour specimen measured 1000 ml. and 50 ml. were used in the test. The weight of the Gooch crucible before filtering was 5.000 gm. The weight of the Gooch crucible after ignition was 5.364 gm.

a. The weight of the barium sulfate is found by substracting the weight of the Gooch crucible before filtering from the weight after ignition. The weight of the barium sulfate is therefore 5.364 gm. minus 5.000 gm., which is 0.364 gm.
b. The weight of sulfur in 0.364 gm. of barium sulfate is found by using the formula:

$$\text{Weight of sulfur} = \text{Weight of BaSO}_4 \times \frac{32.064}{233.402}$$

$$= 0.364 \times \frac{32.064}{233.402}$$

$$= 0.05 \text{ gm.}$$

This is the weight of sulfur in the 50 ml. of urine that were used in the test.

c. To find the weight in the 1000 ml. of the 24-hour specimen:

$$\frac{\text{Weight of sulfur}}{\text{in 24-hour specimen}} = \frac{\text{Weight of sulfur}}{\text{in sample}} \times \frac{\text{Ml. of 24-hour specimen}}{\text{Ml. used in test}}$$

$$= 0.05 \times \frac{1000}{50}$$

$$= 1.0 \text{ gm.}$$

Titratable acidity

The titratable acidity of urine is the total acid present in a 24-hour specimen. The normal values are 200 to 500 ml. of 0.1 N sodium hydroxide. Increased values are found in acidosis.

Folin method

Reagents needed

Phenolphthalein Indicator	(C-54)
Potassium Oxalate	
Sodium Hydroxide, 0.1 N	(C-108)

Procedure

1. Collect a 24-hour specimen of urine, preserving the collections by storing them in the refrigerator.
2. Measure and record the volume in milliliters.
3. Mix. Pipet 25 ml. into a small flask. Add a few drops of a 1% alcoholic solution of phenolphthalein. Add 10 gm. of finely pulverized potassium oxalate. Shake well.
4. Using 0.1 N sodium hydroxide, titrate to a permanent faint pink color. Record the milliliters of 0.1 N sodium hydroxide used for the titration.

Calculation

Calculate the total acidity as follows:

$$\text{Total acidity} = \frac{\text{Ml. of 0.1 N NaOH}}{\text{used in titration}} \times \frac{\text{Ml. of urine in 24-hour specimen}}{\text{Ml. of urine used in titration}}$$

Sample calculation: The 24-hour specimen measured 1000 ml.; 25 ml. of urine were used in the titration; and 5.0 ml. of the 0.1 N NaOH were used in the titration.

$$\text{Total acidity} = 5.0 \times \frac{1000}{25} = 200 \text{ ml. of 0.1 N NaOH}$$

Total solids

The average person excretes about 60 gm. of solids per day, the output varying mainly with diet, exercise, and the functioning ability of the kidneys. If the diet and exercise are controlled, the amount of solids excreted gives a rough index of the functioning ability of the kidneys.

Procedure

1. To estimate the grams of solids in a specimen of urine, multiply the last two figures of the specific gravity by the volume in milliliters and then multiply by the factor 0.0026.
2. Example: The specific gravity is 1.018 and the volume is 1500 ml.

$$\text{Grams of solids} = \frac{\text{Last 2 figures}}{\text{of sp. gr.}} \times \frac{\text{Volume}}{\text{in ml.}} \times 0.0026$$

$$= 18 \times 1500 \times 0.0026$$

$$= 70.2$$

Note: In most methods for the estimation of total solids, Long's coefficient (2.6) is used in the numerator and 1000 is used in the denominator. The above factor of 0.0026 is simply Long's coefficient divided by 1000.

Vitamin C

The urine of the average person contains about 10 to 30 mg. of vitamin C (ascorbic acid) per day. Decreased amounts are found in scurvy.

Part 6

Fecal analysis

In man's digestive tract food is broken down into materials that may be absorbed and utilized by the body. However, not all food products are digested and absorbed. Feces contain the undigested food residue, certain body secretions, such as bile pigments and salts, and large quantities of bacteria. The average normal output of feces is 200 gm./24 hr.

Chapter 23

Fecal analysis

Feces are waste products left in the wake of intestinal digestion and absorption. In disease, deviations from the normal composition may occur. A few qualitative tests are listed.

> Occult blood
> Bile pigment
> Urobilin
> Fats

OCCULT BLOOD

Occult blood may be found in the stool of a person having ulcers or cancer. The patient should be on a meat-free diet for 4 days prior to the test to eliminate a false positive reaction. The following tests may be used to test for occult blood.

Reagents needed for occult blood tests

Benzidine, Saturated, in Glacial Acetic Acid	(C-151)
Hydrogen Peroxide, 3%	(may be purchased)
Glacial Acetic Acid	(may be purchased)
Ethyl Alcohol, 95%	
Orthotoluidine, 4%	(make fresh monthly)

Using a volumetric flask, dissolve 4 gm. of orthotoluidine in 100 ml. of glacial acetic acid. Keep in brown bottle and refrigerate.

Benzidine test

Procedure

1. Take a piece of feces about the size of a pea and place on a spot plate.
2. Add a few drops of a saturated solution of benzidine in glacial acetic acid and mix with the feces, using an applicator stick.
3. Add a few drops of 3% hydrogen peroxide. Mix.

Reaction

A blue to green color represents a positive reaction. Disregard any other color. Report the test as positive or negative.

Guaiac test

Additional reagent needed

Guaiac Reagent (prepare just prior to use)
Into a test tube, place 2 ml. of 95% ethyl alcohol and 0.2 gm. of powdered guaiac. Add 2 ml. of 3% hydrogen peroxide. Mix.

Procedure

1. Take a piece of feces about the size of a pea and place on a spot plate.
2. Add 2 drops of glacial acetic acid and mix with the feces, using an applicator stick.
3. Add a few drops of the guaiac reagent. Mix.

Reaction

A blue to green color is a positive reaction. Disregard any other colors. Report the test as positive or negative.

Orthotoluidine test

Procedure

1. Take a piece of feces the size of a pea and place on a spot plate.
2. Add a few drops of 3% hydrogen peroxide and mix with the feces, using an applicator stick.
3. Add a few drops of orthotoluidine reagent. Mix.

Reaction

A blue to green color is a positive reaction. Disregard any other colors. Report the test as positive or negative.

BILE PIGMENT

Bile pigments are not normally present in feces. It may be found, however, in diarrhea and in obstructive jaundice.

Gmelin test

Reagents needed

Barium Chloride, 10% (C-170)
Nitric Acid, Concentrated

Procedure

1. Using an evaporating dish or mortar, mix 7 ml. of 10% barium chloride with a piece of feces about the size of a marble.
2. After an emulsion is made, filter the specimen.
3. When the funnel is completely drained, then add a few drops of concentrated nitric acid to the filter paper.

Reaction

A display of colors, one of which must be green, is a positive reaction. Report the test as positive or negative.

UROBILIN

Urobilin is normally present in feces. However, it is usually absent in obstructive jaundice.

Schmidt qualitative test

Reagent needed

Mercuric Chloride, 10% (C-198)

Procedure

1. Place a piece of feces in an evaporating dish or mortar and mix thoroughly with 2 ml. of 10% mercuric chloride.
2. Let the mixture stand overnight.

Reaction

If urobilin is present, a deep red color will be evident after 8 hours.

FATS

Refer to Chapter 12 (Lipids) for the quantitative method.

Appendixes

Appendix A

Review questions and answers

The student of medical technology should be able to answer the following 100 questions in elementary chemistry. These questions have been discussed in the first four chapters.

As a convenience, the answers are given at the end of the section.

Review questions

1. What is an element?
2. What is a compound?
3. How many elements are known to exist?
4. What are the three states of matter?
5. What is the atomic number?
6. Name two components of an atom.
7. When an atom is in the neutral or uncombined state, does the number of protons equal the number of electrons?
8. What part of the atom do the protons occupy?
9. What part of the atom do the electrons occupy?
10. What is the basic principle involved in all chemical reactions?
11. Is it true that some atoms give electrons, some take electrons, and some even share electrons?
12. What two general types of chemical reactions are there?
13. What do the majority of atoms need in order to attain a stable structure?
14. What is valence?
15. What determines the valence of an atom?
16. When does an atom acquire a positive valence?
17. When does an atom acquire a negative valence?
18. Are some atoms able to have more than one valence?
19. What is oxidation?
20. What is reduction?
21. What is a formula?
22. What is a radical?
23. What are atomic weights?
24. How do you find the molecular weight of a compound?
25. What is an ion?
26. What are the three classes of compounds that form ions?
27. What is an acid?
28. What is a base?

29. What is a salt?
30. What is neutralization?
31. Name four commonly used acids.
32. Name two commonly used bases.
33. Give the formulas for three commonly used acids.
34. Give the formulas for two commonly used bases.
35. Give the formulas for the following salts: sodium chloride and sodium sulfate.
36. What is the titratable acidity of an acid?
37. What determines the strength of acids and bases?
38. Can the exact strength of dilute acids and bases be expressed by their hydrogen ion concentration?
39. What does the symbol pH stand for?
40. If the hydrogen ion concentration is 10^{-3}, what is the pH value?
41. If the pH value is 7, what is the hydrogen ion concentration?
42. If a solution has a pH of 3, is it acid or basic?
43. If a solution has a pH of 8, is it acid or basic?
44. If the pH value of a solution increases, does the corresponding hydrogen ion concentration increase, decrease, or remain the same?
45. If the hydrogen ion concentration of a solution increases, does the corresponding pH value increase, decrease, or remain the same?
46. Why is it not possible to measure solutions such as 5 N HCl or 8 N NaOH on the pH scale?
47. If a solution has a pH of 7, is it acid, basic, or neutral?
48. Name five common indicators used by the technician.
49. What is the unit of liquid measure?
50. How many milliliters in 1 liter?
51. How many cubic centimeters in 1 liter?
52. Name two general types of pipets.
53. Name two measuring vessels that may be used to measure fluids exceeding 10 milliliters.
54. What is the unit of weight in the metric system?
55. How many milligrams in a gram?
56. If you were called upon to weigh 6.155 grams on an analytical balance, what gram and milligram weights would you select from the weight box?
57. Name two methods of separating solids from liquids.
58. What is a saturated solution?
59. How many grams of sodium chloride are contained in 100 milliliters of an 8% solution?
60. How many milliliters of glacial acetic acid are contained in 200 milliliters of a 50% solution of acetic acid?
61. How many grams of salt are present in 100 milliliters of physiological saline?
62. If the red cells of the blood are placed in an isotonic solution, do they swell, shrink, or remain the same?
63. If the red cells of the blood are placed in a hypertonic solution, do they swell, shrink, or remain the same?
64. If the red cells are placed in a hypotonic solution, do they swell, shrink, or remain the same?
65. Is physiological saline solution isotonic, hypotonic, or hypertonic with respect to red cells?
66. The atomic weight of sodium is 22.9898 grams, and the atomic weight of chlorine is 35.453 grams. How many grams of sodium chloride are in 1 liter of a 1 M solution?
67. How do you find the equivalent weight of an acid?
68. How do you find the equivalent weight of a base?
69. How many equivalent weights of NaOH are there in 1 liter of 2 N NaOH?
70. How many equivalent weights of sulfuric acid are there in 1 liter of 0.1 N H_2SO_4?
71. What does the abbreviation meq. (or mEq.) stand for?
72. Will 5 milliliters of 1 N H_2SO_4 exactly neutralize 5 milliliters of 1 N NaOH?
73. What is a titration?
74. Suppose it required 20 milliliters of 0.1 N NaOH to neutralize 10 milliliters of HCl. What is the normality of the HCl?

75. Suppose it required 2 milliliters of NaOH to neutralize 10 milliliters of 0.1 N oxalic acid. What is the normality of the NaOH?
76. What is a primary standard?
77. Oxalic acid has 2 replaceable hydrogen atoms. If the molecular weight of oxalic acid is 126.066 grams, what is the equivalent weight?
78. If you had to weigh out 6.303 grams of oxalic acid on the analytical balance, what gram and milligram weights would you use?
79. Why is it not possible to weigh out an equivalent weight of NaOH and use it to prepare a 1 N solution?
80. Name the three steps used in the preparation of 1 N NaOH.
81. Is sodium carbonate one of the impurities in sodium hydroxide?
82. Why is NaOH kept in polyethylene containers?
83. Is the approximate normality of a saturated solution of NaOH 5 N, 18 N, or 8 N?
84. Suppose 9.9 milliliters of NaOH are used to neutralize 10 milliliters of 1 N oxalic acid. What is the normality of the NaOH?
85. Suppose you have 1.01 N NaOH, and you wish to make 100 milliliters of 1 N NaOH. How much of the 1.01 N solution do you need?
86. Name the three steps necessary to prepare 1 N H_2SO_4.
87. The atomic weight of H is 1.0080, the atomic weight of S is 32.064, and the atomic weight of O is 15.9994. What is the molecular weight of H_2SO_4?
88. Using the molecular weight derived from the above question, find the equivalent weight of H_2SO_4.
89. How many equivalent weights are there in 2 liters of 2 N H_2SO_4?
90. One milliliter of water weighs 1 gram. Does 1 milliliter of sulfuric acid weigh 1 gram, more than 1 gram, or less than 1 gram?
91. Suppose 11.0 milliliters of 1 N NaOH are required to neutralize 10 milliliters of H_2SO_4. What is the normality of the sulfuric acid?
92. Suppose you have 1.1 N H_2SO_4, and you wish to make 100 milliliters of 1 N H_2SO_4. How much of the 1.1 N solution do you need?
93. Suppose you have 1 N NaOH, and you wish to make 100 milliliters of 0.1 N NaOH. How much of the 1 N solution do you need?
94. Suppose you have 0.1 N H_2SO_4, and you wish to make 100 milliliters of 0.01 N H_2SO_4. How much of the 0.1 N solution do you need?
95. Name two general types of colorimeters.
96. Is this statement true or false? The concentration of a substance in solution is usually determined by a color reaction, the basic principle being the greater the concentration, the weaker the color.
97. Suppose you are using a visual colorimeter and have the following data:
    Reading of standard: 20
    Reading of unknown: 16
    Concentration of standard: 100 mg./100 ml.
    What is the concentration of the unknown?
98. Name the two major steps the technician takes to determine the concentration of a substance in solution.
99. In using a photoelectric colorimeter, name the parts of the three-link chain that is the key to the concentration of a substance in solution.
100. What is the purpose of a filter in a photoelectric colorimeter?

Answers to review questions

1. An element is a substance that is made up of like atoms.
2. A compound is a substance that is made up of different atoms.
3. 102.
4. Solids, liquids, and gases.
5. The atomic number represents the number of protons possessed by an atom.
6. Protons and electrons.
7. Yes.
8. Center or nucleus.
9. Orbits surrounding the nucleus.

10. The tendency of atoms to transfer electrons.
11. Yes.
12. Transfer of electrons and sharing of electrons.
13. An outer orbit made up of 8 electrons.
14. Valence is the combining power of an atom.
15. The number of electrons the atom gives, takes, or shares during a reaction.
16. When it loses an electron.
17. When it gains an electron.
18. Yes.
19. Oxidation is the loss of electrons.
20. Reduction is the gain of electrons.
21. A formula gives the composition of a compound.
22. A radical is a combination of two or more atoms that reacts as a single atom.
23. The atomic weights are the relative weights of atoms.
24. The molecular weight of a compound is found by adding the atomic weights.
25. An ion is an atom that has acquired an electrical charge.
26. Acids, bases, and salts.
27. An acid is a compound containing a hydrogen atom that is capable of ionizing.
28. A base is a compound that contains a hydroxyl radical that is capable of ionizing.
29. A salt is a compound form by the reaction between an acid and a base.
30. Neutralization is a reaction between an acid and a base to form salt and water.
31. Nitric acid, sulfuric acid, hydrochloric acid, and acetic acid.
32. Sodium hydroxide and ammonium hydroxide.
33. HNO_3, H_2SO_4, and HCl.
34. NaOH and NH_4OH.
35. NaCl and Na_2SO_4.
36. Total strength possessed by the acid.
37. The degree of ionization.
38. Yes.
39. The exponent of the hydrogen ion concentration, with the minus sign dropped.
40. 3.
41. 10^{-7}.
42. Acid.
43. Basic.
44. Decrease.
45. Decrease.
46. Because they exceed the limits of the scale.
47. Neutral.
48. Litmus paper, nitrazine paper, Töpfer's reagent, phenolphthalein, and pHydrion.
49. The liter.
50. 1000.000
51. 1000.028
52. Serological pipets and volumetric pipets.
53. Graduates and volumetric flasks.
54. The gram.
55. 1000.
56. Gram weights: 1 and 5.
    Milligrams weight: 100, 50, and 5.
57. Centrifuging and filtering.
58. A saturated solution contains an excess of the solute.
59. 8 grams.
60. 100 milliliters.
61. 0.850 gram.
62. Remain the same.
63. Shrink.
64. Swell.
65. Isotonic.
66. 58.544 grams.

67. Divide the molecular weight by the number of replaceable hydrogen atoms.
68. Divide the molecular weight by the number of replaceable hydroxyl ions.
69. 2.
70. 0.1.
71. Milliequivalent.
72. Yes.
73. A titration is the act of finding the strength of a solution.
74. 0.2 N.
75. 0.5 N.
76. A pure substance that can be made directly into a normal solution.
77. 63.033 grams.
78. Gram weights: 1 and 5.
    Milligram weights: 200, 100, 2, and 1.
79. Because NaOH is not a pure substance.
80. a. Preparation of Slightly Stronger than 1 N NaOH.
    b. Determination of the Exact Normality.
    c. Dilution to Make the 1 N NaOH.
81. Yes.
82. Because it attacks the silicates of the glass.
83. 18 N.
84. 1.01 N.
85. 99.0 milliliters.
86. a. Preparation of Slightly Stronger than 1 N H_2SO_4.
    b. Determination of the Exact Normality.
    c. Dilution to Make the 1 N H_2SO_4.
87. 98.0820 grams.
88. 49.041 grams.
89. 4.
90. More than 1 gram.
91. 1.1 N.
92. 90.9 milliliters.
93. 10 milliliters.
94. 10 milliliters.
95. Visual colorimeters and photoelectric colorimeters.
96. False.
97. 125 milligrams/100 milliliters.
98. a. Treats the solution to produce a color.
    b. Determines the depth of color produced.
99. Concentration, depth of color, and transmitted light.
100. To remove colors that have no correlation with the concentration.

Registry type questions
and answers

Appendix B contains 164 questions of the type found on Registry examinations.

The first part of the section contains 81 multiple-choice questions. The second part contains 83 true-false questions. The answers to all questions are given at the end of the section.

Some problems call for calculations that the average person cannot make "in his head." For these calculations, the student should use scratch paper.

Place a circle or parentheses around the letter that you consider the best answer to the question or problem, as shown below.

Example: Ammonium hydroxide solution is:

a.   acid
(b.) base
c.   neutral

Registry type questions

1. The total number of elements known to exist is:
   a. 90
   b. 96
   c. 102
   d. 98
2. How many gas elements are there?
   a. 2
   b. 80
   c. 10
   d. 92
3. The formula for sodium hydroxide is:
   a. H_2SO_4
   b. NaOH
   c. NaCl
   d. NH_4OH
4. A solution has a hydrogen ion concentration of 10^{-4}. The pH is:
   a. 8
   b. 14
   c. 4
   d. 2

5. A solution has a pH of 7. The hydrogen ion concentration is:
   a. 10^{-9}
   b. 10^{-7}
   c. 10^{-13}
   d. 10^{-4}
6. Töpfer's reagent has a pH range of:
   a. 6.4 to 8.0
   b. 1.2 to 2.8
   c. 6.0 to 7.4
   d. 3.0 to 4.0
7. One liter contains:
   a.   100 ml.
   b.   800 cc.
   c.   500 cc.
   d. 1000 ml.
8. One gram contains:
   a. 1000 mg.
   b.   10 mg.
   c.   100 mg.
   d.   500 mg.
9. For medical laboratory work, the sensitivity of an analytical balance should be:
   a. 0 to 2
   b. 3 to 5
   c. 7 to 9
   d. 8 to 10
10. 20 ml. of 0.1 N NaOH were used to neutralize 10 ml. of an acid. The normality of the acid is:
    a. 0.6
    b. 1.0
    c. 0.2
    d. 0.4
    Note: Use scratch paper for calculations on this problem and any others you desire.
11. 2 ml. of NaOH were used to neutralize 10 ml. of 0.1 N oxalic acid. The normality of the NaOH is:
    a. 2.0
    b. 0.5
    c. 1.0
    d. 1.5
12. Suppose 5 ml. of 1 N NaOH were used to neutralize 10 ml. of HCl. The normality of the acid is:
    a. 0.8
    b. 0.6
    c. 0.5
    d. 1.2
13. Suppose 20 ml. of NaOH of unknown normality were used to neutralize 10 ml. of 0.1 N oxalic acid. The normality of the NaOH is:
    a. 0.10
    b. 0.05
    c. 0.04
    d. 0.25
14. Using phenolphthalein as an indicator, 10 ml. of an acid of unknown normality is titrated to a faint pink color with 8.6 ml. of 0.1 N NaOH. The normality of the acid is:
    a. 1.200
    b. 0.086
    c. 0.760
    d. 1.400
15. Using phenolphthalein as an indicator, it required 7.5 ml. of a base of unknown nor-

mality to titrate 10 ml. of 0.1 N oxalic acid to a faint pink color. The normality of the base is:
   a. 0.133
   b. 0.120
   c. 0.200
   d. 0.500

16. It is desired to make a 1.0 N HCl solution from a 1.2 N solution. The volume of acid needed for 100 ml is:
   a. 89.22 ml.
   b. 82.33 ml.
   c. 86.00 ml.
   d. 83.33 ml.

17. It is desired to make a 1.00 N NaOH solution from a 1.01 N solution. The volume of base needed for 100 ml. is:
   a. 98.0 ml.
   b. 96.5 ml.
   c. 99.0 ml.
   d. 97.8 ml.

18. With a visual colorimeter, the reading of the standard is 20, the reading of the unknown is 16, and the concentration of the standard represents 100 mg./100 ml. The concentration of the unknown is:
   a. 120 mg./100 ml.
   b. 125 mg./100 ml.
   c. 122 mg./100 ml.
   d. 124 mg./100 ml.

19. Using a photoelectric colorimeter, the O.D. reading of the standard is 0.250, the reading of the unknown is 0.125, and the concentration of the standard represents 100 mg./100 ml. The concentration of the unknown is:
   a. 200 mg./100 ml.
   b. 250 mg./100 ml.
   c. 125 mg./100 ml.
   d. 50 mg./100 ml.

20. The daily volume of urine passed by an average healthy person is:
   a.   600 ml.
   b. 2800 ml.
   c. 2400 ml.
   d. 1400 ml.

21. The waste materials found in urine average about:
   a. 60 gm. per day
   b. 25 gm. per day
   c. 35 gm. per day
   d. 96 gm. per day

22. Which one of the following is not used as a preservative for urine?
   a. Formalin
   b. Toluene
   c. Boric acid
   d. Lactic acid

23. The pH of a urine specimen is found to be 6.0. This means that it is:
   a. Acid
   b. Neutral
   c. Basic

24. Which of the following is not a test for albumin in urine?
   a. Robert test
   b. Purdy test
   c. Benedict test
   d. Heller test

25. When glucose reacts with an alkaline copper solution, the copper is:
   a. Oxidized

    b. Unchanged

    c. Reduced

26. Which of the following is not a ketone body?

    a. Acetone

    b. Diacetic acid

    c. Beta-oxybutyric acid

    d. Calcium

27. Which of the following is not a test for bilirubin (bile) in urine?

    a. Smith test

    b. Arnold test

    c. Nitric acid test

    d. Foam test

28. In the benzidine test for occult blood, which of the following reagents is not used?

    a. Hydrogen peroxide, 3%

    b. Glacial acetic acid

    c. Saturated solution of benzidine

    d. Ethyl alcohol, 95%

29. In the Sulkowitch test for calcium in urine, the calcium is precipitated by the following reagent:

    a. Calcium chloride

    b. Ammonium phosphate

    c. Ammonium oxalate

    d. Sodium hydroxide

30. Which of the following is not a quantitative test for protein in urine?

    a. Exton method

    b. Smith method

    c. Kingsbury method

    d. Esbach method

31. Bence Jones protein precipitates out at about:

    a. 25° C.

    b. 50° C.

    c. 90° C.

    d. 100° C.

32. The normal values for the Addis count are exceeded in:

    a. Diabetes

    b. Tuberculosis

    c. Nephritis

    d. Anemia

33. The normal values for the urea clearance test are:

    a. 100 mg./100 ml.

    b. 20 to 50%

    c. 60 to 125%

    d. 50 mg./100 ml.

34. In calculations for the urea clearance test, which of the following data is not needed?

    a. Urea nitrogen value of urine

    b. Nonprotein nitrogen value of blood

    c. Urea nitrogen value of blood

    d. Milliliters of urine passed per minute

35. In the phenolsulfonphthalein (PSP) test, the normal values for total excretion are:

    a. 20 to 40%

    b. 60 to 85%

    c. 90 to 120 mg./100 ml.

    d. 25 to 40 mg./100 ml.

36. Which of the following is not a pregnancy test?

    a. A-Z test

    b. Somogyi-Nelson test

    c. Friedman test

    d. Frog test

37. In 100 ml. of normal blood, the volume of plasma is approximately:
    a. 60 ml.
    b. 20 ml.
    c. 40 ml.
    d. 80 ml.
38. Which of the following is not an anticoagulant for blood?
    a. Sodium oxalate
    b. Heparin
    c. Lithium oxalate
    d. Potassium permanganate
39. The vast majority of chemical blood tests use the following blood preparation:
    a. Plasma
    b. Serum
    c. Protein-free filtrate
40. Which of the following is not a method for the preparation of a protein-free filtrate?
    a. Folin-Wu method
    b. Haden method
    c. Benedict method
    d. Van Slyke method
41. Which reagent is not used in the preparation of a protein-free filtrate?
    a. Sulfuric acid
    b. Sodium tungstate solution
    c. Nitric acid
42. The normal values for true glucose in blood are:
    a. 50 to 70 mg./100 ml.
    b. 70 to 100 mg./100 ml.
    c. 90 to 120 mg./100 ml.
    d. 100 to 130 mg./100 ml.
43. Which of the following is not a test for blood glucose?
    a. Folin-Wu
    b. Newberger
    c. Benedict
    d. Somogyi-Nelson
44. The normal values for blood creatinine are:
    a. 25 to 35 mg./100 ml.
    b. 1 to 2 mg./100 ml.
    c. 2 to 4 mg./100 ml.
    d. 10 to 15 mg./100 ml.
45. Which of the following is not a method for blood uric acid?
    a. Folin
    b. Brown
    c. Newton
    d. Wintrobe
46. The normal values for blood urea nitrogen are 10 to 15 mg./100 ml. of blood. The corresponding values for urea may be found by multiplying these figures by:
    a. 6.75
    b. 2.14
    c. 1.80
    d. 3.25
47. The total nonprotein nitrogen (NPN) of the blood is not increased in:
    a. Nephritis
    b. Pregnancy
    c. Metallic poisoning
    d. Uremia
48. In the Folin-Wu method for total nonprotein nitrogen (NPN), the solution is heated with a flame. This decomposes the nitrogenous substances and forms:
    a. A red precipitate
    b. An ammonium salt

    c. Sodium chloride

    d. Nessler's solution

49. In nephrosis, the total protein of the blood is:

    a. Increased

    b. Unchanged

    c. Decreased

50. The normal values for albumin in serum are:

    a. 10 to 15 mg./100 ml.

    b.   2 to   4 mg./100 ml.

    c. 3.5 to 5.5 gm./100 ml.

    d. 1.2 to 2.3 gm./100 ml.

51. Which of the following is not a method for blood protein?

    a. Greenberg

    b. Frommer

    c. Kingsley biuret reaction

    d. Looney-Walsh

52. To convert total protein in grams/100 ml. to milliequivalents per liter, the following factor is used:

    a. 1.20

    b. 2.43

    c. 6.50

    d. 6.70

53. A solution commonly used as a standard for icterus index determinations is:

    a. Sulfuric acid

    b. Methyl orange

    c. Potassium dichromate

    d. Sodium sulfate

54. The normal values for serum bilirubin are:

    a.   4 to   7 units

    b.   4 to   8 mg./100 ml.

    c. 10 to 15 mg./100 ml.

    d. 0.2 to 0.8 mg./100 ml.

55. The following reagent is used in the Malloy-Evelyn test for bilirubin:

    a. Esbach's reagent

    b. Sulkowitch reagent

    c. Diazo reagent

    d. Thymol reagent

56. In the thymol turbidity test, the thymol solution is buffered to a pH of:

    a. 6.80

    b. 5.25

    c. 8.50

    d. 7.55

57. In health, 100 ml. of serum contains the following weight of total cholesterol:

    a.   10 to   15 mg.

    b. 150 to 250 mg.

    c.   25 to   35 mg.

    d. 250 to 400 mg.

58. The blood amylase is elevated in:

    a. Hepatitis

    b. Carcinoma of the liver

    c. Acute pancreatitis

    d. Cirrhosis of the liver

59. In the Cherry-Crandall method for blood lipase, the following is used as a substrate:

    a. Starch

    b. Sodium glycerophosphate

    c. Olive oil

    d. Rice

60. In the Bodansky method for alkaline phosphatase, the serum, substrate, and buffer are heated for exactly 1 hour at:
    a. 56° C.
    b. 98° C.
    c. 37° C.
    d. 64° C.
61. The normal pH of blood is:
    a. 6.6 to 7.2
    b. 7.3 to 7.5
    c. 6.8 to 7.0
    d. 7.6 to 8.2
62. The normal values for calcium in serum are:
    a. 2.0 to 4.0 mg./100 ml.
    b. 9.0 to 11.5 mg./100 ml.
    c. 10.5 to 15.5 mg./100 ml.
    d. 6.8 to 8.6 mg./100 ml.
63. In the Clark-Collip modification of the Kramer-Tisdall method, the calcium is precipitated by:
    a. Sodium oxalate
    b. Ammonium oxalate
    c. 1 N sulfuric acid
    d. 0.1 N potassium permanganate
64. The actual chloride content of 1000 ml. of normal serum is:
    a. 98 to 109 meq.
    b. 122 to 132 meq.
    c. 170 to 250 meq.
    d. 73 to 95 meq.
65. In the Whitehorn titration procedure for blood chloride, the chloride is precipitated by:
    a. Sodium chloride
    b. Silver nitrate
    c. Nitric acid
    d. Sulfuric acid
66. The normal values for sodium are:
    a. 120 to 140 meq. per liter of serum
    b. 135 to 155 meq. per liter of serum
    c. 80 to 120 meq. per liter of serum
    d. 96 to 108 meq. per liter of serum
67. Normal plasma has a CO_2 combining power of:
    a. 55 to 75 volumes percent
    b. 35 to 55 volumes percent
    c. 70 to 100 volumes percent
68. The equivalent weight of sodium is 23. If you convert 325 mg. of sodium/100 ml. to meq. per liter, the answer is:
    a. 120 meq. per liter
    b. 162 meq. per liter
    c. 155 meq. per liter
    d. 141 meq. per liter
69. The equivalent weight of calcium is 20. If you convert 4.5 meq. of calcium per liter to mg./100 ml., the answer is:
    a. 8.5 mg./100 ml.
    b. 9.0 mg./100 ml.
    c. 6.4 mg./100 ml.
    d. 7.8 mg./100 ml.
70. If you convert 50 volumes percent of carbon dioxide to millimoles per liter, the answer is:
    a. 20.1 millimoles per liter
    b. 24.6 millimoles per liter

    c. 21.4 millimoles per liter
    d. 22.3 millimoles per liter
71. If you convert 22.3 millimoles per liter of carbon dioxide to volumes percent, the answer
    is:
    a. 46 volumes percent
    b. 50 volumes percent
    c. 56 volumes percent
    d. 54 volumes percent
72. The normal values for glucose in spinal fluid are:
    a. 25 to   35 mg./100 ml.
    b. 40 to   70 mg./100 ml.
    c. 70 to 100 mg./100 ml.
    d. 90 to 120 mg./100 ml.
73. Which of the following is not a test for spinal fluid protein?
    a. Pandy test
    b. Ross-Jones test
    c. Lange test
    d. Nonne-Apelt test
74. The normal values for spinal fluid chloride, expressed as sodium chloride, are:
    a. 170 to 250 meq./L.
    b.   98 to 109 meq./L.
    c. 122 to 132 meq./L.
    d.   73 to 95 meq./L.
75. When Töpfer's reagent is added to the gastric fluid, free hydrochloric acid is present if
    the fluid turns:
    a. Blue
    b. Red
    c. Black
    d. Green
76. Which of the following is not used as a stimulant in gastric analysis?
    a. Ethyl alcohol
    b. Histamine
    c. Ewald meal
    d. Coffee
77. Gastric acidity is reported in the following manner:
    a. Hydrogen ion concentration
    b. Degrees of acidity
    c. Mg. of acid/100 ml.
    d. pH
78. In cancer of the stomach, the gastric acidity is usually:
    a. Increased
    b. Normal
    c. Decreased
79. Which of the following is not present in gastric fluids?
    a. Rennin
    b. Hydrochloric acid
    c. Pepsin
    d. Nitric acid
80. The total gastric acidity is a combination of the free hydrochloric acid and:
    a. Lactic acid
    b. The combined acid
    c. Acetic acid
81. In duodenal fluid, which of the following is not tested for?
    a. Bile
    b. Amylase
    c. Trypsin
    d. Albumin

The following statements are either true or false. If the statement is true, place a circle or parentheses around the T; if it is false, place a circle or parentheses around the F.

Example: Gold is an element.	(T)	F

82. Sodium chloride is an element. T F
83. There are more compounds than elements. T F
84. In a neutral uncombined atom, the protons are balanced by an equal number of electrons. T F
85. The electrons bear a positive charge of electricity and the protons a negative charge. T F
86. When an atom takes electrons, it is oxidized. T F
87. Atomic weights are relative weights. T F
88. The molecular weight of a compound is the sum of its atomic weights. T F
89. Sodium chloride does not ionize. T F
90. Hydrochloric acid has a greater degree of ionization than acetic acid. T F
91. There are no hydroxyl ions in acid solutions. T F
92. 10^{-1} equals 0.01 T F
93. There is a seesaw relationship between the hydrogen ion concentration and the pH value; when one goes up, the other goes down. T F
94. The molecular form of a chemical indicator has one color and the ionic form has another color. T F
95. In liquid measure, there are about 15 drops in 1 ml. T F
96. If a pipet is labelled TD, the portion remaining in the tip must be blown out. T F
97. When a solid and a liquid are mixed, the solid is known as the solute and the liquid is known as the solvent. T F
98. Medical laboratories use more molar solutions than normal solutions. T F
99. All 1 normal solutions contain 1 equivalent weight per liter of solution. T F
100. The neutralizing power of a 1 N acid solution is exactly equal to the neutralizing power of a 1 N basic solution. T F
101. Because of its purity, oxalic acid is known as a primary standard. T F
102. Specific gravity is the weight of a liquid as compared with the weight of an equal volume of water. T F
103. In photoelectric colorimeters, the transmitted light strikes a photoelectric cell that generates current proportional to the amount of light reaching it. T F
104. Increased amounts of urine are referred to as oliguria. T F
105. Anuria, the complete absence of urine, is seen in diabetes. T F
106. The organic portion of urine is mostly urea. T F
107. The inorganic substances found in urine are mostly salts. T F
108. Refrigeration is a simple and effective means of preserving urine. T F
109. Urochrome is a pigment found only in pathological urine. T F
110. The normal pH range of urine is 4.0 to 8.0 T F
111. If allowed to stand, acid urine becomes alkaline because urea decomposes and liberates ammonia. T F
112. The normal specific gravity of urine is 1.000 to 1.015. T F
113. True albuminuria is caused by a seepage of albumin from the bloodstream into the urine. T F
114. If urine forms a cloudy precipitate when heated, it always indicates the presence of albumin. T F
115. Most of the tests for sugar in urine are based on the fact that glucose is a reducing sugar. T F
116. When diacetic acid decomposes it liberates acetone and beta-oxybutyric acid. T F
117. Many of the tests for acetone in urine call for the reaction of acetone with sodium nitroprusside to form a complex compound that is purple to red in color. T F

118. Diacetic acid may be found in urine in a severe case of diabetes.   T   F
119. The majority of tests for bilirubin in urine call for the oxidation of bilirubin to various colored compounds.   T   F
120. Urobilinogen is a colorless compound derived from bilirubin.   T   F
121. Ehrlich's method is commonly used to test for urobilinogen in urine.   T   F
122. In diseases of the liver and diseases of a hemolytic nature, large amounts of urobilin may be found in the urine.   T   F
123. Tests for melanin in urine usually call for the oxidation of the colorless compound (melanogen) to the colored compound (melanin).   T   F
124. The presence of Bence Jones protein in urine is considered a significant diagnostic aid in multiple myeloma.   T   F
125. The Addis count is an estimate of the number of casts and cells in a 12-hour specimen of urine.   T   F
126. Urinary amylase is decreased in acute pancreatitis.   T   F
127. Following an attack of gout, the urinary uric acid is decreased.   T   F
128. In the Mosenthal test, the specific gravity of urine is measured at various intervals.   T   F
129. In the phenolsulfonphthalein test for kidney function, the dye is red in acid urine and colorless in basic urine.   T   F
130. The pregnancy test is never positive unless the woman is pregnant.   T   F
131. Under normal conditions, there are no barbiturates in the urine.   T   F
132. During late pregnancy and after delivery, a woman's urine may contain lactose and thus give false positive tests for glucose.   T   F
133. A properly prepared protein-free filtrate is light brown in color.   T   F
134. In the preparation of a protein-free filtrate, the blood is diluted 1 in 10; that is, 10 ml. of filtrate represent 1 ml. of blood.   T   F
135. When the glucose level of the blood rises above normal values, the condition is known as hyperglycemia.   T   F
136. All persons have the same renal threshold value.   T   F
137. In Benedict's test for glucose, the glucose is reduced by a copper solution.   T   F
138. Glucose tolerance tests are based on the fact that a normal individual removes an administered dose of glucose at a faster rate than a diabetic person.   T   F
139. The Jaffé reaction consists of a reaction between creatinine and sodium picrate to form creatinine picrate, which is red in color.   T   F
140. The blood uric acid is decreased in gout.   T   F
141. In the Karr method for blood urea nitrogen, the purpose of the buffer solution is to control the pH.   T   F
142. The normal values for the total nonprotein nitrogen (NPN) are 25 to 35 mg./100 ml. of blood.   T   F
143. As a group, one of the major functions of the blood proteins is to maintain the water balance between the blood and tissues.   T   F
144. In severe nephrosis, an inverted A/G ratio may be found.   T   F
145. Jaundice is characterized by excessive bile pigment, which produces a yellow coloration of the skin.   T   F
146. The icterus index may rise to 40 units before the eyes or skin show the yellow pigmentation of jaundice.   T   F
147. The eating of carrots prior to an icterus index determination will not affect the results.   T   F
148. Serum bilirubin is elevated in obstructive jaundice, hemolytic jaundice, and hepatic jaundice.   T   F
149. The Bromsulphalein (BSP) test for liver function is based on the principle that a healthy liver removes the dye at a slower rate than a diseased liver.   T   F
150. In injecting the dye for the Bromsulphalein test, a tourniquet should be while the injection is being made.   T   F
151. The normal values for the thymol turbidity test are exceeded in infectious hepatitis.   T   F

152. Elevated values for total serum cholesterol may be found in obstructive   T   F
     jaundice, hypothyroidism, and eclampsia.
153. The total serum cholesterol is made up of about 30% free cholesterol and   T   F
     70% cholesterol esters.
154. In the Somogyi-Nelson method for blood amylase, the purpose of the   T   F
     acid sodium chloride is to enable the reaction to take place at optimum
     conditions of pH and electrolyte content.
155. In acute pancreatitis, the blood lipase value is decreased.   T   F
156. The normal values for serum alkaline phosphatase in adults are 2 to 4   T   F
     Bodansky units or 4 to 10 King-Armstrong units.
157. In carcinoma of the prostate, the values for acid phosphatase are usually   T   F
     below normal.
158. The serum calcium is increased in tetany.   T   F
159. The chloride content of 100 ml. of whole blood is the same as the chloride   T   F
     content of 100 ml. of serum or plasma.
160. The normal values for phosphorus are 2.5 to 4.0 mg./100 ml. of serum.   T   F
161. The concentration of potassium is normally 16 to 22 mg./100 ml. of serum.   T   F
162. When the CO_2 combining power of the plasma is increased, the condition   T   F
     is referred to as acidosis.
163. The normal values for spinal fluid protein are 15 to 45 mg./100 ml. of   T   F
     fluid.
164. Decreased values for spinal fluid chloride may be found in acute men-   T   F
     ingitis.

Answers to Registry type questions

1.	c	56.	d	111.	T
2.	c	57.	b	112.	F
3.	b	58.	c	113.	T
4.	c	59.	c	114.	F
5.	b	60.	c	115.	T
6.	d	61.	b	116.	T
7.	d	62.	b	117.	T
8.	a	63.	b	118.	T
9.	b	64.	a	119.	T
10.	c	65.	b	120.	T
11.	b	66.	b	121.	T
12.	c	67.	a	122.	T
13.	b	68.	d	123.	T
14.	b	69.	b	124.	T
15.	a	70.	d	125.	T
16.	d	71.	b	126.	F
17.	c	72.	b	127.	F
18.	b	73.	c	128.	T
19.	a	74.	c	129.	F
20.	d	75.	b	130.	F
21.	a	76.	d	131.	T
22.	d	77.	b	132.	T
23.	a	78.	c	133.	F
24.	c	79.	d	134.	T
25.	c	80.	b	135.	T
26.	d	81.	d	136.	F
27.	b	82.	F	137.	F
28.	d	83.	T	138.	T
29.	c	84.	T	139.	T
30.	b	85.	F	140.	F
31.	b	86.	F	141.	T
32.	c	87.	T	142.	T
33.	c	88.	T	143	T
34.	b	89.	F	144.	T
35.	b	90.	T	145.	T
36.	b	91.	F	146.	F
37.	a	92.	F	147.	F
38.	d	93.	T	148.	T
39.	b	94.	T	149.	F
40.	c	95.	T	150.	F
41.	c	96.	F	151.	T
42.	b	97.	T	152.	T
43.	b	98.	F	153.	T
44.	b	99.	T	154.	T
45.	d	100.	T	155.	F
46.	b	101.	T	156.	T
47.	b	102.	T	157.	F
48.	b	103.	T	158.	F
49.	c	104.	F	159.	F
50.	c	105.	F	160.	T
51.	b	106.	T	161.	T
52.	b	107.	T	162.	F
53.	c	108.	T	163.	T
54.	d	109.	F	164.	T
55.	c	110.	T		

Appendix C

Reagents

PREPARATION OF REAGENTS

In the preparation of reagents, chemicals of the highest purity must be used. Bottles containing these chemicals are usually labelled in one of the following manners: (1) Analytical Reagent, (2) Reagent Grade, or (3) C.P. for chemically pure.

The materials for reagents should be weighed on an analytical balance unless the quantity needed exceeds the capacity of the analytical balance. Then a torsion balance may be used. Materials for standards and buffers must always be weighed on an analytical balance.

When measuring liquid materials, use Class A volumetric pipets unless otherwise specified in the directions. Do not pipet strong acids or alkalies by mouth. Attach a rubber bulb or vacuum line to the mouthpiece when drawing up these materials into a pipet.

Some reagents require adjusting to a certain pH. This must be done using a pH meter. A typical pH meter is illustrated in Fig. 74. The operating procedures vary with the different instruments.

Some solutions decompose when exposed to light. These solutions are stored in brown bottles as directed in certain preparations. Many laboratories make it a practice to store all solutions in brown bottles.

The reagents are listed in alphabetical order with their identification numbers. Directions for preparing the reagents are then given in numerical order. For example, the first reagent is listed as "(C-1) Sulfuric Acid, 2/3 N."

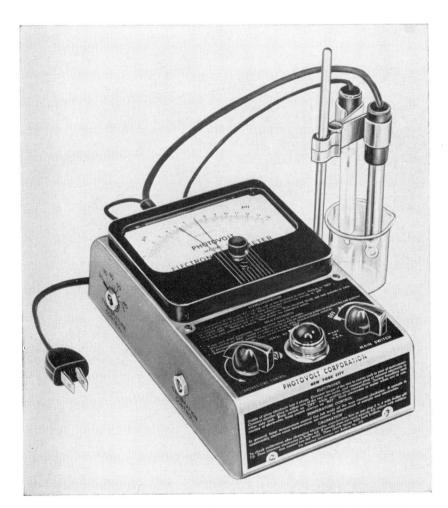

Fig. 74. pH meter. (Courtesy Photovolt Corporation, New York, N. Y.)

Reagents—alphabetical listing

2:2'-Dipyridyl, 0.4%   (C-143)
EDTA Solution   (C-86)
Ehrlich's Diazo Reagent   (C-197)
Ehrlich's Reagent   (C-175)
Esbach's Reagent   (C-182)
Ethyl Alcohol, 95%, containing 0.4% Capryl Alcohol   (C-57)
Exton's Reagent   (C-162)
Ferric Chloride, 5%   (C-189)
Ferric Chloride, 10%   (C-153)
Formaldehyde, 2%   (C-147)
Fouchet's Reagent   (C-171)
Glucose, Stock Standard, 1.0 mg./ml.   (C-9)
Glycerin-Silicate Reagent   (C-16)
Glycine, 7.5%   (C-68)
Gold Chloride, 0.5%   (C-118)
Gram's Iodine Solution   (C-156)
Guaiac Reagent   (C-178)
5-HIAA Standard, 10 mg./100 ml.   (C-188)
Hydrochloric Acid, 0.1 N   (C-25)
Hydrochloric Acid, 0.5 N   (C-128)
Hydrochloric Acid, 1 N   (C-91)
Hydrochloric Acid, 2.0 N   (C-135)
Hydrochloric Acid, 5%   (C-181)
Hydrochloric Acid, 25%   (C-59)
Hydrogen Peroxide, 30%   (C-22)
Iodate, Stock Standard, 100 μg Iodine/ml.   (C-209)
Iodine, Ethyl Alcohol Solution   (C-172)
Iodine Indicator   (C-97)
Iodine Standards   (C-138)
Iron, Stock Standard, 100 mg./100 ml.   (C-144)
Isopropylamine, 5% in Methyl Alcohol   (C-192)
Lactic Acid, 0.1 N   (C-78)
Lactic Acid, 10%   (C-77)
Lead Nitrate, Saturated   (C-201)
Lugol's Solution   (C-174)
Mercuric Chloride, 10%   (C-198)
Mercuric Nitrate Solution, Standard   (C-76)
Molybdate Reagent   (C-93)
Nessler's Reagent   (C-23)
p-Nitrophenol, 10 mM/L.   (C-111)
p-Nitrophenylphosphate, Stock Substrate   (C-103)
Nitrosonaphthol Reagent, 0.1%   (C-185)
NPN Standard, 0.5 mg. N/ml.   (C-24)
Olive Oil Substrate   (C-100)
Orthotoluidine Reagent   (C-177)
Pandy's Reagent   (C-145)
Perchloric Acid, 10%   (C-203)
Phenol Color Reagent   (C-30)
Phenol Reagent of Folin-Ciocalteu, Stock   (C-70)
Phenolphthalein, 0.1%   (C-150)
Phenolphthalein, 1%   (C-54)
Phosphate Buffer, pH 7.0   (C-99)
Phosphate Buffer, 0.1 M, pH 7.4   (C-112)
Phosphomolybdic Acid   (C-10)
Phosphomolybdic Acid, Alternate   (C-11)
Phosphorus, Stock Standard, 0.1 mg. P/ml.   (C-96)
Phosphotungstic Acid   (C-17)
Physiological Saline, 0.9%   (C-34)
Physiological Saline with 10% Methanol   (C-48)

Reagents—directions

(C-1) Sulfuric Acid, 2/3 N

Transfer exactly 19 ml. of concentrated sulfuric acid, H_2SO_4, to a 1-liter volumetric flask containing about 700 ml. of water. Dilute to volume and mix. Standardize.

Note: With phenolphthalein as an indicator, 20 ml. of the above solution should require 13.33 ml. of 1 N NaOH for neutralization. If the solution is too acid, adjust the normality to 2/3 N by dilution.

(C-2) Sodium Tungstate, 10%

Weigh 100 gm. of sodium tungstate, Na_2WO_4, and transfer to a 1-liter volumetric flask. Dissolve and dilute to volume with water. Stopper and mix thoroughly. Store in a Pyrex or polyethylene bottle.

(C-3) Sulfuric Acid, 1/12 N

Pipet exactly 2.3 ml. of concentrated sulfuric acid into a 1-liter volumetric flask containing about 700 ml. of water. Dilute to volume and mix. Standardize.

Note: With phenolphthalein as an indicator, 20 ml. of the above solution should require 16.67 ml. of 0.1 N NaOH for neutralization. If the solution is too acid, adjust the normality to 1/12 N by dilution.

(C-4) Zinc Sulfate, 5%

Weigh 50 gm. of zinc sulfate, $ZnSO_4 \cdot 7H_2O$, and transfer to a 1-liter volumetric flask. Dissolve and dilute to volume with water. Mix thoroughly.

(C-5) Barium Hydroxide, 0.3 N

Weigh 47 gm. of barium hydroxide, $Ba(OH)_2 \cdot 8H_2O$, and transfer to a 1-liter volumetric flask. Dissolve and dilute to volume with water. Mix. Filter if cloudy. Store in a well-closed container with a minimum of air space.

Note: Reagents C-4 and C-5 must neutralize each other. Pipet 10 ml. of $ZnSO_4$ solution into a 250 ml. Erlenmeyer flask. Use a volumetric pipet. Add 50 ml. of distilled water and 4 drops of phenolphthalein indicator. Titrate with the barium hydroxide very slowly until 1 drop turns the solution to a faint pink. If this is done too rapidly a false end point will be obtained. It should require 10 ml. ($\pm$ 0.05 ml.) of barium chloride to reach the end point. If either solution is too strong, adjust with water and titrate. The adjusted or "matched" solutions are now placed into aspirator bottles with the barium hydroxide bottle containing a soda-lime tube in the stopper. The soda-lime tube is to prevent the solution from absorbing atmospheric CO_2. Soda lime is a mixture of CaO and NaOH.

(C-6) Alkaline Copper Reagent (Nelson-Somogyi)

Weigh 24.0 gm. of sodium carbonate and 12.0 gm. of sodium potassium tartrate (Rochelle salt) and transfer to a 1-liter volumetric flask. Add about 250 ml. of water and swirl until all the material is dissolved. Weigh 4.0 gm. of copper sulfate ($CuSO_4 \cdot 5H_2O$) and transfer to a 250 ml. beaker containing about 50 ml. of water. Stir with a glass stirring rod until all crystals are dissolved. Slowly add this to the carbonate-tartrate solution and mix well. Weigh 16.0 gm. of sodium bicarbonate and transfer to the flask (use a powder funnel). Weigh 180 gm. of sodium sulfate and transfer to a 1000 ml. beaker containing about 500 ml. of hot water. Allow this solution to boil for 2 or 3 minutes to expel air; then cool. Add this to the flask containing the other reagents and dilute to the mark with water. Mix thoroughly. If a sediment forms after several days of standing the solution may be filtered.

(C-6a) Alkaline Copper Reagent (Folin-Wu)

Weigh 40.0 gm. of sodium carbonate and transfer to a 1-liter volumetric flask containing about 400 ml. of water. Swirl until all material is dissolved. Add 7.5 gm. of tartaric acid and 4.5 gm. of copper sulfate ($CuSO_4 \cdot 5H_2O$). When this is dissolved, dilute to the mark and mix thoroughly. If a sediment forms, the solution may be filtered.

(C-7) Arsenomolybdate Color Reagent

Weigh 50.0 gm. of ammonium molybdate and transfer to a 2000 ml. beaker or flask containing 900 ml. of water. Mix until all the molybdate goes into solution. Slowly add 42.0 ml. of concentrated sulfuric acid, with constant stirring. Add 6.0 gm. of disodium arsenate ($Na_2HASO_4 \cdot 7H_2O$) and mix. Transfer to a brown, glass-stoppered bottle and place in an incubator at 37° C. for 24 to 48 hours.

(C-8) Benzoic Acid, 0.2%

Weigh 2.0 gm. of benzoic acid and transfer to a 1-liter volumetric flask. Dilute to the mark with water and mix. Benzoic acid dissolves very slowly, so it is best to let this solution stand in a warm place for several hours before using.

(C-9) Glucose, Stock Standard, 1.0 mg./ml.

Carefully weigh exactly 1.000 gm. of glucose on an analytical balance and transfer to a 1-liter volumetric flask. Dissolve and dilute to the mark with 0.2% benzoic acid solution. Mix well and store in a Pyrex or polyethylene bottle.

(C-10) Phosphomolybdic Acid

Place 400 ml. of water and 400 ml. of 10% sodium hydroxide in a 2-liter Erlenmeyer flask. Add 70.0 gm. of molybdic acid and 10.0 gm. of sodium tungstate. Boil for 30 to 40 minutes to remove any ammonia. Cool to room temperature and add 250 ml. of orthophosphoric acid (85%). Mix and transfer to a 1-liter volumetric flask. Rinse the Erlenmeyer flask several times with about 10 ml. of water and add these rinsings to the volumetric flask. Dilute to the mark with water and mix well. Store in a Pyrex or polyethylene bottle.

(C-11) Phosphomolybdic Acid, Alternate

Mix 500 ml. of reagent C-10 with 35 ml. of water and 215 ml. of orthophosphoric acid. When using this reagent instead of C-10, 3 ml. should be used instead of the usual 2 ml.

(C-12) Picric Acid, Saturated

Heat 1 liter of distilled water to boiling in a 2-liter flask or beaker. Remove from heat and add 11.75 gm. of picric acid. (Keep away from an open flame.) Allow to cool to room temperature and filter. Store in a brown, glass-stoppered bottle.
Note: Reagent grade picric acid will have 10 to 12% water added.

(C-13) Sodium Hydroxide, 10% (2.5 N)

Dilute solutions of sodium hydroxide should be prepared by using a nearly saturated solution that has been standardized. If the normality of the concentrated solution is known, then the volume needed to make a dilute solution may be determined with the following formula:

$$Ml. \times N = Ml. \times N$$

Example: If the concentrated solution is 16.67 N and you want 1 liter of 2.5 N NaOH

$$X(ml.) \times 16.67(N) = 1000(ml.) \times 2.5(N)$$

$$X = \frac{250}{16.67}$$

$$X = 15.0 \ ml.$$

Therefore, if 15.0 ml. of 16.67 N NaOH are diluted to 1 liter with water, this would give a 2.5 N solution of NaOH. Titrate with a standard acid solution to check.

(C-14) Uric Acid, Stock Standard, 1 mg./ml.

Weigh 1.000 gm. of uric acid and transfer to a 1-liter volumetric flask (Pyrex). Weigh 0.5 gm. of lithium carbonate and transfer to a 250 ml. Erlenmeyer flask containing 150 ml. of hot water. Add this warm solution of lithium carbonate to the flask containing the uric acid. Shake until all the uric acid is dissolved. Add about 300 ml. of water and 25 ml. of 40% formaldehyde; mix. Add 3 ml. of glacial acetic acid and mix. After the liberated CO_2 has been removed from the solution by shaking, dilute to volume with water. Mix well. Store in a brown bottle.

(C-15) Polyanethol Sodium Sulfonate (Liquoid)

Weigh 2.0 gm. of polyanethol sodium sulfonate (Liquoid)* and carefully transfer to a 100 ml. volumetric flask. Use a funnel. This material is very light and fluffy, so care must be taken to avoid losing any. Wash any material remaining in the funnel down into the flask with about 80 ml. of distilled water. When all the Liquoid is dissolved, dilute to the 100 ml. mark and mix thoroughly. Transfer to a brown bottle and store in a refrigerator.

(C-16) Glycerin-Silicate Reagent

Weigh 50.0 gm. of crystalline sodium silicate "soluble" and transfer to a 1-liter beaker containing 500 ml. of hot water. Stir until dissolved. Add 100 ml. of glycerin. Stir until thoroughly mixed. Allow to come to room temperature. If the solution is cloudy, filter through hardened paper. Store in a Pyrex or polyethylene bottle.

---

*May be obtained from Hoffman-La Roche, Inc., Nutley, N. J.

(C-17) Phosphotungstic Acid

Weigh 50.0 gm. of sodium tungstate ($Na_2WO_4 \cdot 2H_2O$) and transfer to a 1-liter round-bottom flask. Add 400 ml. of water and 40 ml. of 85% orthophosphoric acid. Boil gently under a reflux condenser for 4 hours. Allow to cool to room temperature. Transfer to a 500 ml. volumetric flask. Rinse the boiling flask twice with 10 ml. of water and transfer rinsings to the volumetric flask. Dilute to the 500 ml. mark with water. Mix thoroughly and store in a brown bottle.

(C-18) Sodium Hydroxide, 0.5 N

Prepare by using a concentrated solution of NaOH that has been standardized.

$$Ml. \times N = Ml. \times N$$

(C-19) Uric Acid Special Reagent

To 180 ml. of water, add 80 ml. of phosphotungstic acid (C-17) and 100 ml. of Liquoid solution (C-15). Mix well and store in a brown bottle.

(C-20) Sodium Carbonate, 14%

Weigh 140.0 gm. of anhydrous sodium carbonate and transfer to a 1-liter volumetric flask. Add about 800 ml. of water and mix until all the carbonate is dissolved. Dilute to volume and mix again. Store in a Pyrex or polyethylene bottle.

(C-21) Sulfuric Acid (Digestion Mixture), 30%

Measure 340 ml. of water and transfer to a 1-liter beaker or Erlenmeyer flask. Place the beaker or flask in a large pan of ice for 10 or 15 minutes. *Very carefully* add 150 ml. of concentrated sulfuric acid. This mixture will be very hot! Carefully mix and allow to stand in the ice water until cool. Store in a Pyrex or polyethylene bottle.

(C-22) Hydrogen Peroxide, 30% (Superoxol)

This may be obtained from any Merck supplier. It is a strong oxidant and should be handled with care. Store in a refrigerator when not in use.

(C-23) Nessler's Reagent

Weigh 1000 gm. of sodium hydroxide pellets and dissolve in about 1500 ml. of water. Cool and dilute to 2 liters. Transfer this to a 5-gallon Pyrex bottle and add 8 liters of water. Dissolve 150 gm. of potassium iodide (KI) in about 200 ml. of water. Gradually add 200 gm. of mercuric iodide to the KI solution, with vigorous stirring. Dilute this solution to 2 liters and add to the NaOH solution. Add 2 more liters of water. Stopper and mix thoroughly. Allow to settle for at least 3 weeks. The clear supernatant is siphoned off as needed.
Note: Do *not* make this reagent near the protein-bound iodine area if you are doing PBI's.

(C-24) Stock NPN or BUN Standard, 0.5 mg. N/ml.

Weigh 2.3585 gm. of anhydrous ammonium sulfate, $(NH_4)_2SO_4$, and transfer to a 1-liter volumetric flask. Dissolve and dilute to the mark with 0.1 N hydrochloric acid (ammonia-free).

(C-25) Hydrochloric Acid, 0.1 N (ammonia-free)

Using a 10 ml. serological pipet attached to a rubber bulb or vacuum line, transfer 8.4 ml. of concentrated, reagent grade hydrochloric acid to a 1-liter volumetric flask containing about 700 ml. of water. Dilute to volume and mix. Standardize. Be sure that neither the concentrated nor the dilute acids are exposed to ammonia fumes. *Do not pipet strong acids by mouth.*

(C-26) Urease Solution

Weigh 15.0 gm. of jack bean meal and transfer to a 250 ml. Erlenmeyer flask. Add 10.0 gm. of dry Permutit and 100 ml. of approximately 20% ethyl alcohol (21 ml. of 95% alcohol diluted to 100 ml. with water). Stopper and shake for 30 minutes. Filter in refrigerator. Cover funnel with watchglass. This solution is stable for about 2 weeks when stored in the refrigerator.

(C-27)   Potassium Persulfate, 2.5%

Weigh 2.5 gm. of reagent grade, nitrogen-free potassium persulfate and transfer to a 100 ml. volumetric flask. Dissolve and dilute to volume with water. Prepare a fresh solution weekly. Store in a refrigerator and remove only long enough to obtain the amount needed, as decomposition is rapid at higher temperatures.

(C-28)   Potassium Gluconate, 1%

Weigh 1.0 gm. of potassium gluconate and transfer to a 100 ml. volumetric flask. Dissolve and dilute to volume with water. Prepare a fresh solution weekly and store in a refrigerator.

(C-29)   Buffered Urease Solution

Weigh 150 mg. of urease* and transfer to a 100 ml. volumetric flask. Add 1.0 gm. of ethylenediaminetetra-acetic acid (EDTA). Dissolve and dilute to volume with water. This solution is stable for 1 month when stored in a refrigerator.

(C-30)   Phenol Color Reagent

Weigh 50.0 gm. of reagent grade phenol and 0.25 gm. of reagent grade sodium nitroprusside and transfer to a 1-liter volumetric flask. Dissolve and dilute to volume with water. This solution is stable for at least 2 months if stored in a brown bottle in a cool place.

(C-31)   Alkali-Hypochlorite Reagent

Weigh 25.0 gm. of reagent grade NaOH and transfer to a 1-liter volumetric flask. Add 40.0 ml. of Clorox (commercial bleach). Dilute to volume with water and mix. Store in an amber bottle protected from light and heat. This solution is stable for at least 2 months.

(C-32)   Acetate Buffer

Weigh 15.0 gm. of sodium acetate and transfer to a 100 ml. volumetric flask. Add 1.0 ml. of glacial acetic acid. Dilute to volume with water and mix.

(C-33)   Biuret Reagent

Weigh 45.0 gm. of sodium potassium tartrate and transfer to a 1-liter volumetric flask containing about 600 ml. of 0.2 N NaOH (prepare from a concentrated solution of NaOH that has been standardized). Mix until dissolved. Add 15.0 gm. of copper sulfate, $CuSO_4 \cdot 5H_2O$, and dissolve completely. Add 5.0 gm. of potassium iodide and mix. Dilute to volume with 0.2 N NaOH and mix thoroughly. Store in a Pyrex or polyethylene bottle.

(C-34)   Physiological Saline, 0.9%

Weigh 9.0 gm. of sodium chloride and transfer to a 1-liter volumetric flask. Dissolve and dilute to volume with water. Store in a Pyrex or polyethylene bottle.

(C-35)   Sodium Sulfate, 24.5%

Weigh 245.0 gm. of reagent grade sodium sulfate and transfer to a 1-liter volumetric flask containing about 700 ml. of water. Dissolve and dilute to volume. This solution should be kept in a warm place (26° to 30° C.).

(C-36)   Trichloroacetic Acid, 3%

Trichloroacetic acid crystals are difficult to weigh accurately because they absorb moisture from the air very rapidly. It is recommended that dilute solutions of TCA be made from more concentrated solutions. Measure 300 ml. of 10% trichloroacetic acid (C-63) and transfer to a 1-liter volumetric flask. Dilute to volume with water and mix.

---

*Urease, Type II, about 800 to 1000 Sumner units per gram, Sigma Chemical Co., St. Louis, Mo.

(C-37)   Tsuchiya's Reagent

Weigh 15.0 gm. of phosphotungstic acid and transfer to a 2-liter Erlenmeyer flask containing 1 liter of 95% ethyl alcohol. Add 50.0 ml. of concentrated hydrochloric acid and mix thoroughly.

(C-38)   Sodium Citrate, 5%

Weigh 50.0 gm. of sodium citrate and transfer to a 1-liter volumetric flask. Dissolve and dilute to volume with water. Mix thoroughly.

(C-39)   Potassium Dichromate, Stock Standard, 1%

Weigh 1.0 gm. of potassium dichromate and transfer to a 100 ml. volumetric flask containing about 70 ml. of water. Add 2 drops of concentrated sulfuric acid and dilute to volume. Mix thoroughly and store in a glass-stoppered brown bottle.

(C-40)   Diazo Blank Solution

Transfer 1.5 ml. of concentrated hydrochloric acid to a 100 ml. volumetric flask. Dilute to volume with water and mix.

(C-41)   Sulfanilic Acid, Solution A, 0.1%

Weigh 100 mg. of sulfanilic acid and transfer to a 100 ml. volumetric flask. Add 1.5 ml. of concentrated hydrochloric acid. Dilute to volume with water.

(C-42)   Sodium Nitrite, Stock Solution B, 5%

Weigh 5.0 gm. of sodium nitrite and transfer to a 100 ml. volumetric flask. Dissolve and dilute to volume with water. Store in a refrigerator.

(C-43)   Sodium Nitrite, Working Solution B, 0.5%

Prepare this solution just before use. Mix 1.0 ml. of stock solution B (C-42) with 9.0 ml. of water.

(C-44)   Alkaline Buffer, pH 10.6-10.7

Weigh 24.4 gm. of dibasic sodium phosphate, $Na_2HPO_4 \cdot 7H_2O$, (or 12.92 gm. of Na_2HPO_4) and 3.54 gm. of $Na_3PO_4 \cdot 12H_2O$ and 6.4 gm. of sodium p-toluenesulfonate and transfer to a 1-liter volumetric flask. Dissolve and dilute to volume with water. Check pH and adjust if necessary.

(C-45)   Acid Reagent, 2 M NaH_2PO_4

Weigh 27.6 gm. of $NaH_2PO_4 \cdot H_2O$ and transfer to a 100 ml. volumetric flask. Dissolve and dilute to volume with water.

(C-46)   BSP Standard, 5 mg./100 ml.

Pipet 1.0 ml. of the intravenous test solution (50 mg./ml.)* into a 1-liter volumetric flask. Dilute to volume with water. This diluted standard is stable for 1 week.

(C-47)   Thymol-Barbital Buffer, pH 7.55

Boil 1100 ml. of distilled water for about 5 minutes to drive off CO_2. Allow to cool to about 95° C. Weigh 6.0 gm. of thymol crystals and transfer to a 2-liter Erlenmeyer flask. Add 300 ml. of the hot water. Add 3.09 gm. of barbital, 1.69 gm. of sodium barbital, and 720 ml. of hot water. Stopper and shake flask for 5 minutes. (Vigorous stirring with a magnetic stirrer works very well.) Release pressure from time to time by removing the stopper. Allow to cool to 25° C. and add 20 ml. of water to compensate for evaporation. Seed the solution with about 1 gm. of thymol crystals. Shake the flask vigorously until the supernatant solution becomes clear.

---

*Available from Hynson, Westcott, and Dunning, Baltimore, Md.

Allow to stand at room temperature (25° C.) until the next day. Then filter through Whatman No. 1 paper. Check pH. It must be between 7.50 and 7.60 at 25° C. If the pH is outside these limits, adjustments must be made by altering the ratio of barbital to sodium barbital in a new preparation. Store in a tightly stoppered container to protect it against changes in pH from uptake of CO_2.

(C-48) Physiological Saline with 10% Methanol

Mix 100 ml. of methanol with 900 ml. of physiological saline, 0.9% (C-34).

(C-49) Acetone-Alcohol Mixture

Mix 500 ml. reagent grade acetone with 500 ml. of 95% ethyl alcohol.

(C-50) Digitonin Solution

Mix 525 ml. of 95% ethyl alcohol with 475 ml. of water. Add 5.0 gm. of digitonin and stir to dissolve.

(C-51) Acetic Acid, 10% (v/v)

Measure 100 ml. of glacial acetic acid and transfer to a 1-liter volumetric flask containing about 600 ml. of water. Mix, dilute to volume with water, and mix again.

(C-52) Acetone-Ether Mixture

Mix 200 ml. of reagent grade ether with 100 ml. of reagent grade acetone.

(C-53) Potassium Hydroxide Solution

Weigh 20.0 gm. of reagent grade potassium hydroxide and transfer to a 100 ml. beaker containing 40 ml. of distilled water. Stir until dissolved. Store in a polyethylene bottle.

(C-54) Phenolphthalein, 1%

Weigh 1.0 gm. of phenolphthalein and transfer to a 100 ml. volumetric flask. Dissolve and dilute to volume with 95% ethyl alcohol. Mix.

(C-55) Acetic Anhydride-Dioxane (A-D) Reagent

Mix 600 ml. of reagent grade acetic anhydride with 400 ml. of purified dioxane. This should be done *under a hood.* Store in a brown, glass-stoppered bottle.

(C-56) Cholesterol Standard, 0.2 mg./ml.

Weigh 0.025 gm. of pure, dry cholesterol and 0.0277 gm. of cholesteryl acetate and transfer to a 500 ml. Erlenmeyer flask. Add 240 ml. of acetic anhydride-dioxane mixture (C-54) and heat 15 minutes in a boiling water bath. Cool and wipe outside of flask to remove moisture. Transfer to a 250 ml. volumetric flask. Rinse the Erlenmeyer flask with 5 ml. of A-D solution and add this to the volumetric flask. Dilute to volume with A-D solution and mix thoroughly. Store in a glass-stoppered, brown bottle.

(C-57) Ethyl Alcohol, 95%, containing 0.4% Capryl Alcohol

Pipet 4 ml. capryl alcohol into a 1-liter volumetric flask and dilute to volume with 95% ethyl alcohol. Mix.

(C-58) Potassium Hydroxide, 33%

Weigh 330 gm. of potassium hydroxide pellets and transfer to a 1-liter Pyrex volumetric flask containing about 600 ml. of water. Swirl to dissolve and allow to cool to room temperature. Dilute to volume and mix. Store in a polyethylene bottle.

(C-59) Hydrochloric Acid, 25%

Measure 676 ml. of concentrated hydrochloric acid (37%) and transfer to a 1-liter volumetric flask containing 300 ml. of water. Dilute to volume with water and mix.

(C-60)   Sodium Hydroxide, NaOH, 1.000 N

Prepare from a concentrated solution of sodium hydroxide that has been standardized. Standardize the diluted solution against 1 N acid. Adjust to 1.000 N if necessary.

(C-61)   Thymol Blue, 0.2% in 50% Ethyl Alcohol

Weigh 0.2 gm. of thymol blue and transfer to a 100 ml. volumetric flask. Add 53 ml. of 95% ethyl alcohol and dilute to volume with water and mix.

(C-62)   Uranyl Zinc Acetate Reagent

Weigh 10.0 gm. of uranyl acetate and dissolve in a beaker containing 50 ml. of boiling water and 2.0 ml. of glacial acetic acid. In another beaker, dissolve 30.0 gm. of zinc acetate in 50 ml. of boiling water and 1.0 ml. of glacial acetic acid. Mix the two solutions and heat again to the boiling point. Let the beaker stand overnight at room temperature. Filter and then mix with an equal volume of 95% ethyl alcohol. Place in a refrigerator for 2 days and then filter. This reagent is stable at room temperature.

(C-63)   Trichloroacetic Acid, 10%

Trichloroacetic acid (TCA) is extremely hygroscopic (capable of absorbing water from the atmosphere) and is therefore difficult to weigh accurately. It is recommended that reagent grade TCA be purchased in ¼ pound (113.4 gm.) bottles and that an entire bottle be dissolved and diluted to the desired concentration. To prepare 10% TCA, dissolve and dilute a ¼ pound or 113.4 gm. bottle of TCA (check weight on bottle) to 1134 ml. Store in a Pyrex bottle.

(C-64)   Sodium Standard, 0.64 mg. Na/ml.

Weigh 0.162 gm. of sodium chloride and transfer to a 100 ml. volumetric flask. Dissolve and dilute to volume with water.

(C-65)   Sodium Cobaltinitrite Reagent

A. Weigh 25.0 gm. of cobalt nitrate, $Co(NO_3)_2$, and transfer to a 400 ml. beaker containing 50 ml. of water. Stir to dissolve and then add 12.5 ml. of glacial acetic acid.

B. Weigh 120.0 gm. of sodium nitrite, $NaNO_3$, and dissolve in 180 ml. of water.

Place the beaker containing solution A in a fume hood and to it, add 210 ml. of solution B. Bubble air through this solution until all fumes of nitrous oxide are driven off. Filter. This reagent is stable for about 1 month when stored in a refrigerator.

(C-66a)   Sodium Acetate, Saturated

Heat 100 ml. water to 45° C. and add 130 gm. of sodium acetate, $NaC_2H_3O_2 \cdot 3H_2O$. Mix well and place in a 37° C. water bath overnight. Cool to room temperature and allow excess sodium acetate crystals to settle out.

(C-66b)   Sodium Acetate, Half-Saturated

Dilute the above supernatant solution with an equal volume of water.

(C-67)   Wash Solution, Saturated with Potassium Sodium Cobaltinitrite

Weigh 0.070 gm. of potassium sulfate, K_2SO_4, and dissolve in 100 ml. of water. Slowly add 25 ml of half-saturated sodium acetate and 12.5 ml. of sodium cobaltinitrite reagent. Allow to stand for about 30 minutes and then filter through a sintered glass filter. Wash the precipitate twice with 70% ethyl alcohol and once with 95% ethyl alcohol. Transfer the precipitate to an Erlenmeyer flask and prepare a saturated solution with 10% ethyl alcohol. Allow any excess of the precipitate to remain in the bottom of the flask. Remove and filter a portion of the supernatant on the day of use.

(C-68)   Glycine, 7.5%

Weigh 7.5 gm. of glycine and transfer to a 100 ml. volumetric flask. Dissolve and dilute to volume with water. Add 5 drops of chloroform as a preservative.

(C-69)   Sodium Carbonate, 25%

Weigh 25.0 gm. of anhydrous sodium carbonate, Na_2CO_3, and transfer to a 100 ml. volumetric flask containing about 50 ml. of water. Dissolve and dilute to volume with water and mix. It may be necessary to warm the solution slightly to aid in dissolving the carbonate. Store in a warm place in a polyethylene bottle.

(C-70)   Phenol Reagent of Folin-Ciocalteu, Stock

Weigh 100 gm. of sodium tungstate, $Na_2WO_4 \cdot 2H_2O$, and 25.0 gm. of sodium molybdate, $Na_2MoO_4 \cdot 2H_2O$, and transfer to a 2-liter boiling flask containing 700 ml. of water. Swirl to dissolve and add 50 ml. of 85% orthophosphoric acid and 100 ml. of concentrated hydrochloric acid. Attach a reflux condenser to the flask (apparatus must have ground glass joints) and reflux gently for 10 hours. Add 150 gm. of lithium sulfate, Li_2SO_4, 50 ml. of water, and 2 or 3 drops of bromine. Place the flask in a fume hood without the condenser and boil the mixture for 15 minutes to remove excess bromine. Cool to room temperature and dilute to 1 liter with water. This reagent should be yellow without any trace of a green tint. If it turns green during storage it can be restored by adding 2 or 3 drops more of bromine and boiling again. Store in a refrigerator.

(C-71)   Potassium Standard, 0.2 mg. K/ml.

Weigh 0.446 gm. of potassium sulfate, K_2SO_4, and transfer to a 1-liter volumetric flask. Dissolve and dilute to volume with water. Mix thoroughly.

(C-72)   Standard Silver Nitrate Solution

Weigh 2.907 gm. of silver nitrate and transfer to a 1-liter volumetric flask. Dissolve and dilute to volume. Mix thoroughly. One milliliter is equivalent to 1 mg. of sodium chloride. Standardize against sodium chloride and adjust if necessary. Store in a brown bottle.

(C-73)   Thiocyanate Solution, Standard

Weigh 1.7 gm. of potassium thiocyanate, KCNS, or 1.4 gm. of ammonium thiocyanate, NH_4CNS, and transfer to a 1-liter volumetric flask. Dissolve and dilute to volume with water. Mix thoroughly. Standardize against the standard silver nitrate solution under the conditions called for in the chloride procedure. Adjust if necessary so that 5 ml. of the standard thiocyanate solution are equivalent to 5 ml. of the standard silver nitrate solution.

(C-74)   Diphenylcarbazone Indicator

Weigh 0.100 gm. of diphenylcarbazone and transfer to a 100 ml. volumetric flask. Dissolve and dilute to volume with 95% ethyl alcohol. Mix thoroughly. Store in a refrigerator in a brown bottle.

(C-75)   Standard Sodium Chloride, 10 meq/L. or 58.5 mg.%

Weigh 0.585 gm. of dry sodium chloride and transfer to a 1-liter volumetric flask. Dissolve and dilute to volume. Mix thoroughly.

(C-76)   Standard Mercuric Nitrate Solution

Weigh 3.0 gm. of mercuric nitrate and transfer to a 1-liter volumetric flask containing about 500 ml. of water and 20 ml. of 2 N nitric acid. Swirl to dissolve and dilute to volume with water. Mix thoroughly. Standardize this solution as follows: pipet 2 ml. of standard sodium chloride solution into a small flask, add 4 drops of diphenylcarbazone indicator, and titrate with the mercuric nitrate solution. The number of milliliters of the mercuric nitrate solution used equals the value E used in the calculations of the chloride procedure. The standard mercuric nitrate solution is stable indefinitely.

(C-77)   Lactic Acid, 10%

Pipet 11.8 ml. of concentrated lactic acid (85%) into a 100 ml. volumetric flask. Dilute to volume with water and mix.

(C-78) Lactic Acid, 0.1 N

Pipet 4.4 ml. of concentrated lactic acid (85%) into a 500 ml. volumetric flask. Dilute to volume with water. This solution is stable for about 2 weeks.

(C-79) Sodium Hydroxide, 5 N (carbonate-free)

Prepare by using a nearly saturated solution of sodium hydroxide that has been standardized:

$$\text{Ml.} \times \text{N} = \text{Ml.} \times \text{N}$$

(C-80) Sodium Oxalate, 0.100 N

Dry about 10 gm. of anhydrous sodium oxalate, $Na_2C_2O_4$, in a 110° C. oven for 12 hours or overnight. Cool in a desiccator; then weigh 6.7000 gm. and transfer to a 1-liter volumetric flask. Add about 200 ml. of water and 5 ml. of concentrated sulfuric acid. Swirl to dissolve and dilute to volume with water. Mix thoroughly.

(C-81) Potassium Permanganate, 0.100 N

Weigh 3.2 gm. of potassium permanganate, $KMnO_4$, and transfer to a 1-liter volumetric flask. Dissolve and dilute to volume with water. Mix and allow to stand in a dark place at room temperature for about a week. A sediment of MnO_2 will form. Being careful not to disturb the sediment, slowly pour about 700 ml. of the solution into a brown, glass-stoppered bottle. Discard the remainder. This solution will be diluted and standardized before it is used in the determination of calcium. Store in a refrigerator.

(C-82) Ammonium Oxalate, 4%

Weigh 40.0 gm. of ammonium oxalate, $(NH_4)_2C_2O_4$, and transfer to a 1-liter volumetric flask. Dissolve and dilute to volume with water. Mix.

(C-83) Ammonium Hydroxide, Dilute (0.5%)

Transfer 2 ml. of concentrated (28%) ammonium hydroxide to a flask and add 98 ml. of water. This solution is stable for about a month.

(C-84) Sulfuric Acid, Dilute (1 N)

Transfer 28.0 ml. of concentrated sulfuric acid to a 1-liter Pyrex volumetric flask containing about 600 ml. of water. Swirl to mix and allow to cool to room temperature. Dilute to volume with water and mix.

(C-85) Potassium Hydroxide, 1.25 N

Weigh 70.0 gm. of potassium hydroxide pellets and transfer to a 1-liter volumetric flask containing about 600 ml. of water. Swirl to dissolve. Cool to room temperature and dilute to volume with water. Stopper and mix well. Store in a polyethylene bottle.

(C-86) EDTA Solution

Weigh 0.395 gm. of disodium ethylenediaminetetra-acetate dihydrate and transfer to a 1-liter volumetric flask. Dissolve and dilute to volume with water. Mix well. Store in a Pyrex or polyethylene bottle.

(C-87) Cal-Red Indicator

Weigh 1.0 gm. of "Cal-Red Dilute"* and transfer to a mortar of about 50 ml. capacity. Add 10 ml. of distilled water and grind with the pestle until a homogeneous suspension is obtained. (Not all of the material will dissolve.) This suspension should be stored in a refrigerator and it is usually stable for about 2 weeks. If, however, it does not give sharp end points, then it must be discarded. With some batches of indicator it may be necessary to prepare a new suspension daily.

---

*Scientific Service Laboratories, Inc., Dallas, Texas.

(C-88) Sodium Citrate, 0.05 M

Weigh 14.7 gm. of sodium citrate, $Na_3C_6H_5O_7 \cdot 2H_2O$, and transfer to a 1-liter volumetric flask. Dissolve and dilute to volume with water. Store in a Pyrex or polyethylene bottle.

(C-89) Calcium Standard (1 ml. = 100 μg Ca)

Using an analytical balance, weigh 0.2472 gm. of calcium carbonate, $CaCO_3$, and transfer to a 1-liter volumetric flask. Slowly add 7 ml. of dilute hydrochloric acid (1 part concentrated HCl + 9 parts distilled H_2O). Allow to stand until all $CaCO_3$ is dissolved and then add about 900 ml. of distilled water. Adjust the pH to 6.0 with 50% ammonium acetate. Dilute to volume with water and mix thoroughly. Store in a Pyrex or polyethlene bottle.

(C-90) Ammonium Oxalate, 10%

Weigh 10.0 gm. of ammonium oxalate, $(NH_4)_2C_2O_4$, and transfer to a 100 ml. volumetric flask. Dissolve and dilute to volume with water. Mix well and store in a polyethylene bottle.

(C-91) Hydrochloric Acid, 1 N

Using a 10 ml. serological pipet attached to a rubber bulb or vacuum line, transfer 8.4 ml. of concentrated hydrochloric acid to a 100 ml. volumetric flask containing about 70 ml. of water. Dilute to volume and mix. *Do not pipet strong acids by mouth.*

(C-92) Ammonium Hydroxide, 5%

Mix 20 ml. of concentrated ammonium hydroxide, NH_4OH (28%), with 80 ml. of water. Store in a glass-stoppered bottle.

(C-93) Molybdate Reagent

Weigh 25.0 gm. of ammonium molybdate, $(NH_4)_2MoO_4$, and transfer to a 1-liter volumetric flask containing about 300 ml. of water. Swirl to dissolve. Add 300 ml. of 10 N sulfuric acid (C-94). Dilute to volume with water and mix. Store in a glass-stoppered bottle.

(C-94) Sulfuric Acid, 10 N

Measure 282 ml. of concentrated sulfuric acid and add slowly to a 1-liter Pyrex volumetric flask containing about 600 ml. of water. Carefully swirl to mix. Cool to room temperature and dilute to volume with water. Mix.

(C-95) Reducing Reagent (aminonaphtholsulfonic Acid)

Weigh 14.64 gm. of sodium bisulfite, $NaHSO_3$, and 0.25 gm. of 1-amino-2-naphthol-4-sulfonic acid* and transfer to a 100 ml. volumetric flask containing about 75 ml. of water. Swirl to dissolve. Add 0.5 gm. of sodium sulfite, Na_2SO_3. Dissolve and dilute to volume. Transfer to a brown bottle and store in a refrigerator. If a precipitate forms, filter in the refrigerator so the reagent does not become warm.

(C-96) Phosphorus, Stock Standard, 0.1 mg. P/ml.

Weigh 0.4394 gm. of monobasic potassium phosphate, KH_2PO_4, and transfer to a 1-liter volumetric flask. Add 10 ml. of 10 N sulfuric acid and dilute to volume with water. Mix thoroughly.

(C-97) Iodine Indicator

a. Stock, 0.1 N iodine in 30% potassium iodide
    Weigh 13.0 gm. of elemental iodine and 300 gm. of potassium iodide and transfer to a 1-liter volumetric flask. Dissolve and dilute to volume with water. Mix thoroughly.
b. Working, 0.002 N iodine in 2% potassium iodide
    Pipet 20.0 ml. of stock iodine solution into a 1-liter volumetric flask containing about 600 ml. of water. Add 14.0 gm. of potassium iodide. Dissolve and dilute to volume with water. Mix thoroughly. Store in a brown bottle.

---

*Eastman, purified.

(C-98) Sodium Hydroxide, 0.05 N

Prepare from a concentrated solution of sodium hydroxide that has been standardized.

$$\text{Ml.} \times \text{N} = \text{Ml.} \times \text{N}$$

Standardize this dilute solution against a standard acid solution and adjust if necessary to exactly 0.05 N.

(C-99) Phosphate Buffer, pH 7.0

Weigh 5.785 gm. of dibasic sodium phosphate, Na_2HPO_4, and 3.532 gm. of monobasic potassium phosphate, KH_2PO_4, and transfer to a 1-liter volumetric flask. Dissolve and dilute to volume with water. Mix thoroughly.

(C-100) Olive Oil Substrate

Weigh 5.0 gm. of acacia and 0.4 gm. of sodium benzoate, C_6H_5COONa, and dissolve in 100 ml. of water. Transfer this solution to a blendor and add 100 ml. of pure olive oil. Blend for 10 minutes to obtain a homogeneous emulsion. Store in a refrigerator. Shake vigorously just before using.

(C-101) Thymolphthalein Indicator

Weigh 1.0 gm. of thymolphthalein and transfer to a 100 ml. volumetric flask. Dissolve and dilute to volume with 95% ethyl alcohol. Filter if necessary.

(C-102) Alkaline Buffer, 0.1 M Glycine, pH 10.5

Weigh 7.5 gm. of glycine and 0.095 gm. of magnesium chloride and transfer to a 1-liter volumetric flask containing about 750 ml. of water. Add 85 ml. of 1 N sodium hydroxide (C-60) and dilute to volume with water. Mix thoroughly. Store in a refrigerator.

(C-103) *p*-Nitrophenylphosphate, Stock Substrate

Dissolve 0.100 gm. of *p*-nitrophenylphosphate* in 25 ml. of water.

(C-104) Alkaline Buffered Substrate, pH 10.3 to 10.4

Mix equal volumes of alkaline buffer (C-102) and stock substrate (C-103).

(C-105) Sodium Hydroxide, 0.02 N

Pipet 20 ml. of 1 N NaOH (C-60) into a 1-liter volumetric flask and dilute to volume with water. Mix well.

(C-106) Acid Buffer, 0.09 M Citric Acid, pH 4.8

Weigh 18.907 gm. of citric acid and transfer to a 1-liter volumetric flask containing about 600 ml. of water. Add 180 ml. of 1 N sodium hydroxide (C-60) and 100 ml. of 0.1 N hydrochloric acid (C-25). Dilute to volume with water and mix. Store in a refrigerator.

(C-107) Acid Buffered Substrate, pH 4.8 to 4.9

Mix equal volumes of acid buffer (C-106) and stock substrate (C-103).

(C-108) Sodium Hydroxide, 0.1 N

Transfer 100 ml. of 1 N sodium hydroxide to a 1-liter volumetric flask and dilute to volume with water. Mix.

(C-109) Acetic Acid, 20% (v/v)

Transfer 20 ml. of glacial acetic acid to a 100 ml. volumetric flask and dilute to volume with water. Mix.

---

*Available from Sigma Chemical Co., St. Louis, Mo.

(C-110) Tartrate Acid Buffer, pH 4.8

Weigh 18.9 gm. of citric acid, $C_6H_8O_7 \cdot H_2O$, and 6.0 gm. of L (+) tartaric acid and transfer to a beaker containing about 600 ml. of water. Stir to dissolve. Add 100 ml. of 0.1 N hydrochloric acid (C-25) and mix. Add enough 1.0 N sodium hydroxide (C-60) to bring the pH to 4.8. Use a pH meter. Transfer quantitatively to a 1-liter volumetric flask and dilute to volume with water. Store in a refrigerator.

(C-111) *p*-Nitrophenol, 10 mM/L.

Weigh 0.1391 gm. of *p*-nitrophenol and transfer to a 100 ml. volumetric flask. Dissolve and dilute to volume with water.

(C-112) Phosphate Buffer, 0.1 M, pH 7.4

a. Disodium phosphate, 0.1 M. Weigh 14.2 gm. of disodium phosphate, Na_2HPO_4, and transfer to a 1-liter volumetric flask. Dissolve and dilute to volume with water. Mix.
b. Potassium dihydrogen phosphate, 0.1 M. Weigh 13.609 gm. of potassium dihydrogen phosphate, KH_2PO_4, and transfer to a 1-liter volumetric flask. Dissolve and dilute to volume with water. Mix.
Mix 420 ml. of 0.1 M disodium phosphate with 80 ml. of 0.1 M potassium dihydrogen phosphate.

(C-113) SGOT Substrate, α-Ketoglutarate, 2 mM/L.; *dl*-Aspartate, 200 mM/L.

Weigh 0.0292 gm. of α-ketoglutaric acid and 2.66 gm. of *dl*-aspartic acid and transfer to a small beaker. Add 20 ml. of 1 N sodium hydroxide and stir until the acids are dissolved. Using a pH meter, adjust the solution to pH 7.4 by adding 1 N sodium hydroxide dropwise. Transfer quantitatively to a 100 ml. volumetric flask, using buffer C-112 to rinse the beaker. Dilute to volume with buffer and mix. Add 1 ml. of chloroform as a preservative and store in a refrigerator.

(C-114) SGPT Substrate, α-Ketoglutarate, 2 mM/L.; *dl*-Alanine, 200 mM/L.

Weigh 0.0292 gm. of α-ketoglutaric acid and 1.78 gm. of *dl*-alanine and transfer to a 100 ml. beaker. Add 20 ml. of water and stir to dissolve. Using a pH meter, adjust the solution to pH 7.4 by adding 1 N sodium hydroxide dropwise. This will require about 10 drops. Transfer quantitatively to a 100 ml. volumetric flask, using buffer C-112 to rinse the beaker. Dilute to volume with buffer and mix. Add 1 ml. of chloroform as a preservative and store in a refrigerator.

(C-115) Color Reagent (2,4-Dinitrophenylhydrazine, 1 mM/L.)

Weigh 0.0396 gm. of dinitrophenylhydrazine and transfer to a beaker containing 200 ml. of 1 N hydrochloric acid (C-91). Stir until dissolved. Store in a refrigerator.

(C-116) Sodium Hydroxide, 0.4 N

This may be prepared from a concentrated solution of sodium hydroxide that has been standardized.
Or: Weigh 16 gm. of sodium hydroxide pellets and transfer to a 1-liter volumetric flask. Dissolve and dilute to volume with water. Mix well and store in a polyethylene bottle.

(C-117) Pyruvate Standard, 2 mM/L.

Weigh 0.0200 gm. of pure sodium pyruvate and dissolve in 100 ml. of phosphate buffer.

(C-118) Gold Chloride, 0.5% in water

Weigh 0.5 gm. of gold chloride, $AuCl_3 \cdot HCl \cdot 3H_2O$, and transfer to a 100 ml. volumetric flask. Dissolve and dilute to volume with water. Store in a refrigerator.

(C-119) Bromide, Stock Standard, 20 mg./ml.

Weigh 2.575 gm. of sodium bromide, NaBr, and transfer to a 100 ml. volumetric flask. Dissolve and dilute to volume with water. Mix.

(C-120)   Color Reagent (Ferric-Mercuric Reagent)

Weigh 40.0 gm. of mercuric chloride, $HgCl_2$, and transfer to a 1-liter volumetric flask containing about 800 ml. of water. Swirl to dissolve. Add 120 ml. of 1 N hydrochloric acid (C-91) and 40.0 gm. of ferric nitrate, $Fe(NO_3)_3 \cdot 9H_2O$. When all the ferric nitrate is dissolved, dilute to volume with water and mix.

(C-121)   Salicylate, Stock Solution, 1 mg./ml.

Weigh 1.160 gm. of sodium salicylate, $C_7H_5O_3 \cdot Na$, and transfer to a 1-liter volumetric flask. Dissolve and dilute to volume with water. Add a few drops of chloroform as a preservative. Store in a refrigerator. This solution is stable for about 6 months.

(C-122)   Salicylate, Standard Solution, 0.05 mg./ml.

Pipet 5.0 ml. of stock salicylate solution (C-121) into a 100 ml. volumetric flask and dilute to volume with water. Add a few drops of chloroform as a preservative. Store in a refrigerator. This solution is stable for about 6 months.

(C-123)   Salicylate, Standard Solution, 0.20 mg./ml.

Pipet 20.0 ml. of stock salicylate solution (C-121) into a 100 ml. volumetric flask and dilute to volume with water. Add a few drops of chloroform as a preservative. Store in a refrigerator. This solution is stable for about 6 months.

(C-124)   Trichloroacetic Acid, 5%

Dilute 50 ml. of 10% trichloroacetic acid (C-63) with 50 ml. of water. Mix.

(C-125)   Ammonium Sulfamate, 0.5%

Weigh 0.50 gm. of ammonium sulfamate, $NH_2SO_3NH_4$, and transfer to a 100 ml. volumetric flask. Dissolve and dilute to volume with water. Store in a refrigerator.

(C-126)   Coupling Reagent (Naphthyl Ethylenediamine Solution)

Weigh 0.20 gm. of *n*-(1-naphthyl)-ethylenediamine dihydrochloride, $C_{10}H_7NHCH_2CH_2NH_2 \cdot 2HCl$, and transfer to a 100 ml. volumetric flask. Dissolve and dilute to volume with 95% ethyl alcohol. Mix and transfer to a brown bottle. Store in a refrigerator.

(C-127)   Sulfanilamide, Stock Standard, 0.1 mg./ml.

Weigh 0.100 gm. of pure sulfanilamide and transfer to a 1-liter volumetric flask. Dissolve and dilute to volume with water. Store in a refrigerator.

(C-128)   Hydrochloric Acid, 0.5 N

Using a 5 ml. serological pipet attached to a rubber bulb or vacuum line, transfer 4.2 ml. of concentrated hydrochloric acid to a 100 ml. volumetric flask containing about 70 ml. of water. Dilute to volume and mix. *Do not pipet strong acids by mouth.*

(C-129)   Calcium Chloride, 2.5%

Weigh 2.5 gm. of calcium chloride, $CaCl_2$, and transfer to a 100 ml. volumetric flask. Dissolve and dilute to volume with water. Mix.

(C-130)   Sodium Hydroxide, 0.2 N

Dilute 20.0 ml. of 1 N sodium hydroxide (C-60) with 80.0 ml. of water. Mix well. Store in a polyethylene bottle.

(C-131)   Protein Standard, 3 mg./ml.

Weigh 0.300 gm. of pure albumin* and transfer to a 100 ml. volumetric flask containing about

---

*May be obtained from Sigma Chemical Co., St. Louis, Mo.

50 ml. of physiological saline (C-34). Swirl flask to dissolve and dilute to volume with saline. Stopper and mix. Pour about 3 ml. aliquots of the standard into Pyrex test tubes and freeze for future use. When thawing protein standards, place the tubes in a beaker of water at room temperature. *Never use hot water.* Once a standard has been thawed, do not refreeze. Discard the unused portion.

(C-132) Zinc Sulfate, 10%

Weigh 100 gm. of zinc sulfate, $ZnSO_4 \cdot 7H_2O$, and transfer to a 1-liter volumetric flask containing about 600 ml. of water. Swirl to dissolve and dilute to volume with water. The 10% zinc sulfate and 0.5 N sodium hydroxide solutions should be so related that when 10 ml. of the zinc sulfate are diluted with 50 ml. of water and titrated with the sodium hydroxide, 10.8 to 11.2 ml. of the 0.5 N NaOH are required to produce a permanent pink with phenolphthalein.

(C-133) Zinc Sulfate, Working Solution

Mix 100 ml. of 10% zinc sulfate with 700 ml. of water.

(C-134) Sodium Carbonate, 4.0 N

Weigh 212 gm. of anhydrous sodium carbonate, Na_2CO_3, and transfer to a 1-liter volumetric flask. Dissolve and dilute to volume with water. Mix thoroughly.

(C-135) Hydrochloric Acid, 2.0 N

Measure 167 ml. of concentrated hydrochloric acid, HCl, and transfer to a 1-liter volumetric flask containing about 600 ml. of water. Dilute to volume and mix.

(C-136) Sulfuric Acid, 7.0 N

Measure 195 ml. of concentrated sulfuric acid, H_2SO_4, and transfer slowly to a Pyrex 1-liter volumetric flask containing about 700 ml. of cold distilled water. Place flask in an ice bath. When the contents of the flask cool to the temperature of the bath, swirl the flask to mix and return it to the ice bath for about 10 minutes. Then remove the flask from the ice bath and allow the solution to come to room temperature. Dilute to volume with water and mix.

(C-137) Sulfuric Acid, Dilute

Dilute 800 ml. of 7 N sulfuric acid to 2 liters with water.

(C-138) Iodine Standards

a. Concentrated Stock Standard, 100 $\mu g/ml.$
   Weigh 0.1308 gm. of desiccated potassium iodide, KI, and transfer to a 1-liter volumetric flask. Dissolve and dilute to volume with double-distilled water. Mix thoroughly.
b. Dilute Stock Standard, 0.2 $\mu g/ml.$
   Pipet 2 ml. of concentrated stock standard into a 1-liter volumetric flask. Dilute to volume with double-distilled water and mix thoroughly.
c. Dilute Working Standard, 0.04 $\mu g/ml.$
   Pipet 10 ml. of dilute stock standard into a 50 ml. volumetric flask and dilute to volume with double-distilled water. Mix thoroughly.

(C-139) Ceric Ammonium Sulfate, 0.02 N

Transfer 500 ml. of water to a 1-liter volumetric flask. Add 230 ml. of 7 N sulfuric acid. Weigh 12.65 gm. of ceric ammonium sulfate, $Ce(SO_4)_2 \cdot 2(NH_4)_2SO_4 \cdot 2H_2O$,* and add to the flask. Swirl to dissolve. Dilute to volume with water and mix.

(C-140) Sodium Arsenite, 0.1 N

Weigh 12.99 gm. of sodium arsenite, $NaAsO_2$, and transfer to a 1-liter volumetric flask. Dissolve and dilute to volume with water. Mix.

---

*The ceric salt may be obtained from the G. Frederick Smith Co., Columbus, Ohio.

(C-141) Antifoam Solution

Dissolve 35 gm. of Dow Corning Antifoam AF Emulsion in 500 ml. of water. A Waring blendor will facilitate the mixing of the two ingredients.

(C-142) Trichloroacetic Acid, 20%

Dissolve and dilute a ¼ lb. bottle (see C-63) of trichloroacetic acid to 567 ml. Mallinckrodt trichloroacetic acid AR is recommended because of its extremely low iron content.

(C-143) 2:2′-Dipyridyl, 0.4%

Weigh 0.40 gm. of 2:2′-dipyridyl and transfer to a 100 ml. volumetric flask containing 5 ml. of glacial acetic acid. Swirl to dissolve. Dilute to volume with iron-free water.

(C-144) Iron, Stock Standard, 100 mg./100 ml.

Weigh exactly 0.100 gm. of pure iron wire and transfer to a 100 ml. volumetric flask. Add 50 ml. of 2 N HCl and allow the iron wire to dissolve. This may take several days. When all the wire is dissolved, dilute to volume with water.

(C-145) Pandy's Reagent

Weigh 10 gm. of phenol, C_6H_5OH, and dissolve in 100 ml. of water. Place in an incubator at 37° C. for 2 or 3 days. Use only the clear supernatant solution.

(C-146) Ammonium Sulfate, Saturated

Weigh 80 gm. of ammonium sulfate, $(NH_4)_2SO_4$, and dissolve in 100 ml. of water.

(C-147) Formaldehyde, 2%

Mix 5 ml. of formalin (40% formaldehyde) with 95 ml. of water.

(C-148) Sodium Nitrite, 0.06%

Weigh 0.060 gm. of sodium nitrite, $NaNO_2$, and transfer to a 100 ml. volumetric flask. Dissolve and dilute to volume with water. Mix. Transfer to a brown bottle and store in a refrigerator.

(C-149) Töpfer's Reagent

Weigh 0.5 gm. of dimethylaminoazobenzene and dissolve in 100 ml. of 95% ethyl alcohol.

(C-150) Phenolphthalein Indicator, 0.1%

Weigh 0.1 gm. of phenolphthalein and dissolve in 100 ml. of 95% ethyl alcohol.

(C-151) Benzidine, Saturated, in Glacial Acetic Acid

The benzidine powder must be labelled "for blood tests." Weigh 4 gm. of benzidine powder and transfer to a brown bottle. Add 50 ml. of glacial acetic acid. Shake to dissolve as much as possible. This solution is stable for about 1 month.

(C-152) Sodium Hydroxide, 0.01 N

Pipet 1.0 ml. of 1 N sodium hydroxide (C-60) into a 100 ml. volumetric flask. Dilute to volume with water and mix.

(C-153) Ferric Chloride, 10%

Weigh 10 gm. of ferric chloride, $FeCl_3$, and transfer to a 100 ml. volumetric flask. Dissolve and dilute to volume with water. Mix.

(C-154) Sodium Carbonate, 1%

Weigh 1 gm. of sodium carbonate, Na_2CO_3, and transfer to a 100 ml. volumetric flask. Dissolve and dilute to volume with water. Mix.

(C-155)   Starch, 1%

Heat 100 ml. of distilled water to boiling. Add a mixture of 1 gm. of soluble starch in 5 ml. of distilled water, stirring constantly until the fluid again reaches the boiling point. Let cool. If the solution is to be kept more than a few days, add a few drops of toluol or chloroform and store in a refrigerator.

(C-156)   Gram's Iodine Solution

Weigh 0.4 gm. of iodine and 0.8 gm. of potassium iodide and dissolve in 120 ml. of water. Store in a brown bottle.

(C-157)   Acetic Acid, 1.0%

Pipet 1 ml. of glacial acetic acid into a 100 ml. volumetric flask. Dilute to volume with water and mix.

(C-158)   Acetic Acid, 5%

Pipet 5 ml. of glacial acetic acid into a 100 ml. volumetric flask. Dilute to volume with water and mix.

(C-159)   Sodium Chloride, Saturated

Weigh 40 gm. of sodium chloride, NaCl, and transfer to a flask or beaker containing 100 ml. of hot distilled water. Stir to dissolve as much as possible. Allow any undissolved salt to remain on the bottom of the bottle in which the solution is stored.

(C-160)   Acetic Acid, 50%

Add 50 ml. of glacial acetic acid to 50 ml. of water. Mix.

(C-161)   Sulfosalicylic Acid, 20%

Weigh 20 gm. of sulfosalicylic acid and transfer to a 100 ml. volumetric flask. Dissolve and dilute to volume with water. Mix.

(C-162)   Exton's Reagent

Weigh 200 gm. of sodium sulfate, $Na_2SO_4 \cdot 10H_2O$, and transfer to a 1-liter volumetric flask containing 800 ml. of water. Swirl to dissolve. Add 50 gm. of sulfosalicylic acid. Dilute to volume with water and mix thoroughly.

(C-163)   Robert's Reagent

To 1 liter of distilled water, add magnesium sulfate, with stirring, until no more dissolves. Add 200 ml. of concentrated nitric acid. Mix.

(C-164)   Benedict's Qualitative Reagent

Using the rough balance, weigh out 100 gm. of anhydrous sodium carbonate (Na_2CO_3) *or* 200 gm. of hydrated sodium carbonate ($Na_2CO_3 \cdot 10H_2O$). Place in a Pyrex container. Add about 800 ml. of distilled water. Add 173 gm. of sodium citrate. Heat to dissolve. Cool to room temperature. Using the rough balance, weigh out 17.3 gm. of copper sulfate ($CuSO_4 \cdot 5H_2O$). With the aid of heat, dissolve in 100 ml. of distilled water. Cool to room temperature. With constant stirring, pour the copper sulfate solution slowly into the solution of carbonate and citrate salts. Make up to 1 liter with distilled water. Mix. This preparation keeps indefinitely.

(C-165)   Sodium Nitroprusside, Saturated

Add 40 gm. of sodium nitroprusside (sodium nitroferricyanide) to 100 ml. of water in a brown bottle. Shake to dissolve as much as possible. Allow any undissolved salt to remain in the bottom of the bottle.

(C-166) Sodium Nitroprusside Reagent

Weigh 10 gm. of sodium nitroprusside (sodium nitroferricyanide) and transfer to a flask containing 95 ml. of water and 2 ml. of concentrated sulfuric acid. Mix and store in a brown bottle.

(C-167) Rantzman's Reagent

Weigh 37.5 gm. of ammonium nitrate and 2.5 gm. of sodium nitroprusside (sodium nitroferricyanide) and transfer to a 100 ml. volumetric flask. Dissolve and dilute to volume with water. Mix. Store in a brown bottle. This reagent is stable for about 2 months.

(C-168) Sodium Hydroxide, 40%

Weigh 40 gm. of sodium hydroxide pellets and transfer to a Pyrex 100 ml. volumetric flask containing about 50 ml. of water. Swirl to dissolve. Cool to room temperature, dilute to volume, and mix.

(C-169) Salicylaldehyde, 10%

Place 10 ml. of salicylaldehyde (salicylous acid) in a container. Add 90 ml. of 95% ethyl alcohol. Mix.

(C-170) Barium Chloride, 10%

Weigh 10 gm. of barium chloride and transfer to a 100 ml. volumetric flask. Dissolve and dilute to volume with water. Mix.

(C-171) Fouchet's Reagent

Weigh 25 gm. of trichloroacetic acid and transfer to a flask containing 100 ml. of water. Add 10 ml. of 10% ferric chloride solution (C-153) and mix.

(C-172) Iodine, Ethyl Alcohol Solution

Weigh 0.7 gm. of iodine and 0.5 gm. of potassium iodide and transfer to a 125 ml. Erlenmeyer flask. Add 5 ml. of water and mix. Add 95 ml. of 95% ethyl alcohol and mix.

(C-173) Acetic Acid, 30%

Add 30 ml. of glacial acetic acid to 70 ml. of water and mix.

(C-174) Lugol's Solution

Weigh 5 gm. of iodine and 10 gm. of potassium iodide and transfer to a brown bottle. Add 100 ml. of water and mix.

(C-175) Ehrlich's Reagent

Pour 100 ml. of distilled water into a brown bottle. Add 0.7 gm. of *p*-dimethylaminobenzaldehyde. Carefully add 150 ml. of concentrated hydrochloric acid. Mix.

(C-176) Bromine Water

Cautiously add a few drops of liquid bromine to 100 ml. of distilled water. Mix. Store in a brown bottle. When the solution loses its color, prepare a fresh solution.

(C-177) Orthotoluidine Reagent

Dissolve 4 gm. of orthotoluidine in 100 ml. of glacial acetic acid. Keep in a brown bottle and store in a refrigerator. Prepare fresh every month.

(C-178) Guaiac Reagent

Weigh 1 gm. of powdered guaiac and transfer to a brown bottle. Add 10 ml. of 95% ethyl alcohol and mix. Add 10 ml. of 30% hydrogen peroxide and mix. This reagent is stable for about a month.

(C-179)   Sulkowitch Reagent

Weigh 2.5 gm. of ammonium oxalate and 2.5 gm. of oxalic acid and transfer to a brown bottle. Add 145 ml. of water and 5 ml. of glacial acetic acid. Mix.

(C-180)   Benedict's Quantitative Reagent

The copper sulfate used must be weighed on the analytical balance. All other reagents may be weighed on the rough balance. Weigh out the first four reagents listed below; place in separate labelled containers; and then prepare 5 ml. of the 5% potassium ferrocyanide solution.

Copper Sulfate (crystallized) $CuSO_4 \cdot 5H_2O$	18.0 gm.
Sodium Carbonate (anhydrous) Na_2CO_3	100.0 gm.
(or 200 gm. of crystalline $Na_2CO_3 \cdot 10H_2O$)	
Sodium Citrate (or Potassium Citrate)	200.0 gm.
Potassium Thiocyanate (Sulfocyanate)	125.0 gm.
Potassium Ferrocyanide, 5%	5.0 ml.

Pour about 600 ml. of distilled water into a 1-liter Pyrex beaker. Heat to about 70° C. With stirring, transfer the above weights of sodium carbonate, sodium citrate, and potassium thiocyanate to the beaker. Stir until dissolved. Filter. Dissolve the copper sulfate in about 100 ml. of distilled water. With stirring, slowly add this copper solution to the 1-liter beaker. Now add the 5.0 ml. of the 5% potassium ferrocyanide solution. Mix. Allow the solution to cool. Transfer all of the solution to a 1-liter volumetric flask. Add distilled water to the 1-liter mark. Mix. Five milliliters of this reagent should be reduced by 1.0 ml. of a 1% glucose solution.

(C-181)   Hydrochloric Acid, 5% (v/v)

Dilute 5 ml. of concentrated hydrochloric acid with 95 ml. of water. Mix.

(C-182)   Esbach's Reagent

Weigh 1 gm. of picric acid and 2 gm. of citric acid and dissolve in 100 ml. of water.

(C-183)   Sulfosalicylic Acid, 3%

Weigh 3 gm. of sulfosalicylic acid and transfer to a 100 ml. volumetric flask. Dissolve and dilute to volume with water. Mix.

(C-184)   Sulfuric Acid, 2 N

Measure 56 ml. of concentrated sulfuric acid in a 100 ml. graduated cylinder and transfer to a 1-liter volumetric flask containing about 600 ml. of water. Swirl to mix. Cool to room temperature. Dilute to volume with water and mix.

(C-185)   Nitrosonaphthol Reagent, 0.1%

Weigh 0.100 gm. of 1-nitroso-2-naphthol and transfer to a 100 ml. volumetric flask. Dissolve and dilute to volume with 95% ethyl alcohol. Mix. Transfer to a brown bottle and store in a refrigerator.

(C-186)   Sodium Nitrite, 2.5%

Weigh 2.5 gm. of sodium nitrite, $NaNO_2$, and transfer to a 100 ml. volumetric flask. Dissolve and dilute to volume with water. Mix. Store in a refrigerator.

(C-187)   Sodium Nitrite, 0.5%

Pipet 20 ml. of 2.5% sodium nitrite into a 100 ml. volumetric flask. Dilute to volume with water and mix. Store in a refrigerator.

(C-188)   5-HIAA Standard, 10 mg./100 ml.

Weigh 0.0200 gm. of the mono-dicyclohexylammonium salt of 5-hydroxyindole-3-acetic acid*

---

*May be obtained from Sigma Chemical Co., St. Louis, Mo.

and transfer to a 100 ml. volumetric flask. Dissolve and dilute to volume with 0.1 N sulfuric acid. Mix thoroughly and transfer to a brown bottle. Store in a refrigerator.

(C-189)   Ferric Chloride, 5%

Weigh 5.0 gm. of $FeCl_3$ or 8.3 gm. of $FeCl_3 \cdot 6H_2O$ and transfer to a 100 ml. volumetric flask. Dissolve and dilute to volume with water. Mix.

(C-190)   PSP, Stock Standard, 120 mg./500 ml.

Weigh 0.120 gm. of phenolsulfonphthalein (phenol red) and transfer to a 500 ml. volumetric flask. Add 1 ml. of 10% NaOH. Dilute to volume with water. Mix thoroughly.

(C-191)   Cobalt Acetate, 1% in Methyl Alcohol

Weigh 1.0 gm. of cobalt (ous) acetate, $Co(CH_3COO)_2 \cdot 4H_2O$, and transfer to a 100 ml. volumetric flask. Dissolve and dilute to volume with absolute methyl alcohol. Mix.

(C-192)   Isopropylamine, 5% in Methyl Alcohol

Weigh 5.0 gm. of isopropylamine and transfer to a 100 ml. volumetric flask. Dissolve and dilute to volume with absolute methyl alcohol. Mix.

(C-193)   Sulfuric Acid, 10%

Place about 60 ml. of water in a Pyrex 100 ml. volumetric flask. Place the flask in an ice bath for about 10 minutes. Add 10 ml. of concentrated sulfuric acid to the flask and mix. Allow to come to room temperature. Dilute to volume with water and mix.

(C-194)   Sodium Acetate, 20%

Weigh 33.0 gm. of sodium acetate, $CH_3COONa \cdot 3H_2O$, and transfer to a 100 ml. volumetric flask. Dissolve and dilute to volume with water. Mix.

(C-195)   Ammonium Hydroxide, 10% (w/v)

Measure 36 ml. of concentrated ammonium hydroxide (28%) and transfer to a 100 ml. volumetric flask. Dilute to volume with water and mix.

(C-196)   Ammonium Oxalate, 0.1 M

Weigh 1.42 gm. of hydrated ammonium oxalate, $(NH_4)_2C_2O_4 \cdot H_2O$, and transfer to a 100 ml. volumetric flask. Dissolve and dilute to volume with water. Mix. Store in a refrigerator.

(C-197)   Ehrlich's Diazo Reagent

A. Add about 500 ml. of distilled water to a 1-liter volumetric flask. Add 50 ml. of concentrated hydrochloric acid. Weigh 5.0 gm. of sulfanilic acid and transfer to the volumetric flask. Add distilled water to the 1-liter mark. Mix.
B. Weigh 0.5 gm. of sodium nitrite. Dissolve in 100 ml. of distilled water. Pour into a brown bottle. Mix. Store in a refrigerator.

Place 25 ml. of solution A in a flask. Add 0.5 ml. in solution B. Mix. This reagent must be prepared just before use, as it does not keep.

(C-198)   Mercuric Chloride, 10%

Weigh 10 gm. of mercuric chloride, $HgCl_2$, and transfer to a 100 ml. volumetric flask. Dissolve and dilute to volume with water. Mix.

(C-199)   Calcium Chloride, 10%

Weigh 10 gm. of anhydrous calcium chloride, $CaCl_2$, and transfer to a 100 ml. volumetric flask. Dissolve and dilute to volume with water. Mix.

(C-200)   Zinc Acetate, Saturated Alcoholic Solution

Place 100 ml. of ethyl alcohol in a beaker. Add zinc acetate, with stirring, until no more dissolves.

(C-201)   Lead Nitrate, Saturated

Weigh 75 gm. of lead nitrate, $Pb(NO_3)_2$, on a rough balance and transfer to a 125 ml. Erlenmeyer flask. Add 100 ml. of hot distilled water and swirl to dissolve. Cool to room temperature. There should be some undissolved crystals of lead nitrate remaining in the bottom of the flask.

(C-202)   Barium Chloride, 5%

Weigh 5.0 gm. of barium chloride and transfer to a 100 ml. volumetric flask. Dissolve and dilute to the mark with distilled water. Store in a Pyrex or polyethylene bottle.

(C-203)   Perchloric Acid, 10%

Place about 700 ml. of double-distilled water in a 1-liter Pyrex volumetric flask and *slowly* add 143 ml. of 70% perchloric acid. Swirl to mix and cool to room temperature. Dilute to volume and mix again. Store in a brown glass bottle.

(C-204)   Chloric Acid Reagent

Weigh 500 gm. of potassium chlorate, $KClO_3$, and transfer to a 2000 ml. flask or beaker. Add 900 ml. of double-distilled water and heat on an electric hot plate to dissolve. *Do not use an open flame.* While this solution is still hot, *slowly* add 400 ml. of 70% perchloric acid with stirring. Cool to room temperature; then place in a freezing compartment for 24 hours. Decant and filter through glass wool while cold. Store the chloric acid in a brown glass bottle in a refrigerator. Flush the precipitated salts down the sink with plenty of water.

(C-205)   Chromic Acid

Weigh 3.03 gm. of chromium trioxide, CrO_3, and transfer to a 1-liter volumetric flask. Dissolve and dilute to volume with double-distilled water. Store in a brown bottle.

(C-206)   Arsenious Acid, 0.2 N

Weigh 9.89 gm. of arsenic trioxide, As_2O_3, and 7.0 gm. of sodium hydroxide, NaOH, and dissolve in 100 ml. of double-distilled water. When this is completely dissolved, add 300 ml. of water and 3 drops of phenolphthalein indicator. Add concentrated sulfuric acid dropwise with stirring until the red color disappears. Then add 42 ml. of concentrated sulfuric acid and dilute to 1000 ml. with water. Store in a polyethylene bottle.

(C-207)   Ceric Ammonium Sulfate, 0.04 N

Weigh 25.31 gm. of ceric ammonium sulfate, $(NH_4)_4Ce(SO_4)_4 \cdot 2H_2O$, and transfer to a 1-liter volumetric flask. Add 700 ml. of water and 103 ml. of concentrated sulfuric acid. Mix. Cool to room temperature and dilute to volume. Mix. Store in a polyethylene bottle.

(C-208)   Sulfuric Acid, 10 N, with 100 mg. NaCl/ml.

Weigh 100 gm. of sodium chloride, NaCl, and transfer to a 1-liter Pyrex volumetric flask. Add about 600 ml. of water and swirl to dissolve. *Slowly* add 278 ml. of concentrated sulfuric acid. Cool to room temperature and dilute to volume with water. Store in a Pyrex glass bottle.

(C-209)   Iodate, Stock Standard, 100 μg Iodine/ml.

Weigh 0.1685 gm. of potassium iodate, KIO_3, which has been dried in a vacuum desiccator, and transfer to a 1-liter volumetric flask. Dissolve and dilute to volume with double-distilled water.

(C-210)   Sodium Nitrate, Saturated

Weigh 130 gm. of sodium nitrate, $NaNO_3$, and transfer to a 125 ml. Erlenmeyer flask. Add 100 ml. of hot distilled water and mix. Cool to room temperature. There should be some undissolved crystals of sodium nitrate remaining in the bottom of the flask.

Appendix D

Bibliography

Alba, A.: Medical technology: A review for licensure examinations, ed. 5, Berkeley, 1964, Biotechnical Publications.

Annino, J. S.: Clinical chemistry; principles and procedures, ed. 3, Boston, 1964, Little, Brown & Co.

Bauer, J. D., Toro, G., and Ackermann, P. G.: Bray's clinical laboratory methods, ed. 5, St. Louis, 1962, The C. V. Mosby Co.

Cantarow, A., and Trumper, M.: Clinical biochemistry, ed. 5, Philadelphia, 1955, W. B. Saunders Co.

Davenport, H. W.: The ABC of acid-base chemistry, ed. 4, Chicago, 1958, The University of Chicago Press.

Frankel, S., and Reitman, S. editors: Gradwohl's clinical laboratory methods and diagnosis, ed. 6, vols. 1 and 2, St. Louis, 1963, The C. V. Mosby Co.

Hawk, P. B., Oser, B. L., and Summerson, Wm. H.: Practical physiological chemistry, ed. 13, New York, 1954, Blakiston Division, McGraw-Hill Book Co., Inc.

Henry, R. J.: Clinical chemistry; principles and technics, New York, 1964, Paul B. Hoeber, Inc., Medical Book Department of Harper & Row, Publishers.

Hepler, O. E.: Manual of clinical laboratory methods, ed. 4, Springfield, Ill., 1949, Charles C Thomas, Publisher.

Jaffe, B.: New world of chemistry, New York, 1955, Silver Burdett Co.

Kark, R., Lawrence, J., Pollak, J., Pirani, C., Muehrcke, R., and Silva, H.: A primer of urinalysis, ed. 2, New York, 1963, Paul B. Hoeber, Inc., Medical Book Department of Harper & Row, Publishers.

King, E. J., and Wootton, I. D. P.: Micro-analysis in medical biochemistry, ed. 3, New York, 1956, Grune & Stratton, Inc.

Kleiner, I. S., and Orten, J. M.: Biochemistry, ed. 6, St. Louis, 1962, The C. V. Mosby Co.

Lewis, J. R.: First-year college chemistry, ed. 7, New York, 1951, Barnes & Noble, Inc.

Meites, S., and Faulkner, W. R.: Manual of practical micro and general procedures in clinical chemistry, Springfield, Ill., 1962, Charles C Thomas, Publisher.

Moyer, C. A.: Fluid balance, Chicago, 1952, The Year Book Publishers, Inc.

Natelson, S.: Microtechniques of clinical chemistry, ed. 2, Springfield, Ill., 1961, Charles C Thomas, Publisher.

Page, L. B., and Culver, P. J., editors: A syllabus of laboratory examinations in clinical diagnosis, rev. ed., Cambridge, Mass., 1961, Harvard University Press.

Reiner, M., editor: Standard methods of clinical chemistry, vol. 1, New York, 1953, Academic Press, Inc.

Seligson, D., editor: Standard methods in clinical chemistry, vol. 2, New York, 1958, Academic Press, Inc.

Seligson, D., editor: Standard methods in clinical chemistry, vol. 3, New York, 1961, Academic Press, Inc.

Seligson, D., editor: Standard methods in clinical chemistry, vol. 4, New York, 1963, Academic Press, Inc.

Simmons, S. B., and Gentzkow, C. J.: Medical and public health laboratory methods, Philadelphia, 1956, Lea & Febiger.

Sobotka, H., and Stewart, C. P., editors: Advances in clinical chemistry, vol. 1, New York, 1958, Academic Press, Inc.

Sobotka, H., and Stewart, C. P., editors: Advances in clinical chemistry, vol. 2, New York, 1959, Academic Press, Inc.

Sobotka, H., and Stewart, C. P., editors: Advances in clinical chemistry, vol. 3, New York, 1960, Academic Press, Inc.

Sobotka, H., and Stewart, C. P., editors: Advances in clinical chemistry, vol. 4, New York, 1961, Academic Press, Inc.

Sobotka, H., and Stewart, C. P., editors: Advances in clinical chemistry, vol. 5, New York, 1962, Academic Press, Inc.

Sobotka, H., and Stewart, C. P., editors: Advances in clinical chemistry, vol. 6, New York, 1963, Academic Press, Inc.

Varley, H.: Practical clinical biochemistry, ed. 3, London, 1962, William Heinemann, Medical Books, Ltd.

Wood, J. H., and Keenan, C. W.: General college chemistry, New York, 1957, Harper & Brothers Publishers.

Index